FLUID POWER EQUIPMENT IN MINING QUARRYING AND TUNNELLING

FLUID POWER EQUIPMENT IN MINING QUARRYING AND TUNNELLING

Conference sponsored by the
Fluid Power Transmission Group and
Manipulative and Mechanical Handling Machinery Group of
The Institution of Mechanical Engineers and
British Tunnelling Society
British Compressed Air Society
Institution of Mining Engineers
Association of Mining, Electrical and Mechanical Engineers
Council of Underground Machinery Manufacturers
Institute of Quarrying

London, 12-13 February 1974.

Published by
Mechanical Engineering Publications Limited for
The Institution of Mechanical Engineers
LONDON

CP3 - 1974

ISBN 0 85298 300 X

Set and printed photolitho by William Clowes and Sons Limited, London, Colchester and Beccles, Suffolk. Bound by F J Blissett & Co, Palmerston Works, Roslin Road, Acton, London W 3

Made and printed in Great Britain

CONTENTS

CONTENTS

C18/74

ENERGY REQUIREMENTS FOR IMPACT BREAKAGE OF ROCKS

I. EVANS, DSc, FInstP, FIMinE, CEng

Deputy Director, Mining Research and Development Establishment,
Stanhope Bretby, Burton-on-Trent, Staffordshire

The Ms. of this paper was received at the Institution on 24th July 1973 and acc████ █r publication on 23rd October 1973. 23

The process of mechanisation of roadway drivage in c█ █ines has led to the evolution of the "impact ripper" in which rock at the ripping lip is broken ███ by a succession of blows.

The rock properties likely to enter into the process are █ █dered, and the energy required for breakage is calculated according to the likely mode of rock fail███

It is concluded that the success of a ripper is dictated more ███ ██istribution of gross weaknesses than by the innate strength of the rock. So far as the ██████ concerned, nothing would be gained by exceeding a blow of about 7000 J (5000 ft lbf).

Rocks likely to be difficult ripping subjects can be identified from me█ ████ments of compressive and tensile strength.

LIST OF SYMBOLS

α angle of failure plane with horizontal

β angle between shear plane and reference plane

θ semi-angle of wedge

σ_1 major principal compressive stress

σ_2 minor principal compressive stress

σ_u unconfined compressive strength

ϕ angle of internal friction

ψ angle of friction between material and steel

c cohesion

d depth of cut

E_c energy of failure in shear breakage

E_t energy of failure in tensile breakage

F_c force required to cause breakage by shear failure

F_t force required to cause breakage by tensile failure

n normal stress

R_c force on face of wedge in shear failure

p depth of penetration of wedge

r radius of tip of wedge

s shear stress

t tensile strength

ω length of edge of wedge

INTRODUCTION

1. In coal mining one of th█ ██t difficult operations to mechanise is the ██████king of rock, as required in roadway drivage, █████ "ripping", the action of enlarging the roadw█ ██eading to a long wall-face from seam height ██ █road-head to a value more in keeping with █ ██equire-ments for accessibility by personnel, ███████ient hauling of materials and mineral, and █ ████e ventilation of the workings. The tradit██ ███way is to break down the rock with explosives █ █ this is still widely practised. The draw-b█ that the method is highly labour-intensive, difficult to mechanise, and not fast enough in hard rock to keep pace with the rapid face advan█ which can be brought about by the use of modern power loaders.

2. For this reason there have been in the last few years a number of attempts to mechanise road-heading and ripping. The early machines incorporated developments from coal-cutting practice and incorporated rotating chains or "cutting heads" equipped with picks which were recognisably of coal-cutting lineage, though capable of heavier duty. Many of the machines are now working reliably; at a recent count over 400 machines, of a variety of designs, but fundamentally of this type, were employed in British mines for road-heading and ripping. They are used mainly for use with softer rocks, but these are in fact of quite common occurrence. In a minority of situations, which are nevertheless very important operationally and economically, hard rocks are encountered. Pick-type ripping machines are less satisfactory in this ground. Pick wear tends to be high, the worn picks result in an increase in cutting forces, in power demand and in dust produced. The dust hazard can be mitigated by good design in relation to dust suppression, which fundamentally means the proper use of water in the vicinity of the pick points; but it is always undesirable, and particularly so at the present

1

time when there is wide-spread awareness of the importance of maintaining a good environment at the place of work, no less than in the home and in the community at large.

3. For these various reasons attention has been given recently to the method of breaking rock from the mass by means of heavy blows delivered by a single tool. In coal-mining practice the development stemmed from the study of coal ploughing, where it was thought that the plough could be eased in its progress through the coal by an auxiliary impact unit which came into use when "hard spots" were encountered. The development proved to be aberrant, as well-designed and properly-used ploughs had no need of such help, the "hard spots" turning out to be simply the external symptoms of internal inefficiencies. However, an impact unit, the "Lothians" unit delivering a blow of 1356J (1000 ft lbf) at 120 blow/min had been designed and was available for alternative employment. Experiments in breaking rock seemed promising, and breakage seemed to be accompanied by remarkably little dust. There was thus every incentive to continue with the development of impact rippers, using impact units which derived from civil engineering experience, and which were more practical and robust than the Lothians. These were the Shand "Fluicon" unit 2240J (1650 ft lbf) of up to 180 blow/min; the Ingersoll-Rand "Hobgoblin" 1356J (1000 ft lbf) at up to 600 blow/min; and the Krupp "HM 400", 542J (400 ft lbf) at up to 580 blow/min. These units have been employed on experimental impact rippers at several pits. Results on the whole have been favourable; the rippings (admittedly not usually very hard) have been broken down at a rate which makes the machine an economic possibility.

4. There is uncertainty as to the kind of rock which can be broken down and how it may be characterised. The initial trials have yielded indications that some mining rocks are easy subjects, some are much tougher, and some may be so difficult as to be virtually impossible. It would be useful if rocks came in easily-recognised categories, but this is not the case. It is known that some of the difficult rocks encountered are not extreme in regard to certain specific measurements of strength.

5. For this reason it is thought opportune to attempt here to state briefly what is known about rock strength and the way in which it comes into play in tool behaviour and hence machine performance. As is often the case in mining, theory struggles along somewhat in arrears of practice, and might be thought to be unnecessary were it not for the fact that practice is sometimes brought up short by seemingly unusual conditions. At this stage theory is a useful adjunct to further advance. In the case of pick machines, for example, recent research has increased the efficiency of coal cutters by showing how picks should be designed individually for efficient cutting, and how they should be arranged as a group on a cutting head (Ref. 1). It is possible that similar benefits might be obtained from a study of the mechanics of the breakage brought about by impact rippers.

ROCKS AND ROCK STRENGTH

6. The rocks normally encountered in the vicinity of coal seams are various types of shales and mud-stones, siltstones and sandstones. The basic material, of which shales and mudstones are substantially composed, consists of a cemented paste of clay minerals containing kaolinite, illite, and other compounds. The siltstones are composed of relatively poorly rounded and poorly sorted grains fixed in a matrix of the basic clay material, or of calcareous cement. Coal measures rock frequently demonstrates a clear bedding plane layering, and during the course of geological time other systems of weakness such as slips and joints have developed, both on a micro - and a macro-scale.

7. As might be expected from the variable constitution of rocks, their strength is a complicated concept, and in magnitude is very varied and variable. Progress has been made in the study by extending the concepts which have been found to apply to soils, and which have been embodied into the discipline of Soil Mechanics. Sedimentary rocks are, after all, simply consolidated soils, and it is reasonable to expect that the properties of soils and rocks should be in some way related.

8. From the theoretical point of view, some simplification of the real strength properties of rocks must be sought which will allow the employment of tractable mathematical expressions while at the same time not departing too radically from reality. A simplification which is widely used is that due to Coulomb, first propounded in the study of the resistance of sand to shear. It arises in the following manner.

Consider a specimen of rock to be subjected to a plane stress by principal stresses σ_1 and σ_2 (Figure 1a). As σ_1 is increased for a given σ_2 the specimen is observed to fail by shear.

Figure 1b shows a plane drawn at an angle β to the plane on which σ_1 acts. The external stresses applied to the specimen can be resolved into a normal stress acting on this plane, n, and a shear stress s. Coulomb's equation states that at shear failure the relation between n and s is of the form

$$s = c + n \tan \phi \tag{1}$$

where c is a constant known as the cohesion. The significance of ϕ is discussed below.

9. Soils have little or no tensile strength, and the Coulomb characteristic is thought to terminate when it intercepts the axis of shear stress. Rocks differ from soils in that they have a finite tensile strength. It is usually considered that for them the Coulomb characteristic extends from the region of positive normal stress to that of negative normal stress in a smooth and continuous manner. As it approaches the axis of normal stress it curves around, finally cutting the axis normally (Figure 2). The point at which it cuts the axis is defined as the tensile strength of the rock.

10. An important parameter in consideration of the strength and breakability of rocks is ϕ (Figure 2), defining the variation of shear strength with respect to the normal force on the shear plane. It is known as the 'angle of internal friction'.

When ϕ is large the tensile strength of the material is small in relation to its compressive strength. Such a material might be hard, but it would also be "splittable" or brittle. A lower value of ϕ would confer a 'tough' quality to the material.

TENSILE BREAKAGE

11. It has already been mentioned that coal mining mechanisation gave rise to one of the earliest impact units, the "Lothians", and it is fair to say that many of the theoretical ideas current at the moment on the mechanical breakage of rocks stem from coal mining research. The cutter pick is the basic tool for breaking coal, and the mechanics of its action have been much studied in the research establishments of the National Coal Board.

12. The cutter pick is essentially a wedge, which is used to break mineral away to a free face (Fig. 3). Suppose breakage of the mineral takes place as shown along a plane radiating from the edge of the wedge to the free face. The force exerted by the face of the wedge can be resolved so that it has a component parallel to and a component at right angles to the plane. The normal component will promote tensile breakage, the parallel component shear breakage.

13. In terms of the strength characteristic of coal the two modes are probably inter-related, but certain simplifications can be made. It appears that for coal the tensile strength is so low in relation to its unconfined compressive strength that one is justified in assuming that a purely tensile mode of fracture takes place. The force F_t required to break off a chip of coal is given by the expression (Reference 2).

$$F_t = 2twd \; \frac{\sin(\theta+\psi)}{1-\sin(\theta+\psi)} \qquad (2)$$

where t = tensile strength of coal

w = length of wedge at right angles to plane of diagram

d = depth of cut

θ = semi-angle of wedge

ψ = angle of friction between coal and steel.

14. The energy E_t required to break off the chip is calculated from the finding that the wedge, in penetrating the coal, has to overcome a resistance equal to the compressive strength per unit presented area of the wedge. If p is the penetration at which tensile breakage is precipitated then

$$F_t = \sigma_u . 2wp\tan\theta \qquad (3)$$

where σ_u = unconfined compressive strength of coal.

Hence $E_t = \int_0^p F_t \, dt$

$$= \sigma_u \left(\frac{t}{\sigma_u}\right)^2 wd^2 \; \frac{\sin^2(\theta+\psi)}{[\tan\theta(1-\sin(\theta+\psi))]^2} \qquad (4)$$

Thus while the maximum force for breakage is a function of the tensile strength, the energy is a function of both tensile and compressive strength. To recapitulate briefly: the mode of action of the wedge is such that it must overcome the compressive strength in order to make the entry into the coal that will precipitate tensile rupture.

15. To obtain some sense of the magnitude involved, consider a hard coal for which σ_u = 10,000 lbf/in^2, $t/\sigma_u = \frac{1}{20}$.

Take $d = w = 6$ in, $\theta = 15^\circ$, $\psi = 5^\circ$. For these values of θ and ψ the trigonometric function is close to unity.

Then $E_t = 10,000 \times \frac{1}{400} \times 6^2 \times 6 \times \frac{1}{12}$ ft lbf

$= 450$ ft lbf.

In order to break down coal over the height of a seam a blow of this magnitude would have to be applied to a number of blades over a considerable fraction of the height. There would be some beneficial interaction between the respective breakage patterns, but it would be necessary to cover at least $\frac{1}{3}$ the height of the seam. For a 36 in seam the total blow would therefore be of the order of 1000 ft lbf.

16. The calculation has been based upon the assumption of quasi-static breakage produced by a sharp wedge. The latter assumption is particularly vulnerable in comparison with real conditions. Experiments have shown that the force, and hence the energy, increases significantly as the wedge is blunted according to the relation (Reference 3).

Force $\alpha \; r^{\frac{1}{2}}$ $\qquad (5)$
where r is the radius of the tip of the wedge.

17. Other aspects of impact breakage of coal have been studied by W. T. A. Morgans, but his results are embodied in a Mining Research Establishment report which has unfortunately not been published. However his findings may be summarised as follows:

(1) The energy of the blow must be sufficient to cause fracture by a single application. The coal could endure very many repetitions of lighter blows without breaking.

(2) The processes of impulsive breakage with a single blow do not appear to be significantly different from those of continuous breakage (i.e. by forcing a tool slowly and steadily into the coal). However, energy losses inevitably occur in a real machine delivering a blow, so the nominal power rating of the machine will be greater than would be required from quasi-static reasoning.

18. It arises also as a general finding relating not only to impact breakage but also to steady cutting that the best shape of cutting blade is the simple wedge (Ref. 4). Further, cuts should not be shallow as shallow cuts result in excessive comminution of the material, which wastes energy. Ideally, a square-sectioned cut should be taken, i.e. one in which the depth d is roughly the same as the length of blade w. Some variation from this ideal is permissible, but d/w should not be small.

POSSIBILITY OF SHEAR BREAKAGE

19. As has been mentioned, the theory of breakage for coal rests upon the assumption that t/σ_u is small. This is justified for certain rocks, and recent research by Roxborough show that a number of rocks including limestones and sandstones show the characteristic breakage chip which has been related to tensile failure (Reference 5).

20. For higher values of t/σ_u there is a theoretical possibility that shear breakage would take place more easily than tensile breakage. This is not an easy matter to treat theoretically because of the curvilinear nature of the shear characteristic when associated with a tensile stress acting at right angles to the plane of shear. An approximation can be made by treating the characteristic as linear until it meets the axis of shear stress (Figure 2). This would certainly be incorrect near the axis, but would be tolerable further away.

21. The calculation is given in the Appendix. The result may be stated here: if E_c is the energy of breakage in the shear mode

$$E_c = \sigma_u \left(\frac{c}{\sigma_u}\right)^2 wd^2 \frac{\sin(\theta+\gamma)\cos(\theta+\gamma)\cos^2\phi}{\cos^4\frac{1}{2}(\theta+\gamma+\phi)} \quad (6)$$

All the parameters have already been defined in relation to equations (1) and (2). The characteristic c, the shear strength of the mineral under zero normal load, is not commonly measured, but it can, as shown in the Appendix, be expressed in terms of the compressive stress σ_u and the tensile stress t giving

$$E_c = \sigma_u \left(\frac{c}{\sigma_u}\right)^2 wd^2 \frac{\cot^2\left(\frac{\pi}{4}+\phi/2\right)}{4} \cdot \frac{\sin(\theta+\gamma)\cos(\theta+\gamma)\cos^2\phi}{\cos^4\frac{1}{2}(\theta+\gamma+\phi)} \quad (7)$$

In equation (7) t/σ_u and ϕ are inter-related by the expression

$$\frac{t}{\sigma_u} = \cot^2\left(\frac{\pi}{4}+\phi/2\right). \quad (8)$$

22. Equations (4) and (8) are now directly comparable, the energies for tensile and shear breakage being both expressed in terms of the same parameters. The rock characteristics introduced, the tensile strength and compressive strength are measured as a matter of routine at places like the Mining Research and Development Establishment. This is not to say that the process is easy, or that details are beyond controversy, but to go into details of rock testing would demand an article in its own right. It will have to be sufficient here to state that certain measurements which can be regarded as reasonably valid can be made.

CHARACTERISTICS OF COAL MEASURES ROCKS

23. Figure 4 is a graph on which are plotted the characteristics of certain rocks in terms of tensile strength t and the ratio of tensile to compressive strength. These are specimens which have been taken from the vicinity of coal seams in British pits. They are not necessarily related to ripping sites, actual or prospective, although they do include such specimens. Rather they represent a random selection of rocks which may give an idea of the spread of strength characteristics to be found in practice. They range from hard sandstone

with $\sigma_u \approx$ 30,000 lbf/in^2 and t/σ_u 0.1 to 0.2, to mudstones with $\sigma_u \approx$ 5,000 lbf/in^2 and t/σ_u 0.4 to 0.5.

24. Superimposed on the graph are the characteristics for blows of 1000 ft lbf and 3000 ft lbf calculated from equations 4 and 7, for a wedge of 4 in edge taking a depth of cut of 4 in. The rocks to the left of each characteristic can be broken by a single impact of the appropriate size; those to the right are too strong to be broken by a single impact. The curves for shear and tensile mode of breakage merge together for t/σ_u small, as might be expected, for in this event the shear component of the breaking force is being reduced to a low value by the tensile component acting at right angles to the plane of shear.

It appears that a blow of 1000 ft lbf would be barely enough to break a majority of the rocks, while 3000 ft lbf would be sufficient.

25. It should be remembered that this figure has been arrived at on the assumption of no energy losses in delivering the blow. In practice these would have to be taken into account together with the effect of blunting of the wedge, and the nominal blow would consist of the theoretical figure multiplied by a factor of ignorance. The value of this simply has to be guessed at, and a value of 2 is suggested. The blow required to break down the stipulated buttock for a likely majority of coal measures rocks, i.e. 4 in x 4 in would therefore be 6000 ft lbf, or more roundly, to the degree of accuracy involved, somewhere in the vicinity of 5000 ft lbf.

RATE OF BREAKING OF ROCK

26. Unfortunately this does not mean that if an impact ripper is equipped with a blow of 5000 ft lbf then everything in the garden will be lovely. The ripper may be able to break rock, but in order to be of service as a mining machine it must break it at an economic rate. It is not at all certain that in the tougher rocks this can be achieved. If the rock breaks according to prediction each blow of the 4 in edge chisel at a depth of cut 4 in should dislodge about 30 cu in of rock. However, this is for the configuration of a right-angled buttock of rock which the wedge can attack. After a major chip has been removed the ripper has to do some tidying up before the buttock again presents itself in this form. During the process of tidying less rock will be dislodged per blow, and one can make a reasonable estimate that the average amount dislodged per blow would be no more than 10 cu in.

27. Consider the driving of a tunnel of 120 ft^2 cross-section. It is proposed to advance 10 ft per shift, a reasonable target, using an impact device delivering 5000 ft lbf blows. The amount of rock excavated is 120 x 10 x 12^3 cu in, which will require $\dfrac{120 \times 10 \times 12^3}{10}$ blows.

The average rate of working for a 6 hour shift will therefore be
$$\frac{120 \times 10 \times 12^3}{10} \times \frac{5000}{6 \times 60 \times 60 \times 550} \text{ H.P.}$$

$$= 87.3 \text{ H.P.}$$

Thus virtually 100 H.P. would be required for a machine working flat out at 10 blows/sec, with no allowance for time taken to position the blade, to

4

move the machine, to deal with careful work like profiling the perimeter of the excavation, or to cope with delays or stoppages. It might reasonably be felt that this is not a practical proposition.

28. Yet it is known that 100 H.P. or less is perfectly adequate for an impact ripper in many circumstances, and that rock is brought down at a rate that makes the process economic in relation to the related activities of coal winning and debris removal. The reason is that the ripper makes use of the weaknesses in the rock which have already been referred to. Theory inevitably deal with what might be called the intrinsic strength of the rock substance. The effect of bedding planes, joints, etc., is to reduce the strength of the rock to a very small value. Impact rippers work by exploiting the weaknesses of strata rather than by overcoming their strengths. There is a parallel in the mining of anthracite which is intrinsically very hard, but which has an extensive slip system rendering it easy to work.

29. It is noteworthy that on Figure 4 the rocks which press most closely upon the limiting characteristics of a 3000 ft lbf blow are not the extreme ones, of high σ and high t/σ_u respectively, but those in the medium band for both parameters. The presence of these characteristics would alert the engineer to the possibility of a difficult ripping subject, needing further investigation. Unfortunately a quantitative study of lamination has hardly begun, but is badly needed, so that when used in conjunction with tests for intrinsic strength, subjects for ripping may be recognized.

30. With this realisation the value of the theoretical approach set out in this paper may be questioned. However what it does is to set a reasonable upper limit to what should be aimed at in the matter of a blow. There are, in British mines, not many rocks that could not be broken by a 5000 ft lbf blow. To increase the size of blow would merely be bringing into ambit the small minority of rocks that at the moment are outstandingly tough, a process that would be very uneconomic; and also to "overhit" on the less tough subjects, imparting energy to the broken material, and generating the very dust that the method was designed to alleviate. And this would be at a cost of the employment of considerable power in a restricted situation, and massive machinery to withstand the stresses brought about by imparting high energy.

31. There would also be the problem of providing the impactor unit with a cutting edge able to stand up to such energies of impact. The hard inserts used in mining tools are usually of tungsten carbide, and even for continuous cutting in rock present grades are often subject to severe abrasion and fracture. The problem of providing durable cutting edges would be greatly accentuated in impact cutting of hard rock. This again is a topic which would need its own paper for full discussion.

CONCLUSIONS

1. Theoretical considerations indicate that the susceptibility of rock to impact breakage is a function not only of compressive strength but of tensile strength also. Compressive strength alone is a misleading criterion.

2. Formulae are given for calculating the size of blow required to break a buttock of rock. For a wedge-shaped impactor, of 4 in edge taking a 4 in depth of cut, the intrinsic strength of the majority of coal measures rock in exposures overlying coal seams would not warrant a blow of more than about 5000 ft lbf.

3. Many coal measures rocks could be broken by smaller blows, but if a blow is too small large numbers of repetitions at a given point may be required to cause breakage.

4. The volume of debris produced per blow really decides the viability of an impact ripper. This is related not so much to the intrinsic strength of the rock as to the existence of gross weaknesses, as in bedding planes, slips, etc. It is important to study this aspect of rock strength.

5. In the context of coal mining, bigger blows than 5000 ft lbf with the ripping tool defined in Conclusion (2) would not guarantee economic working against recalcitrant rock, and would add to the problem of machine design, adequate tool life, and environmental protection.

ACKNOWLEDGEMENT

I am indebted to my colleague Mr. J. D. Kibble for the argument in the section "Rate of Breaking of Rock."

This paper is published by permission of the National Coal Board. The views stated are those of the author and not necessarily those of the Board.

REFERENCES

1. Evans, I. and Pomeroy C. D., Strength, Fracture and Workability of Coal, Pergamon Press, 1966.

2. Evans, I. A Theory of the Basic Mechanics of Coal Ploughing, Proc. of Inter-Symposium on Mining Research, London, Pergamon, Vol. 2, 1962. pp. 761 - 798.

3. Dalziel, J. A. and Davies, E., Initiation of Cracks in Coal Specimens by Blunted Wedges. The Engineer, Vol. 217, January 31st 1964 pp. 217 - 220.

4. Pomeroy, C. D. The Breakage of Coal by Wedge Action. Colliery Guardian, Vol. 207, 1963, pp. 642 - 648 and pp. 672 - 677.

5. Roxborough, F. F. Cutting Rock with Picks, The Mining Engineer, Vol. 132, June 1973, pp. 445 - 454.

APPENDIX

Force required to cause failure by shear under action of a wedge

The wedge is of a semi-angle θ and is entered a distance p into the buttock. It is assumed that failure takes place by shear along a plane making angle α with the horizontal (Figure 3). The depth of cut is d, and the wedge has an extent ω at right angles to the plane of the diagram.

If P_c is the force on one face of the wedge (assumed in the first instance to be acting at right angles to the face)

Force parallel to shear plane $= P_c \cos(\frac{\pi}{2} - \overline{\theta + \alpha})$

$$= P_c \sin(\theta + \alpha)$$

Force perpendicular to shear plane $= P_c \sin(\frac{\pi}{2} - \overline{\theta + \alpha})$

$$= P_c \cos(\theta + \alpha)$$

Assuming that failure takes place according to Coulomb's equation

$$s = c + n \tan\phi$$

and remembering that in the configuration being envisaged, n is negative, we obtain

$$\frac{P_c \sin(\theta + \alpha)}{wd/\sin\alpha} = c - \frac{P_c \cos(\theta+\alpha)\tan\phi}{wd/\sin\alpha}$$

giving

$$P_c = cwd \frac{\cos\phi}{\sin\alpha \sin(\theta+\alpha+\phi)} \tag{A1}$$

P_c is minimised with respect to α by putting

$$\frac{dP_c}{d\alpha} = 0$$

giving

$$\alpha = \frac{\pi}{2} - \frac{1}{2}(\theta+\phi)$$

The horizontal force F_c is given by

$$F_c = 2P_c \sin\theta$$

$$= 2cwd \cdot \frac{\cos\phi \sin\theta}{\cos^2 \frac{1}{2}(\theta+\phi)} \tag{A2}$$

Also, in a manner exactly parallel to that relating to equation (4) of the text

Energy of penetration, $E_c = \int_0^p F_c \, dp$

$$= \sigma\left(\frac{c}{\sigma_u}\right)^2 wd^2 \frac{\cos^2\phi \sin\theta \cos\theta}{\cos^2 \frac{1}{2}(\theta+\phi)} \tag{A3}$$

A relation between σ_u, c and t can be obtained in the following way: the Coulomb shear characteristic can be regarded as the envelope of the Mohr circles of stress defining the conditions under which the rock specimens are tested. The Mohr circle for a pure tensile test would pass through the points $n = 0$ and $n = -t$; that for the unconfined compression test would pass through the points $n = 0$ and $n = \sigma_u$. The Coulomb envelope is assumed to extend into the region of negative n in such a manner that it is a tangent to the two circles just mentioned (Figure 5). From the geometry of this system

$$\frac{c}{\frac{1}{2}t} = \tan(\frac{\pi}{4} + \frac{\phi}{2}) \tag{A4}$$

We may write $\sigma_u \left(\frac{c}{\sigma_u}\right)^2 = \sigma_u \left(\frac{t}{\sigma_u}\right)^2 \left(\frac{c}{t}\right)^2$ \hfill (A5)

The value of c/t from (A4) may be substituted in (A5) and hence in (A3). At the same time we may take account of the existence of an angle of friction ψ between steel wedge and mineral. This advances P_c to an angle ψ with the normal to the face of the wedge, and therefore in effect increases θ, the semi-angle of the wedge, to $\theta + \psi$. Finally,

$$\frac{E_c}{wd^2} = \sigma_u \left(\frac{t}{\sigma_u}\right)^2 \frac{\tan^4(\frac{\pi}{4} + \frac{\phi}{2})}{4} \cdot \frac{\sin(\theta+\psi)\cos(\theta+\psi)\cos^2\phi}{\cos^4 \frac{1}{2}(\theta+\psi+\phi)} \tag{A6}$$

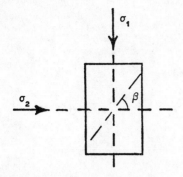

Fig. 1(a): Principal Stresses

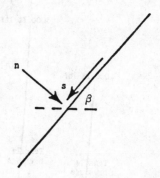

Fig. 1(b): Stresses on Shear Plane

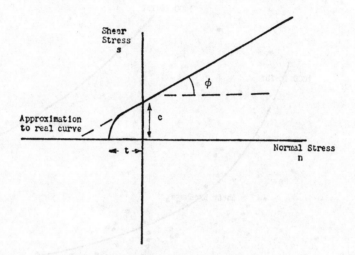

Fig. 2: Illustrating Coulomb's Equation for
Shear Failure

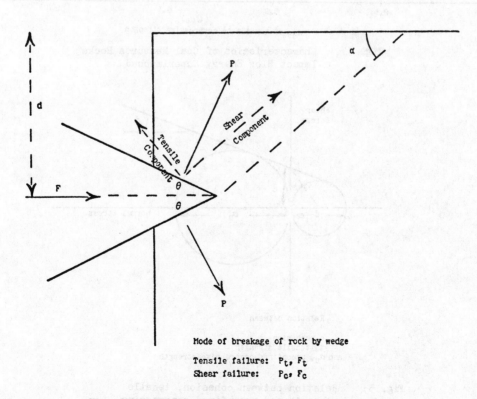

Mode of breakage of rock by wedge

Tensile failure: P_t, F_t

Shear failure: P_c, F_c

Fig. 3: Mode of breakage of rock by wedge

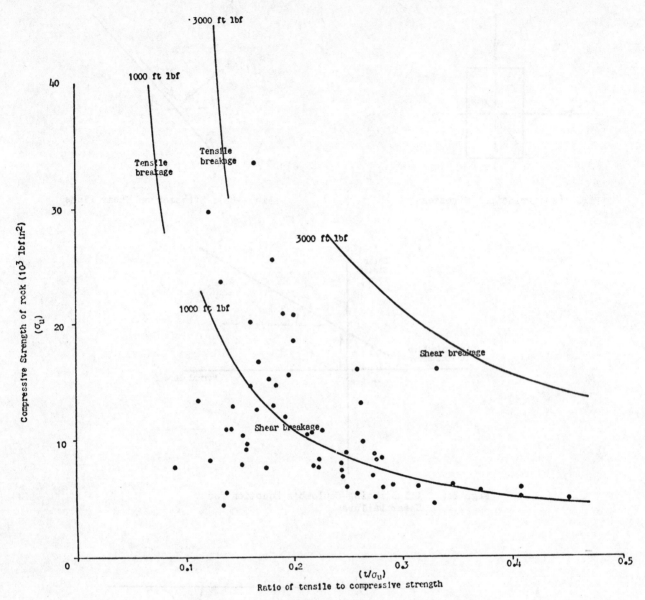

Fig. 4:   Characteristics of Coal Measures Rocks
           Impact Blow Energy Superimposed

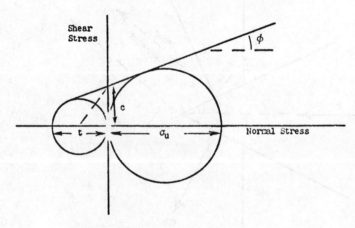

Relation between

    c, cohesion
    t, tensile strength
and σ_u, unconfined compressive strength

Fig. 5:   Relation between cohesion, tensile
           strength and unconfined compressive
           strength.

STRAIN WAVES IN AN IMPACT

J. FURBY, PhD, BEng(Hons)

Director and General Manager, Marwin Mining Tools Limited,
Town Green Street, Rothley, Leicestershire LE7 7QA

The Ms. of this paper was received at the Institution on 24th July 1973 and accepted for publication on 23rd October 1973. 33

SYNOPSIS The effectiveness of an impact Breaker is dependent - but not directly so - on the amount of piston energy it transmits to the Breaker Steel. To use the available energy most efficiently in the rock breaking process, it is necessary to consider the fundamental parameters of piston/steel diameters, steel length, piston impact, velocity and machine thrust and steel point shape. The Author sets out to describe research results which suggest those conditions of operation under which there will be maximum energy input to the Breaker Steel.

INTRODUCTION

1. This paper is written to provide a technical background to the more practical papers describing experience with impact units which is the theme of to-day's discussions. Whilst the principles outlined here apply to the percussive field generally, they have been centred around the high energy hydraulic impact tipper because of the particular features of this unit - such features as low blow rates with high blow energies, and relatively large diameter short working tools.

2. The hydraulic impact unit is relatively new as a practical and reliable mining tool. As with hydraulics generally, the use of high pressures permits very much higher energies per unit of size and weight than with comparable pneumatic units. They also offer such benefits as reduced noise levels and better mechanical operating conditions than pneumatic hammers but these advantages must be set against the obvious increase in complexity of the hydraulic unit and the accumulated wisdom of 100 years of design experience with pneumatic hammers.

3. Every attempt has been made to minimise the mathematical sophistication with which this subject is usually surrounded.

LIST OF SYMBOLS USED

Δ = Total displacement within the pulse
c = Pulse Velocity in material
V = Velocity of piston at impact
As = Area of rod
Ap = Area of piston
E = Young's Modulus
g = Gravity constant
l = Length
ϵ = Strain
σ = Stress
t = Time for pulse to travel an indicated distance.
U = Energy in Wave-form
ρ = Density of material

BASIC CONCEPTS

Generation of a Strain Pulse

1. It has been exhaustively demonstrated that when a piston strikes a long rod a longitudinal strain pulse is generated at the interface of impact and will travel away from this plane in two directions, i.e., down the rod and back up the piston. It is necessary to describe the way in which this strain pulse is generated and its subsequent behaviour within the rod, in order to appreciate those characteristics of a hammer which influence its performance.

2. Impact is basically an energy conversion process. The kinetic energy in a moving piston is used to chip, crush and cleave the rock. It is important to appreciate that the rod is simply a means of transmitting the piston energy and providing it at the cutting edge, in a suitable form for this purpose.

3. Before outlining the manner of wave propogation, it is necessary to state the assumptions made to simplify the analysis. These are:

   1). In the rod and piston plane sections remain plane during the passage of the strain pulse.

   2). Piston and rod axes are collinear and the impacting faces are parallel immediately prior to impact.

   3). Forces at the interface of impact are equal.

4. The piston and rod are considered to be composed of a large number of discrete particles. When impact occurs the moving piston strikes the stationary rod. The rod particles at the interface of impact are given a displacement and hence a velocity away from the plane of impact. These particles transmit this motion to adjacent particles which in turn transmit it to their neighbours and in this way a

pulse of compressive strain travels down the rod. Since the piston is subject to the same forces a similar pulse of compressive strain travels along the piston in a direction away from the plane of impact.

5. It will be apparent that the compressive strain in those particles of the rod at the impacted surface will drop to zero as, and when, the piston is no longer in contact with the rod end. As a consequence, piston energy can only be transmitted to the rod if the piston and rod are in contact. Once they have separated, even though there is energy remaining in the piston, it cannot be made available to do useful work in rock breaking.

6. It can be shown that the strain pulse will travel along the rod and piston at the speed of sound in the material which for steel is about 5200 m/sec. This velocity is given by

$$C = \sqrt{\frac{Eg}{\rho}} \qquad (1)$$

Reflection of a Strain Pulse

1. It is necessary to discuss reflection of strain pulses at boundaries in order to explain subsequent wave behaviour. In the compressive pulse the particle motion and the pulse motion travel in the same direction. When such a pulse impinges on the free end of the rod it is reflected back up the rod towards the piston. There has, however, been no restraint on the particle motion which continues in its original direction of travel, i.e. away from the point of impact. This situation results in the strain pulse approaching the free end as a compressive pulse but being reflected as a tensile pulse. Because the particle motion is still away from the point of impact, it draws the rod away from this point and the overall rod movement is away from the piston.

2. Two important results stem from this pulse behaviour. Firstly, there will always be a change of strain in the pulse from compressive to tensile or tensile to compressive under conditions of free end reflection. The second is that during the reflection of a pulse at a free end, the stress level at this point is zero but the particle displacement is twice the normal in the wave-form.

3. The alternative extreme is the fixed end condition. During reflection, particle displacement is prevented, displacement and pulse motion are in the same direction and there is no change in the sign of the reflected pulse. Hence a compressive whilst a tensile pulse will be reflected as tensile. At the reflecting surface particle displacement will be zero but the stress level will be twice the maximum in the incident wave.

4. All pulse reflections following impact will fall some way between these two extremes of fixed and free end reflection. The behaviour and effectiveness of the cutting edge of the chisel of a hydraulic hammer will be controlled by a combination of these two conditions. All rod movements following impact can be explained by these rules of reflection and particle displacement, and it is the behaviour of the strain pulse within the rod that determines the overall rod movement.

5. The simplest case to examine, is that of a short piston and a long rod of equal diameters.

FIGURE 1

6. After impact the compressive pulse is generated in the piston and travels up the piston to the rear face. Here it is reflected as a tensile wave and because the particle velocity and displacement are away from the interface of impact, they draw the piston away from contact with the rod when the wave arrives back at the interface of impact. Hence the strain level at the interface drops to zero and the wave-length of the pulse in the rod is thus determined. In this case the wave-length is $\frac{2l}{c}$ with a strain level of ϵ.

7. As a result the rod is shorter than its original length by $\epsilon \times c.t$ and it is the relaxation of this strain at the rod end which causes the cutting edge or point of the chisel to penetrate the rock. The end conditions at the rod/rock interface will determine how far the rod as a whole, will move forward into the rock or whether the wave will be partially reflected as compressive to cause a reaction backwards through the chisel and against the hammer and its mountings.

8. Figure 2 shows research results to demonstrate the movement of a rod under free end conditions after impact. Rod movement was measured at the cutting edge whilst the gauge station was halfway down the rod. Hence there was one movement of the rod end of 2Δ for every two occasions when the pulse passed the gauge station.

FIGURE 2

9. Figure 3 shows how the pulse causes the overall rod movement from both fixed and free ends. It also illustrates the way in which the piston contact with the rod is controlled by the reflection at the working end.

FIGURE 3

10. After impact, the wave will subsequently continue to travel up and down the rod - hopefully with energy abstracted at the cutting edge on some of the occasions when it arrives there - until either energy abstraction of the internal friction of the rod material cause it to die away. Since the internal damping capacity of steel is about 1%

per 3 metres, then under free end
conditions the wave would travel up and
down the rod perhaps 100 times stressing
the rod, before it decayed to zero. This
situation, even with energy being
abstracted is shown in Figure 4 taken
from some rock drilling research.

FIGURE 4

Pulse Behaviour at a Section Change

1.   The final concept to be explained
before an understanding of rod movements
can be achieved is that of pulse behaviour
at a change in cross-sectional area.
Under these circumstances part of the wave
is reflected at, and part is transmitted
through, the change in section. The signs
of the reflected and transmitted pulses
are determined by the sign of the incident
wave and the ratio of areas at the change
in section. The importance of this concept
is that it permits a wave shape to be
established under conditions when the
piston is bigger in cross section than the
rod. Such a wave shape is shown in
Figure 5. It will be seen that the basic
step is still 2l/c but that these steps
continue at reducing strain levels until
the strain level in the piston falls to
zero. This assumes however, that the rod
is long enough to prevent reflection of
the pulse from the working end throwing
the piston away from the impacted surface,
when the pulse returns to the plane of
impact.

FIGURE 5

2.   Also as will be shown in the next
section, the maximum stress generated in
the rod is influenced by the maximum
diameter of the piston.

Reflection at the Rock Surface

1.   It has been stated that every
conceivable rod end condition will fall
intermediate between the two extremes of
fixed and free end. In the case of the
chisel in a hydraulic hammer the first
pulse will travel down the chisel 'till
the leading edge of the wave meets the
rod/rock boundary. Initially the
resistance to the relaxation of the
strain in the pulse will be low and so
the point or cutting edge will start to
penetrate the rock. As reflection of
the leading edge of the wave commences
the particle displacement in the rod end
will be 2Δ because reflection of the
pulse will be as from a free end.

2.   However, as reflection and thus
penetration proceeds, and the rock
beneath the cutting edge deforms
elastically to permit the free end
reflection, the resistance of the rock to
penetration increase. This in turn
gradually changes the end conditions at
the rod/rock boundary from free to some
intermediate condition between free and
fixed. Hence the full leading edge of
the pulse is not reflected as tensile and
eventually pure fixed end conditions
develop as resistance to penetration
increases. From that point the wave-form

will follow the original strain/time curve.
The end conditions will completely inhibit
the movement of the cutting edge into the
rock at that point where superimposition
of the incident and reflected wave-forms
exhibits coincidence. This is shown in
Figure 6.

FIGURE 6

3.   By measuring the energies in the first
incident and first reflected wave-forms,
it is frequently found that less than 40%
of the piston energy is actually used to
penetrate the rock. Because rock is
chipped and crushed by rod end displacement under the action of a compressive
pulse, the only energy available for
further penetration is that which was
reflected as tensile at the first
reflection. Under the free end conditions
obtaining at the struck end of the rod,
this tensile leading edge will be reflected
as compressive to provide further rock
penetration potential. But because the
greater part of the total reflected wave is
usually compressive the overall rod
movement will be towards the piston,
preventing further penetration and causing
a reaction on the machine mounting. The
thrust of the mounting is then required to
force the rod back into contact with the
rock before the next blow but this won't
happen until the wave has travelled up
and down the rod many times.

4.   This situation is illustrated in
Figure 7.

FIGURE 7

After the line AB on the reflected wave,
no more penetration of the rock can occur
leaving all the strain energy represented
by ABCD, to oscillate up and down the rod,
stressing it but doing no useful work and
serving only to move the rod as a whole
away from the rock thus causing reaction
on the hammer mounting.

5.   Therefore, reverting to the previous
figure, the lower the strain amplitude at
which coincidence is exhibited, the
greater the percentage of available energy
used, and the less there is available to
move the rod away from the rock. Also
the longer is the rod life because of the
lower residual stress levels in the pulse
after reflection.

Quantities in the Wave

1.   It is only necessary to state the
equations which allow the parameters to the
pulse to be determined.

$$\text{Displacement } \Delta = \frac{c}{E} \int_0^l \sigma \, dt \qquad (2)$$

and is the area under the strain/time
characteristic in the rod.

Under free end conditions Δ is given by

$$\Delta = \frac{2c}{E} \int_0^l \sigma \, dt \qquad (3)$$

11

The energy in the wave-form in the rod is given by

$$U = \frac{Ac}{E} \int_0^\ell \sigma^2 \, dt \qquad (4)$$

The maximum stress in the wave-form generated in the rod is given by

$$\sigma = \frac{c\rho V}{1 + \frac{As}{Ap}} \qquad (5)$$

to unity. Hence $\sigma = \frac{c\rho V}{2}$

Practical Considerations

1. The conditions required for a successful hammer will now be outlined under the general headings as set out below:

    1). Piston Diameters and Length

    2). Piston Velocity

    3). Blow rates and Thrust

    4). Energy Wastage.

Piston Diameters and Length

1. Because the rods are short it is advantageous to have a ratio of diameters of rod and piston close to unity. The reason for this is that if the piston diameter were markedly larger than the rod diameter, the wavelength of the pulse would be relatively long - as shown in Fig. 8 - unless the piston was comparatively short. Under these conditions energy levels to the rod would be low because of low piston weight.

FIGURE 8

2. When the wavelength is long compared to the rod, the first reflected wave would have moved the piston away from the struck end of the rod before it had delivered all of its energy to the rod. To avoid this situation the rod length needs to be greater than half the wavelength of the pulse generated.

3. It is acknowledged that a unit in which the piston is bigger in diameter than the rod could work very well but it would be somewhat wasteful of energy as well as inducing higher than necessary stresses in the rod by virtue of the $\frac{As}{Ap}$ term in Equation (5). It would also require greater energy input for a given work out-put in order to obtain the same impact velocity for the same piston length. It will also be apparent that a unit in which $\frac{As}{Ap} > 1$ could be effective whilst reducing the strain level in the rod for the same impact velocities.

4. The rod length is prescribed by virtue of the conditions that the pulse length needs to be less than twice the rod length whatever piston diameter is used. Therefore it is desirable to have the piston diameter close to the rod diameter and the piston shorter in length than the rod.

Piston Velocity

1. Piston velocity at impact is related to the concepts of thresh-hold energy level and plastic deformation at the interface impact.

2. In the latter case Equation (5) holds:-

$$\sigma_{max} = \frac{c\rho V}{1 + As/Ap} \qquad (5)$$

ie. max, is directly proportional to impact velocity - See Fig. 9 and a very high striking velocity could be expected to result in plastic deformation or rupture of the struck end of the rod. It can be shown by analysis that this limit for steels in a minimum of about 70 metres per second at impact.

FIGURE 9

3. This then establishes the upper limit of impact velocity although obviously for the longest service life of the tool the lowest piston velocity consistent with chosen hammer performance is the correct one

4. There is, however, a lower limit of impact velocity which is related to the concept of thresh-hold energy level. It has already been explained that during the first reflection of the generated pulse the rock beneath the cutting edge will be deformed elastically before it is degraded, chipped or crushed. Hence if the energy level delivered to the cutting edge were only sufficient to deform the rock elastically, then no material would be broken out. Hence the first consideration of impact velocity must be to raise it so that there is sufficient displacement in the rod pulse actually to chip or crush the rock beneath the tool cutting edge in order to facilitate cutting edge penetration which will in turn force the adjacent areas of rock apart causing the material fail in tension and cracks to propogate - hopefully towards a free edge or surface.

5. Moreover, if the cutting edge were to be inserted into a cleat or crack in the rock, the pulse reflections at the cutting edge would be almost totally free end reflections causing the rod as a whole to be "caterpillared" forward into the crack thus propogating the crack. If the material is homogeneous and massive however the complex reflection described in a previous Section would occur and crack propogation would require more blows and higher energies per blow.

6. Also the softer the rock the greater will be the tensile component of the first reflected wave, the smaller the overall particle motion towards the piston and the less the rebound energy imparted to the piston and, through the chisel, to the hammer mountings.

7. The harder the rock the greater will be the compressive component of the reflected wave-form, the greater the overall particle motion towards the hammer and the greater

the rebound forces on the hammer.

8. When using a wedge shaped tool - and a point is just a special case of this - as the rock is chipped and crushed beneath the cutting edge it tends to be extruded back through that area between the face of the wedge and the crater the wedge is producing. The energy level in the tool must be high enough to force this extrusion to permit the cutting edge to work against a reasonably free rock surface.

9. Since it has also been shown that the volume of a crater caused by a wedge shaped cutting edge is proportional to the blow energy - albeit not directly so - then the biggest single factor affecting penetration will be blow energy. Since piston velocity in isolation is not a significant factor in penetration then the most satisfactory solution is to obtain higher energies with larger pistons and lower velocities to reduce strain levels in the tools, i.e., long slow blows at high energy levels.

Blow Rates and Thrust

1. It has been explained that after impact the wave-form will travel up and down the rod continuously until a combination of energy abstracted at the cutting edge, and internal friction in the rod material causes complete decay of the pulse - See Fig.3

2. As soon as the rod returns to quiescence after a piston blow then it is ready to receive its next blow. The only proviso in choosing blow rates is that the stresses generated by one blow should not be superimposed on - and therefore cumulative with - the stresses generated by the preceding blow.

3. Hence if one assumes 100 pulse reflections - and there would certainly be less than 100 if energy were abstracted from the wave-form on one occasion only - with a rod length of 0.8 metres then there could be

$$\left\{ \frac{5200}{100 \times 0.8} \right\} \text{ Blows per second.}$$

with superimposing stress levels as set out above i.e. 65 blows per second or 3900 per minutes.

4. However, there is a practical limitation to high blow rates. It will be appreciated that reaction caused by pulse reflection occurs after each blow. This reaction is, in effect, the force of the rod thrusting against the chuck of the hammer and thence onto the mounting which is counteracted by the thrust that the machine provides to hold the chisel against the rock.

5. Obviously the more frequently this reaction occurs - i.e. the blow rate - the higher must the thrust be to counteract it. Hence optimum thrust must

increase with blow rate and blow energy. This then is the practical limitation on increasing the blow rate of such an hydraulic hammer as we are discussing.

Energy Wastage

1. When a piston strikes a rod three types of strain wave are generated. Only two are important in terms of the design and performance of a hydraulic hammer. In the foregoing only longitudinal pulses were mentioned because these are the pulses which cause rock penetration by the tool. It has been explained that this is brought about by particle displacements in a direction along the rod axis. Certain assumptions about the conditions of impact were also made namely:-

   1). That the piston and rod axes are collinear.

   2). That the impacting faces are parallel immediately before impact.

2. If these conditions are met, only longitudinal pulses are generated. But in any mechanical device tolerances, clearances, and wear prevent such conditions being achieved. This leads to flexural waves being generated simultaneously with the longitudinal waves during impact. The worse the impact conditions, the greater the proportion of available piston energy is channelled into flexural waves. The principal feature of flexural waves is that particle motion is in a direction perpendicular to the rod axis and therefore they can under no circumstances assist the process of rock penetration by the cutting edge but do add significantly to rod stress levels and ultimately earlier rod failure.

3. The hydraulic hammer is capable of being designed with a long front bush to hold and support the tool; small clearances - by virtue of its lubrication systems - to ensure collinearity of piston and tool shank; and ground surfaces on the piston and tool shank to ensure excellent mating of the impacting surfaces.

4. These design features are not readily available in say pneumatic tools. The hydraulic hammer designer can utilise a greater percentage of the available piston energy than can his less fortunate colleague in the percussive tool field.

5. Finally it has been clearly shown that as the tool levers out the rock, extremely high bending stresses can be generated by the superimposition of the static and dynamic strain levels. It is, therefore, essential that the tool diameter and piston diameter bechosen with these stress levels in mind before selecting the piston length and velocity. Certainly maximum total stress levels below about 20 T/▢"should be considered essential to provide an acceptable service life for a tool manufactured from a very high strength alloy steel.

6. A study of the impact systems of a number of hammers currently being marketed has revealed one case in which the principles outlined above have been followed. By a fortunate coincidence this hammer - marketed by Shand - has been found to be highly effective in NCB ripping operations underground. A principal advantage of this unit is that its very low level of rebound or reaction against its mounting permits it to be slung from the roof arches, without moving these arches during ripping operations.

7. In addition the ratio of the times taken on the piston return stroke and impact stroke is about 9:1 resulting in a slow return and a consequent saving in hydraulic energy. At the same time the piston acceleration is high enough to give a high energy blow to the working tool.

8. Finally it can be shown by calculations that the stress level in the working tool is within the limits stipulated above.

CONCLUSIONS

1. The foregoing has set out the design conditions required for acceptable service life from hammer and tool. It is only fiar to comment that because of design complexity, the only accurate way of establishing how efficient is the impact in such a unit, is to measure the strain wave-forms in the tool under operating conditions. Obviously end conditions will change as the tool first of all penetrates and then cleaves the rock it is working. Obviously stress levels will be raised by the superimposition of static and dynamic stresses. Obviously more energy will be available more effectively from a sharp cutting edge than from a blunt one. Only analysis of strain wave-forms will give a complete and accurate picture of energy utilisation under working conditions and the stress levels to be found in the tool.

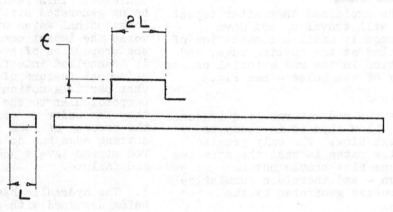

Fig.1

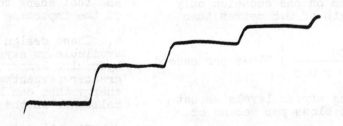

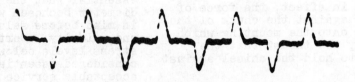

Fig.2

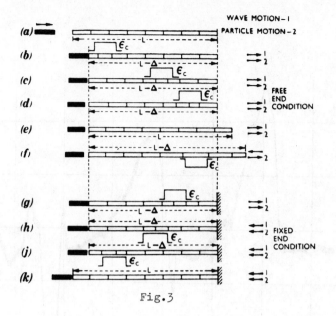

Fig.3

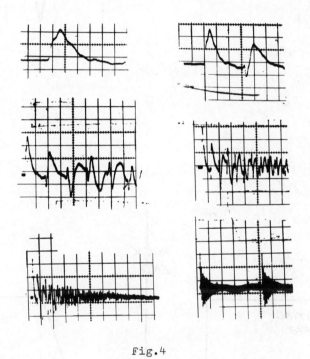

Fig.4

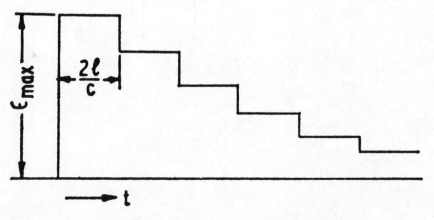

Fig.5

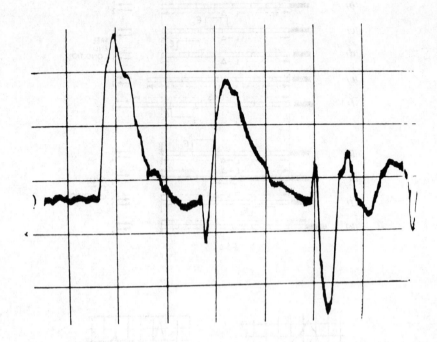

Fig.6

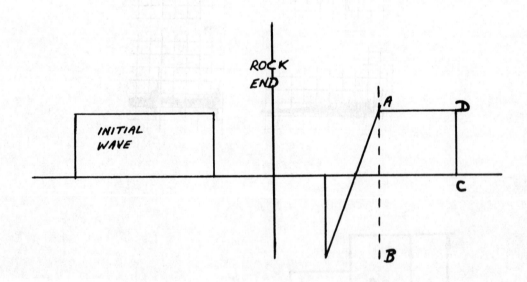

Fig.7

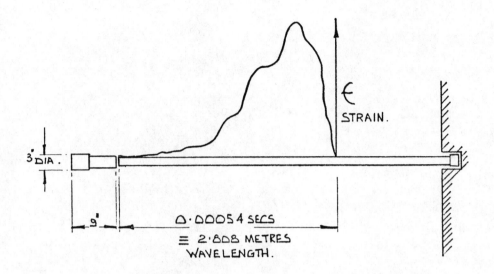

3" DIA.

9"

0·00054 SECS
≡ 2·808 METRES
WAVELENGTH.

$\in$
STRAIN.

Fig.8

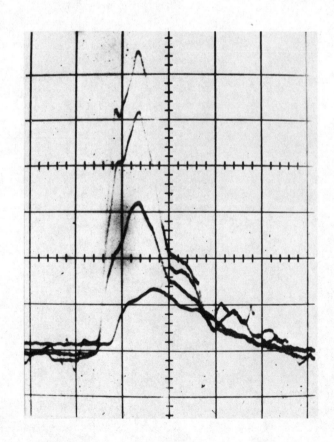

Fig.9

C20/74

SOME RECENT DEVELOPMENTS IN PERCUSSIVE ROCK DRILLING FOR MINING, QUARRYING AND TUNNELLING

J. HODGE, MA, FIMechE
Director, Holman Brothers Limited, Camborne, Cornwall

The Ms. of this paper was received at the Institution on 10th August 1973 and accepted for publication on 23rd October 1973. 43

SYNOPSIS   The development of rigs for mounting rock drills is sketched, with particular emphasis on the trend towards an increasing degree of automatic operation of as many functions as possible. Percussive drilling machines are also discussed; up to the present time they have been almost exclusively pneumatically powered, but there is increasing interest in the potential of hydraulic operation. A new method of rock extraction being developed for reef mining in South Africa is described.

INTRODUCTION

1.   There are two major aspects of rock drilling which can be considered to some extent separately, irrespective of whether the operation is above or below ground. These are the machines themselves which actually drill the holes, and the means of mounting and controlling them. The latter has probably received less attention in the literature - which is not extensive outside the specialised journals - and will be discussed first.

DRILL SUPPORT SYSTEMS

2.   The earliest rock drills needed mechanical support, simply because they were too heavy to be held up in the required position by hand, unless they were drilling vertically downwards, as in shaft sinking, or quarrying. The mountings were of a simple design, known as "bar and column". One or more columns in the form of cast iron or steel tubes were fixed vertically between the roof and floor of the tunnel in which drilling was taking place, either by means of wedges or by simple screw jacks. A bar was then clamped at right angles to the column or columns and the rock drill clamped to this. The axis of the rock drill could be swivelled in two planes about the point of support and the bar could be moved up and down, and the rock drill along it, to change the position in space. Whilst swivelling involved little effort, shifting the support point was hard work; both involved "spanner work" and were slow and cumbersome. The forward feed of the drill was by means of a hand operated feed screw - like the lead screw of a lathe. "Crowding" - that is moving the whole drill and its cradle close to the face before starting to drill, to enable the full depth of hole corresponding to the feed length to be utilised, was limited and difficult.

3.   Whilst drilling speeds were comparatively low, and manpower cheap, this system served well, but increased performance has led in two different directions. One has resulted from the improvements in power/weight ratio, leading to light but powerful machines which can be hand held. These are very useful and flexible, but inevitably their performance has been again increased to the point where they need some mechanical support, especially in awkward positions, such as drilling a horizontal hole high in a tunnel, or a vertically upwards hole.

Apart from weight, the output of a machine (represented as it is by the momentum of the blows delivered by the piston) limits the ability to hold it by hand.

4.   The direct result of the up-grading of the light hand held drill was the introduction of the "airleg" (first in Germany in 1938). This consisted of a simple pneumatically operated piston and cylinder which was attached in some way to the rock drill, and fed with air from the main supply via a teed-in line, with a separate pressure control valve of some kind. The end of the cylinder (or of the piston rod) was provided with a spike to enable it to get a hold on the floor of the workings, either in the rock itself or in a previously anchored chain or "ladder". The force available from the airleg could be applied to assist in supporting the weight of the drill and also to apply forward thrust. Since the angle of the airleg to the axis of the drill varies continuously it is not possible to balance all the forces, vertical and horizontal, all the time, even by varying the air pressure in the leg. Therefore some manual balancing force has to be applied, but this is usually small over a good proportion of the face area and can be controlled in practice by continuous variation of the airleg pressure, as appreciable departures from the optimum forward thrust do not usually have a large effect on drilling speed. However, for very small or very large angles of the airleg to the axis of the machine, considerable physical effort is still necessary.

5. The importance of accurate control of thrust on the drilling efficiency of a percussive machine is dependent on several factors, most important being the ground conditions and the available rotation power. Assuming that the rock bring drilled is hard and homogeneous, there is a minimum thrust which will serve to maintain good contact between the bit and the rock (which is dependent on the momentum being transmitted to the bit). Below this value the percussive energy is largely wasted and drilling speed falls off rapidly, as well as allowing more energy to be absorbed in the parts of the machine itself, with greatly increased risk of failures. Provided the rotational power is ample, considerable increases of thrust above the threshold value do not have a very large effect on drilling speed, though of course in all cases there is an upper limit at which stalling will occur and

drilling effectively cease. Also the rate of bit wear increases rapidly with high thrusts in abrasive ground. With limited rotational power the thrust is much more critical, simply because the margin of thrust between maintenance of contact and stalling is much smaller. Also in broken, soft or fissured rock excessive thrust is liable to cause the bit to jam.

6. The introduction of airlegs was undoubtedly a very major step forward in rock drilling with comparatively small, lightweight machines. The further improvements in their design which have taken place recently have been related to ease of control and operation. By incorporating suitable air passages from the backhead/handle region of the drill through the cylinder and the hinge mechanism to the airleg, all the controls for the drill and the leg have been grouped together so that they can be operated as conveniently as possible. The number of controls (and of air passages) required has been increased by the use of 'retractable' (i.e. double acting) airlegs, which add greatly to the facility with which the toe of the leg may be retracted and brought forward to a new foothold as the drill progresses into the rock. The pressure air has been transmitted to the lower side of the piston either through a hollow piston rod or by an external duct, which now often takes the form of a double walled tube.

7. It is often thought, quite wrongly, that the design of this important adjunct to the rock drill is a simple matter - just another air cylinder. This is not the case and the combination of dirt, acid water, very heavy vibration and side loadings, with general rough handling, does in fact present quite a substantial problem, to achieve reliability and a reasonable life within tight cost and weight limits. A variant of the airleg machine is the stoper. In this, which is intended for drilling more or less vertically upwards, the airleg is attached rigidly in line with the drill, usually co-axial with it.

8. The mountings and controls for heavier machines, whether used above or below ground, have become much more complex in the past few years. This has happened for several reasons - the introduction of heavier equipment which necessitates power handling, the need to keep down expensive labour costs and to increase productivity, the desire for greater accuracy of drilling, and so on. The first major improvement was the introduction of hydraulic rams for positioning the drill carriage. Whereas for the light, basically handheld machine, pneumatic cylinders are adequate and convenient as there is usually no alternative power source available and the forces required are not large, the heavy types are usually required to drill longer holes and, therefore, stability and accuracy of alignment become more important. Hydraulics can provide the larger forces required, compactly, and enable the drill carriage to be locked firmly into position, with very little bounce, apart from general flexing of the structure. On a large rig there is no great difficulty in providing the small amount of hydraulic power required for positioning rams, especially as this is not needed at the same time as power to operate the drill. The simplest solution is to use an air motor to drive the hydraulic pump - not an efficient means of energy conversion (perhaps about 10% overall, from prime mover to hydraulic output), but this is not important. Alternatively, of course, an electric motor or a small auxiliary engine can be used. On some small rigs hand pumped hydraulics are used. Given a hydraulic system, this can be used to operate a large number of different motions - lift, swing, slew, dump and crowd. These enable the drill to be positioned almost anywhere within the reach of the boom, covering a wide range of angular positions. The limitations are provided by mechanical interference, which usually results in small blind spots which cannot be reached without moving the base of the machine. Further recent refinements have been the provision of telescopic extending booms to increase the reach, and of 'roll-over' mechanisms which enable the drill carriage to be placed below or alongside the boom, so helping to eliminate blind spots, and are also useful when it is necessary to drill horizontal holes as close to the floor as possible. Naturally the feed mechanism to drive the drill along its carriage has also become power operated, either a pneumatic or hydraulic motor is used to drive the feed screw or chain; sometimes a straight drive from a cylinder is used.

9. Having achieved the maximum flexibility of positioning, within the limitations of the size of the boom and drill cradle, further development has been concentrated on reducing the amount of effort and skill required of the operator. For tunnelling (whether for civil engineering or mining purposes), it is often necessary to drill a number of holes accurately parallel to its axis. The longer the holes (and hence the 'pull' per round), the more accurate they should be for a successful blast. In order to make the tunnel as nearly as possible the required size and thereby to avoid the need for subsequent trimming or for filling the overbreak with concrete - both expensive and time consuming - the peripheral holes must be accurately drilled at a small angle outwards from the axis. To achieve these objects a number of rigs have been fitted, in recent years, with automatic means of keeping the drill carriage parallel to the tunnel axis (assuming that the machine is set up in the correct alignment in the first place, of course). One example is the Holman Autopanto which operates by means of a hydraulic servo system. The rig itself and the circuit for the control mechanism are shown in Figures 1a and 1b. As will be seen, the rig is equipped with a linear actuator for roll-over and this, together with the available motions of the drill carriage, enables it to cover the face very effectively. This system also has the advantage that it is easy to arrange for an override of the automatic parallel motion, so that holes can be drilled at an angle when desired. The mechanism will then return to parallel motion on operation of the appropriate control without any need for re-setting. There are other systems which operate on a purely mechanical pantograph linkage system, where this facility is more difficult to arrange.

10. The next step in automating a rig of this kind is to arrange for automatic collaring (i.e. starting the hole), drilling with the correct feed pressure, stopping at the end of the drill travel, rapid retraction and shut off. Mechanically this is not difficult, but is of considerable assistance in enabling one operator to supervise two or more machines. A system using some of these features is incorporated in the large drill rigs, shown in Figure 2. which have recently been supplied for a tunnelling contract in Rumania. These do not have the automatic parallel motion feature, though this could be added, but there are several other features of note, such as adjustable platform height for the upper drifter, provision for coupling two rigs side

by side with a hydraulically operated bridging
section on the platform, (though each can be towed
separately over rough ground and manoeuvred into
position), hydraulically positioned explosives
charging cab and so on. The automatic feed system
is operated pneumatically by means of the circuit
shown in Figure 3.

11. The ultimate stage of sophistication which has
so far been attempted, in a rig of this kind for
hard rock tunnelling, is to automate the drilling
of the entire "round" or sequence of holes. No
system of this kind is yet known to be available as
a standard product on the market, but there have
been several prototypes. One was applied to the
Autopanto (shown in Figure 4) and this was displayed
at the International Mining Equipment Exhibition in
London in 1969. In this the automatic feed and retract cycle is followed by automatic movement of the
boom to the next hole position. This is controlled
by a metal (or plastic) "punched card" template and
operated by a pneumatic fluidic circuit. This is
appropriate in most circumstances, requiring very
little power, being fireproof and resistant, if
properly enclosed, to most of the hazards of the
environment in which it must operate.

12. There are, in fact, many possible systems of
operation and control for this type of equipment.
The essentials are reliability, safety and reasonable simplicity, with ease of changing the pattern
of holes to be drilled. It is, of course, one thing
to make a rig like this work satisfactorily in an
experimental shop and quite another to achieve a
real advantage in actual tunnelling operations. It
remains to be seen whether one can often enough find
sufficiently consistent rock conditions, for long
enough at a time, to enable a pre-programmed drilling pattern to be successfully used, cutting out the
element of operator's judgement when he approaches
each fresh round. So far as the author knows there
is insufficient experience yet available to give an
opinion on this point, but there is no doubt that if
it can be made practical, some system of this kind
can both provide substantial savings in time and
manpower and also enable the operator to retire to
a less noisy and safer position while the round is
being drilled, being available mainly to deal with
broken, stuck or blunt steels and bits.

13. Above ground, for both quarrying and civil
engineering, the bulk of drilling is of near
vertical holes, which are usually much longer than
those drilled underground for tunnelling. Whereas
in the latter a single drill rod is usually sufficient (up to about 4m. depth of hole), above ground
holes are often upwards of 15-20 m. in depth.
Naturally this precludes the use of one-piece drill
rods (or tubes with down-the-hole drills), and this
results in a need for drill rod handling equipment.
Whilst rods or tubes are up to about 3m. long they
can be handled manually, but increasing drilling
speeds, achieved by more powerful drills or by the
use of higher air pressures, put a premium on the
time involved in adding a length of rod, which becomes a significant factor in determining overall
drilling rates. Also even a rod of this size is not
the nicest thing to have to manhandle in an unstable,
near-vertical position, perhaps near the edge of a
quarry or a cutting, in a gale and rain. So everything - speed and safety, amenity and economy -
indicates the need for automation of this feature.

14. The usual method is by means of a magazine
(sometimes, when of a rotary type, known as a
'carousel') attached to the vertical mast and holding
the maximum number of rods or tubes required for one
hole. This can be actuated, pneumatically or hydraulically, into position to add or retrieve one rod
at a time and there is also a mechanism for making
or unmaking the screwed joints. With a system like
this the height of the mast (and hence the length
of individual rods) is determined largely by consideration of stability and transport of the rig itself. A hoist is provided to assist with the loading and unloading of the magazine.

15. Rigs for use above ground are usually mounted
on caterpillar tracks, as they have to operate over
very rough ground. Propulsion may be either by means
of an auxiliary engine on the rig (via hydraulic
pumps and motors) or by compressed air motors powered by the (towed) compressor which operates the rig
and hammer mechanisms. This is a singular "lifting
oneself by one's own bootstraps" sort of operation,
inefficient in terms of power, but simple and
effective for the short distances usually required.
There has recently been a greatly increased tendency
to provide a cabin for the driller, especially in
the larger rigs, to give him protection from the
weather and from noise. This, of course, in itself
poses a need to enable the rod changing and other
functions to be carried out by remote control.

DRILLING MACHINES

16. Actual drilling machines in use today are of
two main types. One is the conventional percussive
hammer with some kind of rotation mechanism to index
the bit, which is itself at the end of a drill steel
or string of steels. Only the bit goes down the hole,
the machine staying outside, and therefore its size
is independent of the size of hole. The other
involves the hammer complete with its bit, which is
closely attached, going down to the bottom of the
hole on the end of a tube which guides it and transmits working fluids and rotational torque to it -
the down-the-hole drill.

17. The latter have so far been exclusively pneumatically powered, though hydraulics would have
some positive advantages if certain difficulties
were to be overcome. Naturally, the hammer itself
must be smaller than the hole it drills and, making
allowance for an annulus to allow the escape of
drilling detritus and exhaust air, and the thickness
of the cylinder wall, which normally has to contain
some air passages, as well as an inherent need for
robustness of construction, the ratio of hammer
piston area to hole area is limited. The smaller
the absolute size of the hole, the more onerous is
the limitation and largely because of this, and
therefore, the difficulty of getting a reasonable
drilling performance, there have been very few
hammers of this type designed to drill holes less
than 75 mm in diameter. The tendency towards bigger
machines is also emphasised by the fact that they
are used for relatively deep holes (in quarrying,
well drilling and civil engineering) because the
greater the depth the greater their potential
advantage over the conventional machine in performance and accuracy. Provided that the effect of air
pressure loss in the feed tubes can be kept lower
than that of energy losses in drill steel couplings,
the rate of loss of drilling speed with hole depth
will be lower for the down-the-hole machine than for
the conventional one. Naturally, deeper holes tend
to be larger in diameter than shallow ones, as the
explosive energy input required is greater, apart
from possible difficulties in charging small holes,
and in drilling them straight.

18. One of the major determinants of drilling speed is the ratio of piston area to hole area, and Figure 5 shows how this varies for a typical range of machines for holes from 80 mm to 150 mm diameter. These were not all designed at the same time and techniques have developed, but the tendency to a more advantageous ratio in the bigger sizes is evident. In any attempt to push these figures significantly higher, serious attention must be paid to maintenance of reliability and ability to clear drilling chips.

19. Piston weights and strokes, detailed valve design and many other factors affect performance also of course, but except by using complex devices such as tandem piston arrangements, the only other basic method of getting more power into a down-the-hole hammer is by increasing the pressure of the operating fluid. A semi-empirical equation often used by designers of percussive drills (of both basic types) is:

$$\text{Drilling speed} \propto \frac{P^{3/2} \; A^{3/2} \; S^{1/2}}{W^{1/2}}$$

Where P is the mean pressure in the cylinder
A is the effective piston area exposed to that pressure
S is the piston stroke
W is the piston weight.

So the design process seeks to optimise drilling speed in accordance with this formula, but also bearing in mind two more basic factors. These are the stresses in the piston, steel and bit generated by the impacts, and the air consumption (or prime mover power consumption in the more general sense). Stresses are determined by impact velocity, allied to the geometry of the piston and of the bit (and steels if any). The geometry of the various elements is important in that it determines the effects of reflected waves superimposed upon the primary stress waves, which are themselves mainly dependent on impact velocities. This applies to all types of percussive machines operated by fluid pressure acting on a piston, but especially with down-the-hole machines the limitations on space soon lead to consideration of the possibilities of higher pressures, after optimising the other factors. (For example, in the case of one particular machine, increasing the air pressure ratio from 6.4 to 11.2 bars resulted in an increase of drilling speed by a factor of 2.16 - not far off the value given by the $P^{3/2}$ value, which would have been 2.30). In practice it is necessary to re-tune a machine to suit particular pressures, otherwise it will either be overstressed at the higher values or under utilised at the lower end of the range. Such re-tuning (involving changes in piston weight and stroke mainly) will tend to flatten the curve and reduce the advantage of higher pressures. Nevertheless it is usually economical to operate at as high a pressure as possible because, even though the compressor is more expensive and air consumption higher, the increase in output more than pays for these factors when all labour and depreciation costs are taken into account. This tendency to higher pressures has been taking place over the past decade or more and whereas nominal air pressures of 7 bars were the rule, they now go up to 17 bars with 12 bars as a common level.

20. The use of higher pressures not only increases the forces acting on the piston, giving higher blow energies, but also improves the clearance of detritus from the hole bottom. The quantity of air exhausted in this region is increased and also the pressure, since full expansion within the machine is

impractical. These effects contribute significantly to improved performance and help to keep down the rate of bit wear by reducing the grinding action of loose dust and chips round the bit head. On the other hand excessive flushing air velocities around the hammer can cause serious erosion.

21. One of the most interesting features of recent years has been the success of the button bit, where the tungsten carbide 'cutters' take the form of a large number of small hemispherical ended inserts, distributed strategically over the face of the bit, instead of the more usual chisel-like cutting edges. The button type can give improved performance in some types of rock, especially the medium-hard limestones which account for a great deal of quarrying in this country. Though they cannot be re-sharpened their effective life in the right kind of rock can be very favourable, and they now take a substantial share of the total market. Recently chisel ended buttons have been used, and improved matching of body and button materials has made more practicable their use in more abrasive rocks.

22. The 'conventional' types of rock drill - out of the hole machines - have made substantial advances also, but these have been mainly as logical and gradual improvements along anticipated paths of development. The smaller hand or airleg supported machines have become lighter in relation to their power, but have nevertheless been uprated to near the limit of what it is reasonable to expect an operator to handle, for a shift at a time. In particular airleg controls have become more sophisticated, including power retraction and incorporation of all the controls, together with those of the drill itself, on the backhead. This certainly makes operation much more safe and certain, especially with a very powerful machine. It is interesting that in some parts of the world, notably the Far East, it has been necessary to produce machines of the same type, but somewhat less powerful and lighter in weight, so as to be suitable for the physique of the local miners. (Figure 6). Mining at high altitudes (up to about 5000 m in South America) also introduces similar physical limitations.

23. In the past few years there has been a rapidly increasing emphasis on noise reduction - very necessary, as in a heading with several machines operating simultaneously noise levels can be in excess of 130 dBA, which is very much above that at which permanent damage to hearing occurs, without protection. Though there seems little prospect of significantly reducing the noise emanating from the struck steel, the exhaust noise can be greatly reduced. First attempts to achieve this were mainly by means of clipped on plastic (usually polyurethane) mufflers, which were effective in noise control and were surprisingly durable, even in the very arduous conditions of operation. These have been largely superseded by permanently attached metal mufflers, which though generally giving about the same degree of sound attenuation, satisfy the regulations in some countries or provinces, which insist that it shall not be possible for the operator to remove the muffler. Also some mine managements appear to be happier with metal mufflers than with polyurethane on grounds of durability, though this is probably more psychological than real. A significant limit to exhaust noise control is set by the need to avoid icing, in adverse conditions. However, with careful design the exhaust noise can be reduced to a level where the 'bark' has been taken out of it and it does not contribute significantly to the overall level. Individual ear protection remains essential, but is much more likely to be effective when muffled

machines are used.

24. Incidentally one of the less-realised advantages of the down-the-hole drill is that its exhaust air expansion occurs at the bottom of the hole, so that noise both from this source and from the percussive action is largely eliminated and it is only the compressor and any rig ancillaries that are a cause of trouble in this respect.

25. The bigger, rig mounted 'drifters' have developed from being simply larger versions of the hand-held machines to more specialised and versatile forms. Many now use separate rotation motors, rather than relying on the usual rifle bar gear for indexing the bit. This has a number of advantages particularly where the need is for long holes underground, for block caving operations, and considerable rotation power is required. Rotation speed can be controlled independently of piston feed, which is valuable when rock consistency varies, especially in crushed or broken zones. Rotation power is not so liable to be reduced by wear as with a rifle bar, and the ability to reverse rotation is very useful for coupling and uncoupling extension rods. The motors may be mounted on the front or the rear of the machine, but the drive is through the chuck which holds the steel, via a reduction gearbox. Occasionally a feed motor is also incorporated in the back end of the machine. So far there has been little tendency to use higher air pressures with machines of this type - it is easier to use a slightly larger machine to get more power - but there has been an increasing realisation of the importance of pressure losses and leaks in pipelines which for many years have reduced effective pressures at the working faces, especially in mines, to values much lower than the nominal 6-7 bars provided by the compressor. In many cases substantial gains have been made in this respect, but there is often still scope for further worthwhile improvements.

HYDRAULIC PERCUSSIVE MACHINES

26. There is little doubt that the most interesting aspect of the development of rock drills in the next few years is the extent to which hydraulics will be accepted as an alternative power medium to pneumatics for percussive mechanisms. For many years the potential of hydraulics has been an attraction - especially the ability to use high pressures with economy of power and so to pack high performance into small space, with no exhaust noise. In the 1920's Dormans of Stafford made a hydraulic drifter; one of its serious limitations at that time was the 'hose' which consisted of ball jointed lengths of steel pipe; hardly a convenient arrangement. After many frustrating attempts, by many different companies, there is now a small number of machines actually on the market, but insufficient experience as yet to judge their long term prospects. Undoubtedly the lack of success of a number of efforts was due to a failure to realise the special needs and hard times experienced by equipment used in mining - hydraulic expertise is of little value without this. In addition however, there are numerous highly practical side effects to be taken into account when comparing hydraulic and pneumatic operation and which can tilt the balance in particular circumstances. It is obvious that the application to down-the-hole machines would give the opportunity of getting much more power into the bit. However, this has so far not been done, probably mainly because of the practical difficulties of making satisfactory

joints between tubes (bearing in mind the dirty working conditions) to deal with flow and return of the hydraulic fluid as well as with the flushing air or water. A simplification might be possible by the use of an "AC" or standing wave hydraulic system which needs no return pipe, but no successful machines based on this principle have yet emerged and the need for frequent changes in feed pipe length might also prove a problem with this approach.

27. For rig mounted drifters the problems are different and not so difficult. Weight, handling qualities and hose vibration and wear are of minor importance compared with hand held machines. Present day pneumatic machines of the most powerful types are already working with individual blow energies which are near the limit for transmission through strings of coupled rods without resulting in too frequent fractures; some are near the limit in other respects, such as piston stresses. So apart from noise reduction, the main advantages of hydraulics must be sought either in the ability to increase blow frequencies (and hence power output) and/or to increase overall efficiency. Both should be possible, especially the latter as overall efficiencies for pneumatic drifters (from prime mover to rock drill piston energy) are now in the region of 15-20%, so there is obviously room for improvement. However, it should be remembered that, desirable though an increase of efficiency would be, the proportion of the total cost of driving a tunnel due to the power used for drilling is very small - a few percent only - so big cost reductions cannot be expected from this source. Increased drilling speed should probably be the primary aim.

28. Amongst the secondary advantages of the pneumatic system which would be sacrificed by the use of hydraulics are the ventilation and cooling provided by the exhaust (together with undesirable fogging, in some circumstances). Probably more important is the relative insensitivity of the pneumatic machine to dirt, water and general rough handling. Hydraulic machines certainly must be serviced in clean conditions, by reasonably skilled fitters. Any dirt or mishandling can cause expensive damage, whereas pneumatic machines can put up with a surprising amount of abuse. Leaks in hydraulic lines are not permissible, whereas in pneumatics they represent only a loss of power. Probably the pump needs to be reasonably close to the drill when a hydraulic system is used and this necessitates putting a prime mover underground. Introduction of hydraulics to existing mines is likely to be a much slower process, because of this and the existing air distribution system, than it is for civil tunnelling or quarrying. Fire risks may be increased due to this and to any leaks. The cooling system will discharge heat fairly near the working face. Many other arguments can be adduced on both sides, and it is probably true that only extensive practical experience by users will decide the real merits of the case; different conclusions may well emerge from different operating circumstances. There is certain though to be a substantial effort to establish hydraulics as the working fluid in percussive machines in the near future.

SLOTTING

29. An interesting development which has been taking place in South Africa over the past several years consists of an attempt to adopt what is called 'selective mining'. Since the 'reef' in

which the gold is contained is very thin (often of the order of 100 mm in thickness) it would be highly desirable to remove this separately from the 'country' rock above and below it, which must also be moved in order to keep the stope wide enough to work in. This would greatly reduce the amount of material that had to be raised to the surface and milled to separate the metal, as well as having other substantial advantages. The first attempts used a slotting machine operating like a shaping machine, with a cutter actuated by a hydraulic ram, which is used to cut slots above and below the reef, which can then be broken out relatively easily and taken away in large chunks, before tackling the waste rock. This method has problems due to the very large forces required, making the whole equipment very heavy, and to the wear on the tool and the difficulty in making it stiff enough to cut a slot which is quite deep in relation to its width. However, considerable progress has been made and extensive tests are still being carried out.

30. Another alternative method being tried is to cut the slots by means of a percussive machine, similar to a small rock drill, mounted so that it can be traversed laterally as well as fed forward into the rock. This has considerable advantages in lightness and simplicity, using largely conventional basic equipment, familiar to the miners, but also encounters problems of tool life and of control, as any tendency to 'dig in' during traversing, if a softer spot is encountered, can lead to heavy side loads and to stalling. Again an encouraging degree of success is being achieved and tests are continuing. Apart from the immediate problems of cutting the slots economically and quickly, the changes required in the whole mining operation if such methods are widely introduced will be such that full evaluation of the consequences will take some time. It will be interesting to see, if slotting proves successful in the specialised conditions of the South African gold mines, to what extent it finds applications in other mining and civil engineering techniques.

Fig.1a. Holman Autopanto drill rig

24

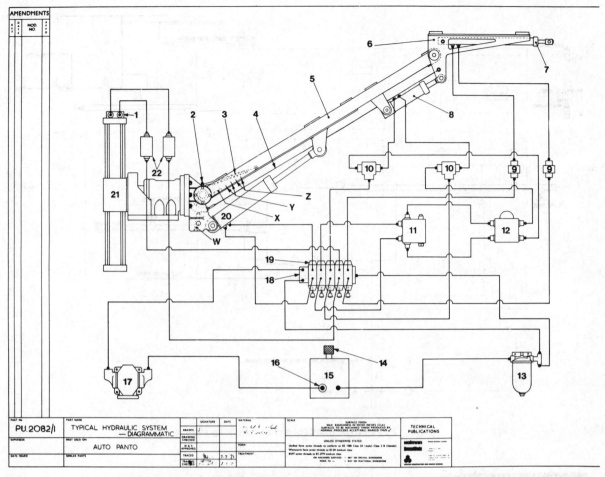

AMENDMENTS

PU.2082/1   TYPICAL HYDRAULIC SYSTEM — DIAGRAMMATIC

AUTO PANTO

TECHNICAL PUBLICATIONS

Fig.1b. Automatic control circuit for Autopanto

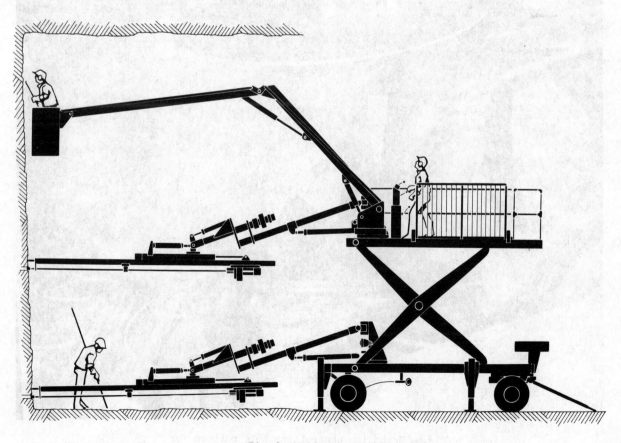

Fig.2. Heavy drill rig

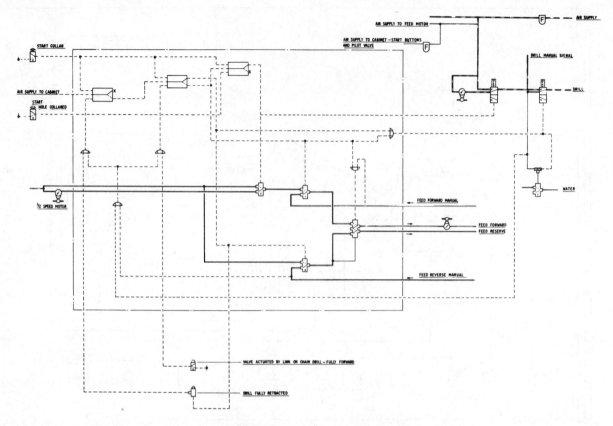

Fig.3. Automatic drill feed system

Fig.4. Mechanism controlling hole pattern for
a complete round

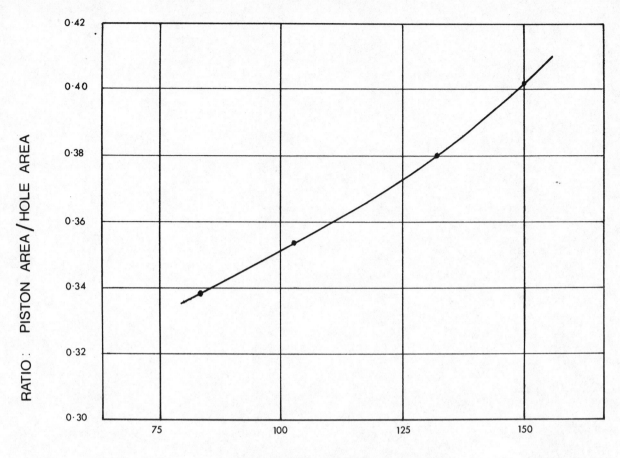

MINIMUM HOLE DIA (mm)

Fig.5. Ratio of piston area to hole area in a
family of down-the-hole drills

Fig.6. Holman Silver Spear airleg drill

MINIMUM HOLE DIA (mm)

C21/74

MODERN MINING AND TUNNELLING DEPEND ON A GOOD COMBINATION OF COMPRESSED AIR AND HYDRAULIC POWER

L. OTTOSSON

Technical Director, Atlas Copco MCT AB, S102 60 Stockholm 4, Sweden

T. I. CAMERON, BSc(Hons), FICE, MIStructE

Manager, Technical Development Field Service, Atlas Copco MCT AB,
Maylands Avenue, Hemel Hempstead, Hertfordshire

The Ms. of this paper was received at the Institution on 23rd July 1973 and accepted for publication on 24th October 1973.

SYNOPSIS   In developing modern mechanized equipment for mining, tunnelling and quarrying, hydraulic components are used to an increasing extent for positioning feeds, booms, etc. In the paper, examples will be given of these developments. Some examples of actions taken to reduce noise, dust and vibration from mechanized equipment will also be given.

INTRODUCTION

1.   All kinds of mechanical equipment used for different types of rock excavation works, such as open pit mining, underground mining, tunnelling, and so on, often work under very severe and difficult conditions. The rock is usually hard and abrasive. Underground there is a lot of humidity in the air and from the rock itself a lot of water, sometimes very corrosive, often pours over the machinery. Working spaces are often very small, and very limited in geometrical shape. On the surface, equipment is subjected to all extremes of weather, and dust and mud are always present. Nevertheless, the miner or the contractor demands high capacity from this machinery, and also high reliability.

2.   The limited dimensions of working space mean that the designer has to design this equipment in such a way that the equipment still gives a high production capacity. This means that a designer certainly has to use all his ingenuity and all his know-how to be able to solve the different problems.

3.   One of the most widely used energy media to power mining equipment is compressed air. Under the conditions mentioned, compressed air has several advantages, such as:-

It is possible to get high power from small dimensions, for example from piston motors and vane-type motors.

For powering percussive rock drills, compressed air has for a long time been almost the only energy medium to be used.

Compressed air can be distributed over long distances.

Leakage of compressed air does no harm. On the other hand, in many cases it just makes the ventilation still better and provides a cooling effect in hot mines.

Compressed air can also be used in control systems, and also for example in air cylinders for opening chutes and similar devices.

4.   During the last 10 - 20 years, however, we have seen how compressed air is used in combination with other types of energy media, such as hydraulic, and in some cases also different types of electrically controlled valves are used in today's mining and contracting machinery. The combination of different types of energy media is interesting also from historical point of view. If we go back 100 - 120 years, we can see how water was used to compress air, and this compressed air was then used for powering percussive rock drills. Today you can see examples of the other way of using these two energy media. In much of our mining equipment today, we can see how compressed air is used for powering a hydraulic pump, and this pump is then used for positioning hydraulic cylinders, or even powering hydraulic motors.

5.   In the following we will give some examples of how compressed air equipment and different types of hydraulic equipment are used together, and how, during the later years, hydraulics is coming more and more into the picture.

UNDERGROUND ROCK DRILLING EQUIPMENT

1.   In the middle of the 19th century in different countries, people were engaged in developing a mechanized percussive rock drill to replace the man with his sledge hammer and his drill steel. In the first attempt one tried to use steam to move the piston back and forth in a cylinder. However, it was very soon found out that steam was not a good medium to be used underground in tunnels; the atmosphere was too hot, and there was too much humidity in the air. Therefore, very soon, compressed air was used as an energy medium. One of the first Alpine tunnels to be driven by compressed air was the Mont Cenis, in Switzerland. It was started by hand-drilling but in 1861 the Italian Sommeiller invented a compressed air rock drill which was put to work there. At that time it was necessary to have nine spare rock drills for each one working, as the reliability was not better than that.

2.   During the years at the end of the 19th century and in the beginning of the 20th, we could see how the capacity of the compressed air-driven rock drill was increased and the reliability became better and better. The rock drills were both hand-held and mounted on simple feeds and other devices. Not before the beginning of the 1940's did a major step forward take place. This was the introduction of a light self-rotating pusher-leg fed rock drill with

cemented carbide-tipped drill steel. This became known as the "Swedish Method" which also meant "one man, one machine" instead of the two men generally required up to that time. In this case, compressed air was also used to feed the rock drill steel into the hole, and to take some of the weight of the rock drill from the man.

3. In the 1950's the demand for mechanization of rock drilling equipment had become even more insistent. Therefore, in the middle of the 50's, the light rock drill was mounted on a type of mechanical device on which the rock drill was sliding and pushed forward still by using an air leg. This meant that the weight of the rock drill itself was not so important any more, as the man had not to lift the rock drill for every hole he drilled. Therefore it was possible to increase the size of the rock drill, and thereby also the penetration speed.

4. The first boom was moved by hand. It was very soon found out that if hydraulic cylinders were installed to lift the boom, and to push it sideways, quite a lot of physical demand from the driller was taken away. This was in Europe the start of the first hydraulic boom to carry a feed for a rock drill and the rock drill itself.

5. The first mechanical devices were best suited for drilling parallel holes. However, in many cases it is necessary to drill holes at an angle to the line of the tunnel or drift, and therefore other types of booms have been designed, such as this shown on illustration No. 1, a present day design. In this type of boom, the feed for the rock drill can be swung in almost all directions, both horizontally and vertically. All the movements of the different parts of the booms and the feeds are actuated by hydraulic cylinders. The reason why hydraulic cylinders have been chosen here is that it is possible to position the feed or the boom in an exact position when the hydraulic fluid is locked in between valves, and the reason why it is not flexible is that hydraulic fluid is not compressible. This is a feature that is necessary for this type of equipment, as we want to drill a hole in an exactly preset direction and at a pre-set point. In this case it is not possible to use air cylinders, as the air is compressible, and that means that one cannot get a fixed setting of the feed with air cylinders.

6. Before hydraulic cylinders were used, different types of mechanical components were tried, such as long feed screws and similar things to actuate the boom. However, the conditions in the tunnel or in the mine where there are a lot of rock cuttings from the hole flowing over the feed screw or mechanical linkages, make it almost impossible to get these parts to stand up, and here the hydraulic cylinders and the hydraulic system have shown very big advantages, as it is a much easier problem to keep all the water and cuttings out from the cylinder by good sealing around the piston rod. The prime mover for the hydraulic pump, that powers these cylinders, is normally an air-driven motor. Here you can see the first example of how compressed air and hydraulics are working together. To move such a rig from place to place in the mine or tunnel, it is most convenient to use diesel power. Although the carrier is articulated, in order to negotiate the sharpest curves it is also necessary to be able to swing the booms while on the move. For this purpose an auxiliary hydraulic pump is driven by the diesel engine.

7. It is also interesting to note that the parallel-holding facility on these booms is accomplished by a purely hydraulic system as shown in fig. 2 in diagram form. Some types of feeds for the rock drill are also hydraulically operated. The hydraulic pump for these purposes is normally air motor driven, as it can be undesirable to have the diesel engine operating at the working face for the relatively small power output required. Such a pump is shown in fig. 3.

8. In illustration No. 4 a further type of underground mining rig is shown, the Simba 322. This very modern design, for long-hole drilling, incorporates noise-damped rock drills and a vibration-free operator's platform. These features have been built into the rig from the beginning and were not added to an existing design. As in the previous example, all movements of the feeds are made by hydraulics, again supplied by an air-hydraulic pump.

SURFACE DRILLING EQUIPMENT

1. The development of surface drilling equipment has proceeded from the hand-held light rock drill through simple mechanical feeds and rigs to the heavy rock drill mounted as shown in the example in illustration No. 5. This example is used for deep-hole drilling in quarry benches and open pit mines. Here the boom, carrying the feed and rock drill, has been mounted on a crawler carrier. The whole carrier is driven by two compressed air piston motors, one to each track. Compressed air is used to drive the crawler, to power the rock drill feed, to drive the percussion and rotation of the rock drill and it is also used for flushing the drilled hole of all cuttings. An air-driven hydraulic pump supplies hydraulic cylinders which are used to actuate all the movements of the boom carrying the feed beam and also the position of the feed itself. To enable the carrier to traverse rough and uneven ground, it is necessary to arrange that the tracks may oscillate to equalize pressure on the ground. This is arranged through twin hydraulic cylinders which are interconnected to control the relative movements of the tracks. Fig. 6.

2. In illustration No. 7 another type of surface drilling equipment can be seen. Here two rock drills with feeds have been mounted on twin booms, and again mounted on a crawler. The principle of design is the same as in the previous picture. The main difference in this case is that electrically controlled valves have been introduced for actuating the hydraulic cylinders used for positioning the feed. This means that the operator can adjust the feed to the right hole angle and bearing standing at the side of the feed and working with two small levers. However, the operator can also operate the cylinders for swinging and lifting the booms from the rear part of the carrier, which is of great advantage when he is travelling over rough terrain, and to be able to balance the carrier he often has to adjust the position of the rock drill and the feed. In this design electrical power comes from a small battery which is mounted in the control console at the rear of the carrier. There is also an option for a generator driven by an air motor. Fig. 8 shows the schematic layout of the electrical system.

3. Environmental regulations in some countries demand an extremely low level of dust in the vicinity of the drilling equipment and it has become necessary to extract all the dust and chippings from the hole and prevent them reaching the atmosphere.

In illustrations 9 and 10 can be seen the latest type of dust control equipment, mounted on the carrier. The apparatus consists of a hood around the drill stem connected by a flexible hose to a dust collector and filter. It is wholly operated by compressed air. The sealing of the hood and the automatic operation of the collector depend on the Coanda effect and the creation of a partial vacuum.

EXPLORATION EQUIPMENT

1. Up to this point descriptions have been given how hydraulic components have been used to solve problems of positioning rock drills and feeds on different types of air powered equipment. However, during the last few years hydraulic energy has been used more and more as a power transmission medium. An example of this is the diamond core drill, shown in illustration No. 11. This core drill is built up of a rotation unit, a feed and a positioning device for the feed, and on the left of the picture can be seen the hydraulic power pack which is either air, electric or diesel-driven. The reason that there is also an air-driven unit is that in many mines there is a compressed air system, but not an electric system with the capacity needed to power this drill. The total power required is around 25 H.P. Most of the power is used for rotating the diamond bit, the core barrel and the drill string, and the other part of the hydraulic energy is used for advancing and retracting the rotary drill head.

2. In core drilling with conventional types of equipment, rod handling has been completely manual and has been very time-consuming. In this new design the whole rod handling system has been mechanized so that the making and breaking of joints, the addition of further rods or the removal of rods extracted from the hole is accomplished by the rotary head, the chucks in the centralizer and the feeding device working through hydraulic interlocks.

UNDERGROUND LOADING EQUIPMENT

1. A further extensive application of compressed air underground is its use to power loading equipment. In illustration No. 12 can be seen an example of a compressed air-driven loader. In this design there are two vane-type or piston-type air motors powering the wheels, one compressed air motor powering the movements of the bucket and a cylinder tipping the body.

2. The steering of the loader is accomplished by a drive-and-brake arrangement which means that when the right hand side wheels are under power and the left hand side wheels are braked, the loader swings to the left. The left hand side wheels can also be reversed and that means that the loader more or less turns around its central vertical axis. Of course these movements can also be accomplished in the opposite sense. This gives extremely high manoeuverability in a very restricted working space.

3. In many cases these types of loaders are working under newly exposed rock faces, which means that it should be an advantage if the operator of the loader could be standing behind the loader without any danger of falling rock from the roof. Such a device has also been designed, and in this case electrically operated valves have been used to control the loader. As can be seen in illustration

No. 13, the operator is standing at the side of the loader, carrying a small box in front. On this small box he has two levers, which exactly replace the two levers on the side of the loader which he is normally working with. On the control box there is also an emergency stop button, which, if pushed, stops all movements of the loader. In this design, the electric supply comes from a small generator mounted on the loader itself and driven by a small vane-type air motor. See layout in fig. 14.

4. On the original design of this loader an air cylinder was used to raise the body for dumping the load. The air cylinder occupied most of the space between the wheels. In spite of the fact that a very large diameter air cylinder was used, practical experience showed that under certain circumstances it was neither powerful enough nor fast enough in its action. The designer therefore had to choose another system. A small hydraulic pump was installed, powered by an air motor, and the air cylinder replaced by a hydraulic cylinder. As the hydraulic system works at a much higher pressure than that possible for an air system, adequate power and speed became available from much smaller equipment. Here is another example of how air and hydraulic systems work together.

5. In modern mining there is a definite trend towards bigger and bigger equipment. Illustration No. 15 shows a new type of loader, where the same principle is used as in the previous example, i.e. there is a bucket loading into a big body. However, in this case the capacity of the loader has been considerably increased. The bucket size has been increased to 1 m^3, and the body has been increased up to 5 m^3.

6. There is also a demand from many mines that it should be possible to carry the load quite a distance, say from 100 up to 200 or 300 metres. In this case it can often be troublesome to have an air hose connected to the loader. Firstly air pressure is lost through the long hose, and secondly the hose is very troublesome to take care of when travelling long distances, wear of the outside of the hose is also high and, as power requirements increase, the hose diameter increases, causing still further handling difficulties. An investigation showed here that it would be an advantage to use diesel hydraulic power for this type of loader.

7. The main design of the loader is an articulated type, where the front part and the rear part can swing in relation to each other, and there is also a certain amount of twisting between the two parts. To get good manoeuvrability, the designer put in a hydraulic motor close to each wheel, and so obtained a 4-wheel drive, as the diesel engine then powers two hydraulic pumps - one for each pair of wheels. The cylinders actuating the bucket and the body are of course also hydraulic and powered from a third pump. As another feature to reduce the number of hydraulic cylinders, the designer has had an ingenious idea, where the body is locked to the rod of the big cylinders normally moving the bucket. When the body is locked to the rods for the bucket cylinders, the rods lift the body and empty it into the ore pass.

8. Another small detail in the design is the hydraulic cylinder situated below the body and just behind the bucket, so that in the lowest position of the bucket an extra push forward is obtained by this cylinder, and helps the digging capacity of

the machine in that way.

HYDRAULIC POWER FOR PERCUSSIVE ROCK DRILLS

1.   At the beginning of this paper it was mentioned
that compressed air energy was almost the only energy medium used for percussive rock drills. However, during recent years attempts have been made
in several countries to develop percussive rock
drills which are hydraulically powered. One of the
reasons why it has taken such a long time for the
introduction of a hydraulic percussive rock drill
is that hydraulic fluid, as opposed to compressed
air, is not compressible.

2.   It must be possible to take care of
the kinetic energy in the piston. If the shank
adapter is not in the right place, and the piston
is just hitting air, then in a pneumatic rock drill
there is an air cushion which absorbs the kinetic
energy and then throws the piston back again. With
a hydraulic fluid, this is not possible. If a piston hits a fluid volume, there are immediately very
high shocks with high pressures in the fluid, and
the peaks of these pressures are so high that they
can easily break parts of the rock drill. Therefore,
other ways have to be found to take care of these
shock waves. One way is to put in some kind of
accumulators, which reduce these high pressure peaks.

3.   In a rock drill, driven by hydraulic fluid,
there are also sealing problems around the piston,
and with the high velocity at which these pistons
work - being thrown forward and back again - these
sealing problems seem not easy to solve.

4.   Certainly, there have been a lot of problems,
and mention has been made of the most difficult ones
to solve. However, these have now been solved, and
this means that today hydraulic percussive rock
drills can be seen working, for example in Swedish
mines and underground chambers. Illustration No. 16
shows a rig incorporating drills of this type.

5.   What advantages can you gain by using hydraulic
fluid instead of compressed air? A few could be
mentioned here, such as the high energy capacity of
hydraulic fluid compared with compressed air. In a
hydraulic system, working pressures are around 200
bar, compared to the 5 - 6 bar used in a pneumatic
rock drill. This means that the dimensions of the
rock drill will be reduced for the same amount of
power. Another advantage is that there is a much
higher efficiency with the hydraulic system than
with the compressed air system. This is a thing
that means quite a lot when coming up to high power
consumption for powerful types of rock drills.

6.   On the environmental side, another advantage
is that exhaust noise is completely absent. In the
hydraulic rock drill there is a closed system, and
hydraulic fluid is returned to the pump. The main
source of noise is then the drill string, and this
is a much more difficult problem to reduce than to
reduce the exhaust noise from a pneumatic rock drill.
However, the noise level from a hydraulically powered percussive rock drill can be 10 - 15 dB lower
than for a comparable air-driven machine.

7.   Another advantage is that there is no fog at
all around the rock drill, and that is because there
is no cold exhaust causing humidity in the air to
precipitate as mist and fog. Freezing problems are
also completely eliminated.

8.   However, disadvantages can also be found with
this system of powering a rock drill. For example,
hydraulic energy cannot be transmitted through very
long hoses or net systems. Therefore the hydraulic
power pack must be mounted as close to the rock
drill as possible, i.e. on the rig itself.

CONCLUSIONS

In the paper examples have been given of how compressed air and hydraulic power are working together
to build up sturdy equipment, that can take the
rough handling, has the capacity necessary to do
the job in mines and tunnels, and has also the reliability that a mine manager and a contracting
engineer demand from the equipment.

In some cases electric energy or diesel power has
been added to the two other media, and it can thereby be seen how the manufacturer tries to design his
equipment to give the best possible output and economy for the customer.

However, during recent years it can also be seen
how hydraulic power is coming more and more into
the picture, not only for positioning booms and
feeds, as it was in the beginning, but in recent
times also for powering loaders, rotary drills, and
also percussive rock drills.

Fig.1. Wheel-mounted hydraulic boom rig

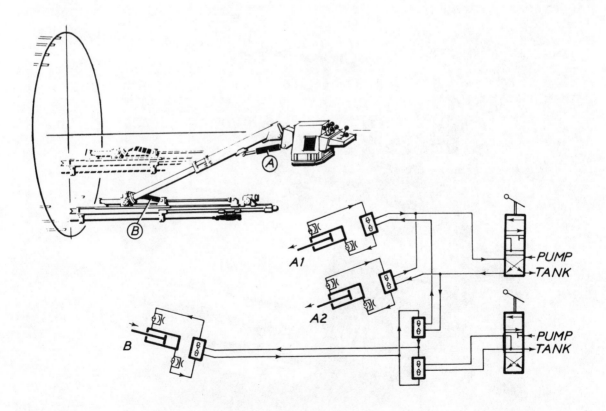

Fig.2. Hydraulic layout for parallel holding

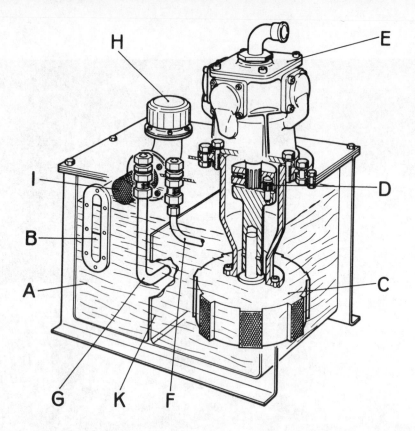

A. Oil tank	F. Pressure connection
B. Sight glass	G. Return connection
C. Hydraulic pump	H. Filler cap
D. Flexible coupling	I. Strainer
E. Pump motor	K. Baffle

Fig.3. Arrangement of air-driven hydraulic pump

Fig.4. Long-hole drill rig, Type Simba 322

Fig.5. Track mounted heavy rock drill

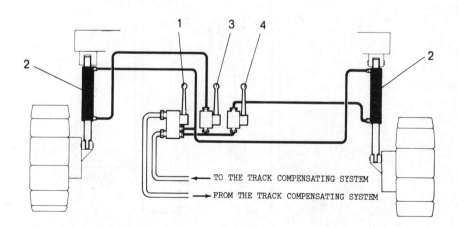

← TO THE TRACK COMPENSATING SYSTEM

→ FROM THE TRACK COMPENSATING SYSTEM

1. Control valve
2. Compensating cylinder
3. Stop cock for left compensating cylinder
4. Stop cock for right compensating cylinder

Fig.6. Hydraulic compensating system for tracks

Fig.7. Twin-boom tracked drill

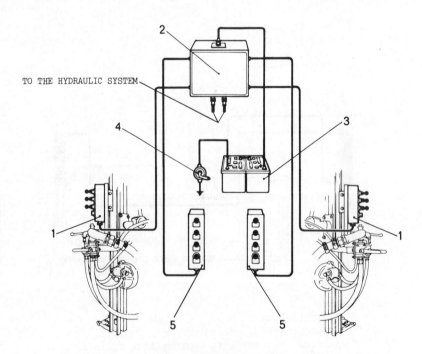

TO THE HYDRAULIC SYSTEM

1. Control box (placed on feed)
2. Junction box
3. Accumulators
4. Switch
5. Control box (placed on bonnet)

Fig.8. Electrically operated drill control system

Fig.9. Dust control equipment mounted on tracked drill

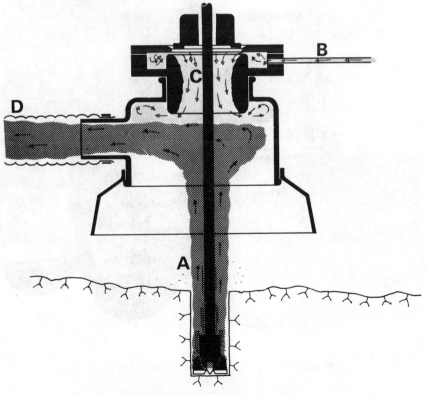

Fig.10. Principle of dust extraction equipment

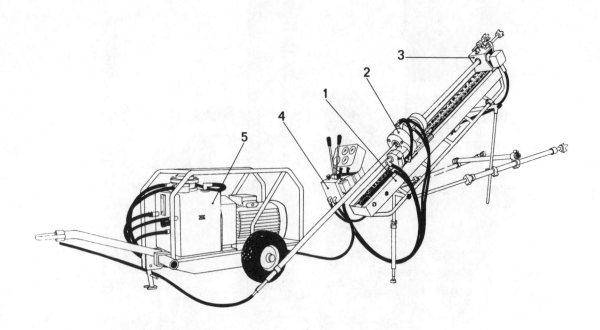

Fig.11. 'Diamec 250' diamond core drill

Fig.12. Compressed air driven mine loader

Fig.13. Remote control of mine loader

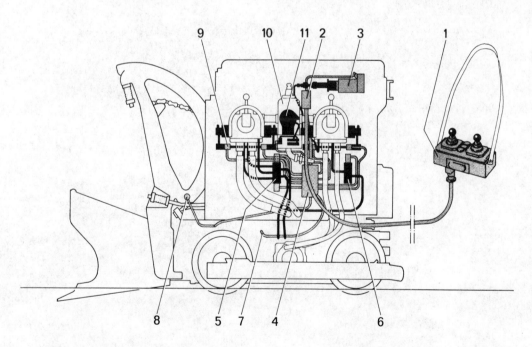

1. Control box
2. Terminal for control box
3. Generator
4. Junction box
5. Electric valve, 4-way
6. Electric valve, 3-way
7. Lead to stop cylinder
8. Breaker for limiting the throw
9. Electric valves
10. Lubricator with main valve
11. Emergency stop

Remote control for track-bound loader

Fig.14. Layout of loader remote control

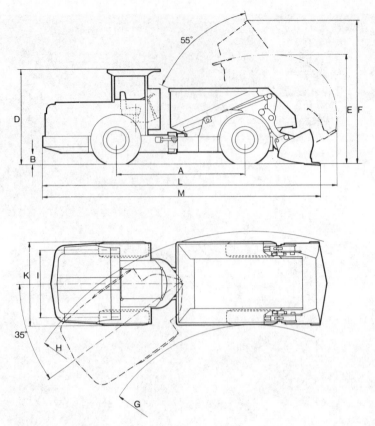

Fig.15. 'CAVO D710' mine loader

Fig.16. Hydraulic percussive rock drill rig

C22/74

A REVIEW OF CURRENT WORK ON THE CUTTING AND FRACTURING OF ROCKS BY HIGH PRESSURE WATER JETS

K. MOODIE, MSc

Fluid Mechanics Section, Safety in Mines Research Establishment,
Red Hill, off Broad Lane, Sheffield S3 7HD

G. TAYLOR, HNC

Fluid Mechanics Section, Safety in Mines Research Establishment,
Red Hill, off Broad Lane, Sheffield S3 7HD

The Ms. of this paper was received at the Institution on 30th August 1973 and accepted for publication on 23rd October 1973. 33

SYNOPSIS   The paper summarizes the research being carried out on the possible application of high-pressure water jets for rock breakage.   Equipment for producing jets at pressures up to 1800 MN/m^2 is described.

It appears that there are two ways of utilising the jet for rock breakage: (i) traversing the jet across the rock to cut grooves in it, and (ii) firing short pulses of water at the rock to induce fractures.   Results indicate that the former method is more effective in soft rocks than hard ones whilst for the latter the opposite is the case.   Most of the experimental results suggest that water jets are at present less efficient than conventional machines, but there are a few notable exceptions.

INTRODUCTION

1.   In recent years there has been considerable interest in high-pressure water jets for various applications ranging from the cutting of thin sheet materials to the breaking of hard rocks.   In April 1972 the 1st International Symposium on Water Jet Cutting Technology (ref. 1) was organised by the British Hydromechanics Research Association at the University of Warwick. Thirty-five papers were presented, dealing with all aspects of the topic.   A second symposium is to be held at Cambridge in April 1974.

2.   The present interest in high-pressure water jets can be traced to work carried out in Russia during the late 1950s.   Water jets were used to cut coal at relatively low pressures of up to 30 MN/m^2.   Later higher pressures were used to cut and fracture both rocks and coal.

3.   In the last few years researchers in other countries have followed the Russian lead and examined these and other applications of water jets.   In America, particularly, experimental work on hard-rock breaking and coal cutting is well advanced.   Research into the cutting of thin sheet materials has led to industrial installations of commercial equipment.   In America a production plant which has now been in operation for nearly two years is used for cutting thick cardboard with water pressures up to 300 MN/m^2.

DEFINITIONS AND THEORETICAL RELATIONSHIPS

4.   A high-pressure water jet is taken in this paper to be one which has a stagnation pressure in excess of 50 MN/m^2.   The stagnation pressure is by definition the pressure obtained when the fluid jet is brought to rest isentropically, or the pressure measured along the centre line of the jet in a plane at right angles to it.   Jet velocity is related to the stagnation pressure by Bernoulli's equation (ref. 2):-

$$p_S - p_O = \tfrac{1}{2} \rho_O v_O{}^2 \qquad (1)$$

where p_S is the stagnation pressure, p_O is the static pressure of the jet, ρ_O is the density of the jet. and v_O its velocity.   Usually $p_S \gg p_O$, so that the expression reduces to

$$p_S = \tfrac{1}{2} \rho_O v_O{}^2 \qquad (2)$$

5.   This expression assumes that the fluid is incompressible and is valid for pressures up to about 700 MN/m^2.   At higher pressures one must consider compressibility and adiabatic-expansion effects within the nozzle.   A more complicated relationship (ref. 2) results:-

$$v_O = \frac{2\gamma A}{(\gamma - 1)} \frac{p_O}{\rho_O} \left[\left(\frac{p_S}{p_O} \right)^{\gamma - 1} - 1 \right] \qquad (3)$$

where ρ_S is the density of the fluid in the reservoir, and γ and A are constants.

6.   The power consumption σ through the nozzle is given by the expression:-

$$\sigma = \frac{\pi d^2}{4} v_O \, p_S \qquad (4)$$

where d is the nozzle diameter.   A discharge coefficient of unity has been assumed.

7.   The variation of power consumption with stagnation pressure and nozzle diameter is shown in Fig. 1, which demonstrates that large power consumptions are possible using relatively small nozzle diameters and high stagnation pressures.   The variation of jet thrust with power consumption is shown in Fig. 2.   The effect of compressibility can be observed from Fig. 3 for stagnation pressures up to 1500 MN/m^2.

APPLICATIONS

8.   There are at present four main types of application of high-pressure water jets.   With each type can be characterised a range of pressures and of nozzle diameters (Fig. 4).   The most well established application is cleaning and descaling of various

materials (eg the internal surfaces of boilers). This application uses a continuous flow of water at pressures up to 100 MN/m^2; such pressures can be provided directly by pumps. The cleaning jet is attached to a hand-held lance and used by a suitably protected operator; the nozzle diameters are kept small so that the jet thrust is low enough for the operator to hold the lance comfortably.

9. A second area of application is the cutting of thin sheet materials. This application usually requires a high quality of finish along the cut edges of the material, which is achieved by using nozzles which give a coherent jet - one which does not diverge until well downstream of the nozzle exit. The nozzle diameters are small (of the order of 0.02 mm) to keep both the power consumption and wastage of material to a minimum; pressures may be as high as 700 MN/m^2. This form of equipment is particularly suited for profile cutting, as the jet is almost a point cutter.

10. The two applications using the widest range of nozzle diameters and jet pressures are the cutting and the fracturing of rock. For cutting of rock, a jet is moved across the rock surface, cutting a groove into the rock. Fragments of rock are eventually broken away by the force of the jet itself; or they may be removed by using a mechanical cutter to dislodge the weakened rock from between the grooves. For this purpose the water jet must run continuously, and thus the power that can be supplied to the system limits the practicable combinations of nozzle diameter and jet pressure. At present the largest practical power consumption is in the region of 1000 kW; the combinations of jet pressure and nozzle diameter which do not exceed this are shown in Fig. 4.

11. Rock breaking or fracturing can be obtained by firing short bursts of fluid at the rock from a stationary nozzle. Systems for doing this use energy-storage devices rather than a continuously operating pump, stored energy (accumulated over a period) is rapidly released, driving the system for a short period at high power; the mean power requirements can thus be a good deal smaller than the peak consumption; although reasonably high power input may still be required if a high repetition frequency is needed. This method of operation does not restrict the size of nozzle or the operating pressure, as is the case with a continuously operating system. Laboratory rigs based on this principle have used the widest range of nozzle diameters and jet pressures (Fig. 4).

EQUIPMENT

12. It is desirable to have a pulse-free flow for cutting thin sheet materials; this is achieved by using a low-pressure water pump to operate a double-acting intensifier, which minimises pressure fluctuations as the piston reaches the end of its travel. (Any small changeover fluctuations that do occur can be damped out by using a reservoir). These systems use very small-diameter nozzles and thus little power; they are made as light as possible for ease of rapid movement over the work piece when profile cutting. Such systems are now commercially available; at least two types on the market operate at pressures up to

300 MN/m^2.

13. In constrast, equipment for use at higher pressures is still in the experimental stage; it is bulky and lacks the refinements of production equipment. Further commercial development should remedy these disadvantages.

14. Experimental work on rock cutting has shown that at constant pressure the groove depth cut increases with nozzle diameter over a limited range; thus for high efficiency it is necessary to work at high power consumption levels. Two types of laboratory rig used for rock-cutting research are shown in Fig. 5. These systems produce jets that have duration of only a few seconds. The jets run continuously for this time after which the systems have to be recharged before being operated again. The system shown in Fig. 5(a) uses a compressed-air reservoir to store the necessary energy. The system is operated by releasing the compressed air through a fast-opening valve on to the piston of an intensifier, which is driven forward, expelling the water trapped in the high-pressure chamber through the nozzle. After which the reservoir is isolated and the air in the intensifier vented. Water is then pumped into the high-pressure chamber of the vessel through a non-return valve; driving the piston back to its starting position and filling the chamber ready for the next experiment.

15. An alternative to this scheme is shown in Fig. 5(b). Compressed gas is stored in a reservoir connected directly to the intensifier piston, thus exerting continuous pressure on the piston. The system is operated by a hydraulic pump with an output pressure greater than the compressed gas pressure. The pump drives fluid on to the return side of the intensifier piston, and at the same time the high-pressure chamber is filled through the non-return valve. The system is operated by rapidly venting this 'cocking' fluid, thus allowing the piston to be driven forward by the compressed gas.

16. These layouts are both used for experimental work. For practical applications the scheme shown in Fig. 5(b) would be preferred on grounds of efficiency. Both systems can produce high-pressure pulses of water lasting for a few milliseconds if a vessel just big enough to contain the required amount of water is used. They can also be made repetitive, and are capable of reaching their peak pressure very quickly.

17. Two other systems used for producing pulses of water are shown in Fig. 6; these are often called "water cannons". Fig. 6(a) shows a system rather similar to those of Fig. 5, with the important difference that the high-pressure piston is not in the high-pressure chamber at the beginning of its stroke. The system is operated by pumping water into the intensifier, thus driving the piston backwards and compressing the gas behind it. When the vent valve is opened the water is released allowing the piston to be accelerated by the gas pressure. The piston traps some water in the high-pressure chamber as it enters. A system of weak shocks and pressure waves is set up in the trapped column of water, which is forced out through the nozzle. The initial peak pressure can be of the order of 1500 MN/m^2 before the steady-state pressure, which depends on the intensification ratio and

the driving pressure, is established.

18. A different system is shown on Fig. 6(b). The high-pressure chamber takes the shape of a long convergent nozzle up to 2 m long. A quantity of water is placed at the entry to the nozzle. A gas-driven piston impacts on the water and forces it down the nozzle. Unsteady flow conditions and a complex system of oblique pressure waves are produced in the water, which is accelerated to a high velocity as it travels towards the nozzle exit. Devices such as this have been used for experimental rock breaking both in Russia and in the USA. They have produced the highest reported pressures and power consumptions used in experimental work. They have the disadvantage that they are difficult to make repetitive.

19. At present water-jet systems seem unlikely to exceed a pressure of about 1500 MN/m^2, because it is unlikely that with currently available materials pressure vessels can be made to withstand higher pressures than this and still have a reasonable fatigue life. (But it seems probable that they will be developed to withstand an infinite number of life cycles at lower pressures up to 700 MN/m^2). Special steels, such as vacuum remelted En 26 steel, maraging steel, or tungsten carbide, have to be used for constructing the pressure vessel. In "double-cylinder" design, tungsten carbide is used for the inner cylinder; this is surrounded by an outer cylinder of a more ductile material providing protection if failure should occur. The end fittings and pipe connections are machined into the outer cylinder.

20. Seals in high-pressure vessels present a substantial problem. Common practice has been to use standard hydraulic seals combined with anti-extrusion rings, which have a limited life. Improved sealing arrangements will be necessary for commercial applications. The dynamic sealing of the piston is particularly difficult; one promising solution involves abandoning the seal altogether and using a close-fitting piston lapped to fit the cylinder bore. This allows a small but acceptable amount of leakage.

21. The nozzles are usually made from hard materials such as tungsten carbide, industrial diamonds or sapphires. The internal surface is polished to reduce friction and wear. Nozzle diameters from 6 mm to 0. 02 mm are used; those with small diameters are difficult to manufacture and clogging can occur unless the fluid is properly filtered.

ROCK CUTTING

22. The potential advantages of high-pressure water-jet techniques for rock-cutting and fracturing have led to considerable research activities in many countries.

23. It is hoped that if high-pressure water jets are used in coal mining their advantages will outweigh any disadvantages, making them safer overall than conventional machines. They should eliminate the frictional sparks which can ignite firedamp and the make of airborne dust is likely to be considerably smaller. The rate of wear in the nozzle is constant and is not affected by the type of rock being out, so that the

rapid pick wear and high replacement costs associated with conventional machines working in very hard rocks are eliminated. Another advantage is the very low thrust associated with a high-pressure jet, even at high power consumptions; the thrust/power ratio is therefore low and does not limit the power that can be applied to the rock face, as sometimes occurs with conventional machines.

24. A knowledge of the efficiency of these processes is clearly important. A convenient measure of efficiency (one used by most researchers) is the amount of work required to remove unit volume of rock. This is often termed the 'specific energy'. The volume of rock removed is influenced by the way the jet is used, by the jet pressure, by the traversing speed, and by the type of rock. Clearly the lowest achievable specific energy should be aimed at. One attractive method consists of cutting a series of grooves in the rock, so spaced that the material is cut away in square sectioned strips. The specific energy for this process is given by the expression $\frac{2\sigma}{sx^2}$ (ref. 2) where σ is the power consumed, s the traversing speed of the jet, and x the groove depth. Alternatively material between the grooves may be removed by some mechanical means. In some cases this can reduce the specific energy needed to half that required when using jets alone. In general, it is important that calculations of specific energy should be made so as to indicate the overall efficiency of the rock-removal process. The volume of material actually removed by the water jet itself (in the case decribed above, the volume of the grooves alone) may be seriously misleading in this respect.

25. Space does not permit a summary of the activities of the many groups investigating applications of high-pressure water jets; further information is given in the literature (ref. 1). A few are worthy of special mention, especially as an indication of the specific energies which can be achieved.

26. Summers (ref. 3) at the University of Missouri has investigated the cutting of soft limestone using jet pressures up to 350 MN/m^2. He concludes that the highest pressures and smallest nozzles do not necessarily give the best performance. The lowest specific energy values obtained are about 3000 J/cc.

27. Researchers at Oak Ridge National Laboratory (ref. 4) have investigated the cutting of three types of rock, Berea sandstone (compressive strength 43 MN/m^2), Indiana limestone (55 MN/m^2) and Georgia granite (56 MN/m^2). The jet pressures for optimum cutting efficiency were found to be less than 70 MN/m^2 for all but the granite. Large nozzles about 2 to 6 mm in diameter gave the best results, and the minimum specific energy (for the Berea sandstone) was 500 J/cc.

28. Investigations at the Illinois Institute of Technology Research Institute (ref. 5) included measurements of the crater volume produced by jets at pressures up to 1200 MN/m^2; the minimum specific energy was 4×10^3 J/cc. This very high value is explained by the method adopted for calculation of specific energy; the crater is formed entirely by the jet, and no material is removed by auxiliary means.

29. Japanese investigators (ref. 6) have been considering water-jets in conjunction with mechanical gear cutters for rapid tunnelling. The jet cuts grooves in the rock and the intervening material is then removed by the mechanical cutters. No specific energy values are quoted, but the investigators suggest that the material removed by a single pass of the disc cutter is increased by 2 to 5 times as a result of pre-cutting by the water jet.

30. Moodie and Artingstall (ref. 2) have shown that the efficiency of rock removal varies with jet pressure and traversing speed. The best results recorded by them are a specific energy of 320 J/cc when cutting in Darley Dale sandstone (compressive strength 46 MN/m^2), and 140 J/cc in Red Woolton sandstone (compressive strength 36 MN/m^2).

ROCK FRACTURING

31. If instead of traversing the jet across the rock the nozzle is kept stationary and a short pulse of fluid is fired at the rock, fracturing can be produced around the point of impact in certain types of rock. It is believed that the action of the jet is similar to hydraulic rock bursting. The jet quickly drills a hole into the rock; water trapped in the hole is then pressurized by the incoming jet. If the pressure is sufficiently high fracturing of the rock occurs. The technique has the advantage that energy-storage devices can be used. This method of rock breakage is under active investigation.

32. At IITRI (ref. 5) experimental work has used jet pressures of up to 1200 MN/m^2 and nozzles of 1 mm diameter. Unconfined blocks of sandstone and granite were broken. No specific-energy values have been published; but the authors believe that the technique is sufficiently effective to warrant further research. Portable equipment suitable for field trials is being constructed.

33. Research by Exotech Inc. (ref. 7) has shown that pulsed water-jets can break blocks of granite and sandstone at specific-energy levels of 13-100 J/cc. Unconfined blocks of rock were used for these tests, and the specific-energy is smaller than would be expected.

34. Cooley (ref. 8) has investigated the possibilities of using a water cannon for breaking rock. This device fires slugs of water lasting for about a millisecond at its peak pressure; it has been used at pressures estimated to be as high as 1800 MN/m^2. Specific-energy values at 500 J/cc were deduced from trials on unconfined blocks of rock. A portable water cannon is being built for field trials.

35. Experimental work by Moodie and Artingstall (ref. 2) has shown that 30 cm cubes of Pennant sandstone (compressive strength 56 MN/m^2), confined by vertical and horizontal pressures to represent the loading on rock underground at about 400 m depth, can be broken with a specific energy of 8 J/cc. An unconfined 90-cm cube of the same material has been fractured at a specific energy level of 12 J/cc. This research is continuing with an experimental rig designed for use in quarries and open-cast coal sites.

EFFICIENCY OF WATER-JETS COMPARED WITH CONVENTIONAL MACHINES

36. The most efficient conventional tunnelling machines are generally those using pick cutters (ref. 9). Such machines achieve overall specific energy levels of 6 to 25 J/cc, but they cannot be used in rocks with compressive strengths greater than 100 MN/m^2, because of excessive pick wear. Roller and disc cutters are used extensively for tunnelling but are less efficient than picks, minimum specific energies of 25 to 125 J/cc are typical. Cutters of this kind have a greater resistance to wear, but require high thrusts; this requirement limits the types of rock in which they can be used.

37. Results obtained for water-jet cutting and fracturing indicate that the specific energy of the process is in most cases higher (ie less favourable) than would be achieved by conventional machines. It should however be noted that so far no published measurements are available based on field experiments. The best specific-energy results obtained are shown in Fig. 7 in which the specific energy is plotted against rock compressive strength. A tentative view, based on Fig. 7, is that medium/soft rocks are cut more effectively than the harder rocks, whilst these can be fractured more efficiently than cut.

CONCLUSIONS

38. Most specific-energy values so far measured are probably higher than would be economically acceptable. It is only in the fracturing of medium/hard rock and in the cutting of soft rock that sufficiently encouraging results have been obtained. A practical machine based on these results might operate with an overall specific energy value of 20 J/cc, which compares most favourably with conventional machines. (But this comparison is made from results obtained from tests on only one type of rock, and clearly further investigations would be desirable).

39. At present there are insufficient data to indicate whether a tunnelling machine using water jets is feasible. But at the specific-energy values which at present seem likely such a machine cannot be expected to appear attractive unless water jets offer other advantages to compensate for their comparative inefficiency. One such advantage might be the ability of a water-jet to apply a great deal more power to the rock face than a conventional cutter, because of its extremely low thrust/power-consumption ratio; faster extraction rates would thus be possible and the process though less efficient might still be cheaper per unit of rock extracted.

Contributed by permission of the Director
Safety in Mines Research Establishment, Department of Trade and Industry

REFERENCES

1. 1st International Symposium on Jet Cutting Technology. BHRA Fluid Engineering. Cranfield April 1972

2. MOODIE K. and ARTINGSTALL G. Some experiments on the application of high-pressure water-jets for mineral excavation. Proceedings of 1st Int. Symp. on Jet Cutting Tech. BHRA Cranfield, April 1972

3. SUMMERS R.A. The effect in change on energy and momentum levels on the rock removal rate in Indiana limestone. Proceedings of 1st Int. Symp. Jet Cutting Tech. BHRA Cranfield, April 1972

4. McCLAIR W.C. and CRISTY G.A. Examination of high pressure water jets for use in rock tunnel excavatation. ORNL-HUD-1. Oak Ridge National Laboratory, Jan. 1970

5. SINGH M.M. and HUCK P.J. Rock fracture by high speed water jet. IIT Research Institute, Illinois, 60616, Dec. 1970

6. HOSHINO K. et al. Rock cutting and breaking using high speed water jets and 'TBM' cutters. Proceedings of 1st Int. Symp. Jet Cutting Tech. BHRA Cranfield, April 1972

7. Exotech Inc. Water jet technology. Hydromechanics Inc. Rockville, Maryland 20852

8. COOLEY W.C. Optimizing the efficiency of rock disintegration by liquid jets, Final Report, Terraspare Incorporated. Report No. TR-4051, Dec 1971

9. DALZIEL J.A. A review of different methods of rock breakage underground. MRE Report No. 255, 1968

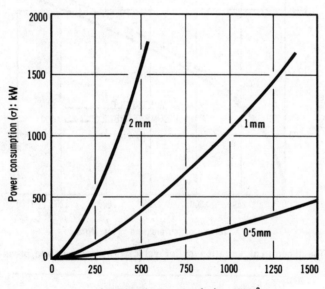

Fig.1 - The theoretical variation of power consumption with jet stagnation pressure for three nozzle diameters

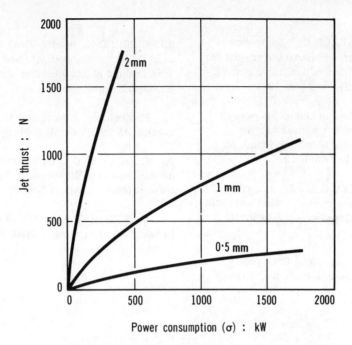

Fig.2 - The theoretical variation of jet thrust with power consumption for three nozzle diameters

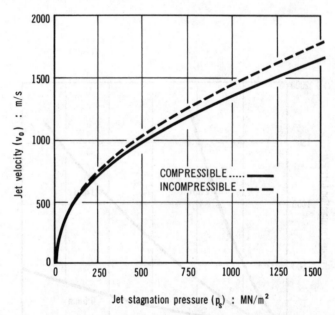

Fig.3 - The theoretical variation of jet velocity with stagnation pressure

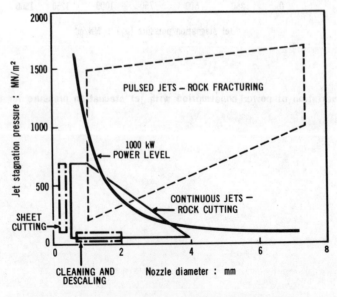

Fig.4 - The application for high-pressure water jets

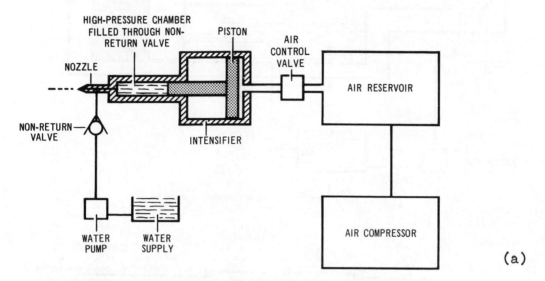

Fig.5(a) - Air operated intensifier system

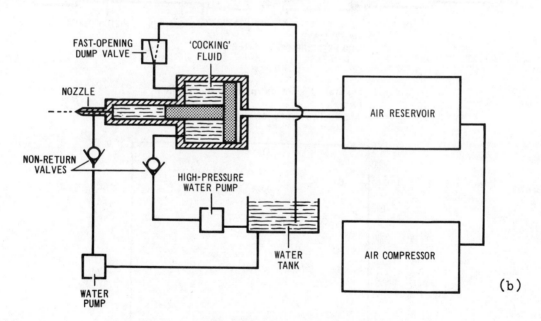

Fig.5(b) - Hydraulically operated intensifier system

Fig.5 - Two types of intensifier systems

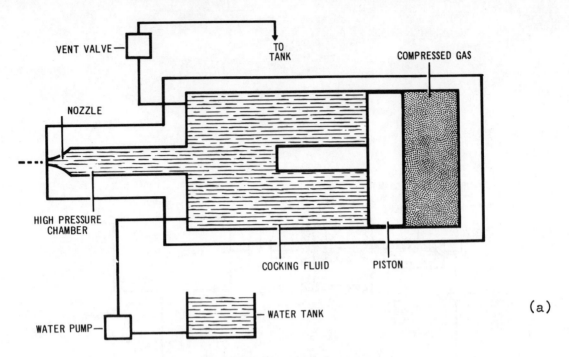

VENT VALVE

TO TANK

COMPRESSED GAS

NOZZLE

HIGH PRESSURE CHAMBER

COCKING FLUID

PISTON

WATER PUMP

WATER TANK

(a)

Fig.6(a) - Hydraulically operated water cannon

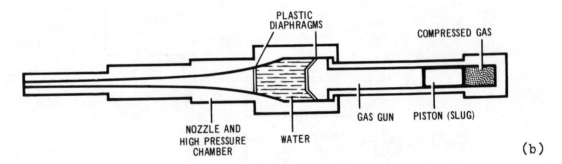

PLASTIC DIAPHRAGMS

COMPRESSED GAS

NOZZLE AND HIGH PRESSURE CHAMBER

WATER

GAS GUN

PISTON (SLUG)

(b)

Fig.6(b) - Impact extrusion water cannon

Fig.6 - Two types of water cannon

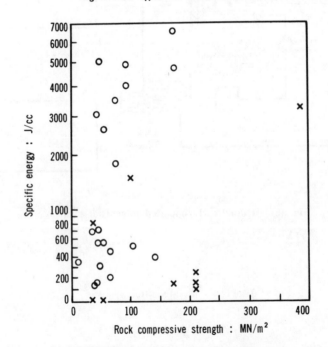

Specific energy values obtained using traversing jets ....o
Specific energy values obtained using pulsed jets x

Fig.7 - The variation of specific energy with rock compressive strength

48

C23/74

BOOM RIPPING

A. H. MORRIS, MIMechE

Chief Engineer, Mechanical Development and Workshops Branch, National Coal Board,
Mining Research and Development Establishment, Ashby Road, Stanhope Bretby,
Burton-on-Trent, Staffordshire

The Ms. of this paper was received at the Institution on 31st July 1973 and accepted for publication on 23rd October 1973. 34

SYNOPSIS

The origins of mechanisation of rippings and the introduction of boom ripping in particular are discussed.

The duty required of a ripping machine, and the problems peculiar to this development are outlined.

Certain mechanical and hydraulic problems which have arisen are brought out.

The compromise between operational needs and the ideal cutting requirements is also explained.

INTRODUCTION

1. Ripping in coalmining terms is the taking down of rock above a void where coal has already been extracted, in order to form a roadway of required cross-section and height. Until relatively recently this operation was almost always carried out by drilling and blasting, and it is only in the last 10-15 years that any attempts have been made to mechanise this process. Ripping machines are the outcome.

2. In order to understand the work and function required of a ripping machine, it is necessary to consider first the strata on which it has to work. The maximum compressive strength of coal is about 42 N/mm^2 and the average somewhere between 21 and 28 N/mm^2. The rocks that lie above the coal may include any combination of fireclay, mudstone, shales and sandstone, and in parts of South Wales a very hard rock known as pennant sandstone. Fireclay is fairly soft, generally not much harder than the coal; shales, mudstones and siltstone will go up to a compressive strength of, say, 90-96 N/mm^2. The sandstones may start at a lower figure than this, but can go as high as 172-207 N/mm^2, although this is unusual. The practicability of cutting these rocks with a ripping machine does not depend entirely upon the compressive strength of the rock but also upon its nature, and we find that a well-laminated rock, having a fair number of pre-existing cracks and fractures even though it may be of high compressive strength, can often be more easily ripped than a homogenous rock of lower compressive strength. A further important factor is its quartzitic content since abrasivity and hence the rate of wear on picks is largely dependent on this aspect. The production of sparks and dust is also very much affected by the abrasivity of the rock.

3. The machines that have been applied to cutting rippings by the use of picks have been the Joy ripper, the Greenside ripper and later the Anderson Mavor and Dosco boom rippers. In design theory, the Joy ripper and the Greenside ripper should have been well suited to the task by reason of their solid anchorage in the roadway and their accurate profiling of the roadway shape leading to snugly fitting supports, etc. However, only about 10 of these machines still continue in operation for reasons that will be explained and have been largely replaced by boom rippers.

4. The mechanisation of rippings was in the first place somewhat naturally attempted by using the same type of cutting pick that had been used in the successful mechanisation of 90% of all coal-getting in British coalmines (See Figure 1). Typically, such a pick had a strong shank that incorporated a quick fastening-and-release device and a tungsten-carbide tip brazed on at the working end. When considering the problems encountered in employing any type of ripping machine it is necessary to look at the action of a pick working in rock. The general aim is to produce a machining effect similar in principle to that produced by a cutting tool used on metals in machine-tool practice. Instead of having the material moving against a stationary tool, however, it is of course necessary in coalmining to move the tool against the material and the pick is pressed against the rock and traversed along its surface for this purpose, with the object of obtaining tool penetration and producing a broken rock debris. The success of this process is very much dependent on the strength of the pick, the linear and axial forces which can be applied to it, the linear speed of the pick, and of course, the resistance of the rock. Where the combination of applied forces and strength of pick are greater than the strength of the material, successful cutting is obtained. In the opposite case, inefficient cutting takes place; indeed in certain cases of extreme rock hardness and low machine capacity, rubbing the pick along the rock is all that is achieved, with very undesirable economic and environmental results. Heat produced by the prictional effect of this action often precludes the application of picked machines. On smaller picks the rapid build up of frictional

heat can often destroy the brazing which secures the carbide tip to the pick or can cause very rapid wear of the pick tip, to such an extent that the bluntness of the tool seriously affects cutting efficiency and operational safety; even if neither of these occurs it is possible for the build-up of heat to ignite a mechane/air mixture such as may be present in our collieries. Deterioriation of picks results in the production of dust, another major coalmining hazard. It has been found in laboratory work and by field experience that the way to avoid these problems is to employ the slowest possible linear pick speed, and an adequate force, and thus achieve deep penetration. Where this approach has been taken to its limit, on for instance the Atlas Copco/Habbager tunnelling machine, and where massive cutting picks have been used with linear speeds as low as 0.127 m/sec combined with very high thrust and traversing forces, it is claimed that rocks up to 207 N/mm^2 compressive strength have been cut successfully. An additional refinement in this machine was water-cooling of the picks themselves, but any cessation of water flow led rapidly to the heat build-up mentioned previously.

5. The cutting requirements mentioned above should be easier to realise where conditions are constant, i.e. where rock is of a consistent nature and the machine is of a type which can hold the pick steadily to its work. In fact, the kinds of rock usually found in coal-measure strata are fairly well laminated and contain pre-existing cracks; they are thus not consistent and offer widely varying degrees of resistance to the passage of the cutting picks and so seriously affect pick speed and penetration. This situation also means that a pick 'impacts' to some extent and can suffer damage or the loss of its tip. Also, because of the need to employ machines which are of such a size and horsepower that they can be readily installed in fairly confined spaces and yet leave access for the passage of men and materials to the working face, it is not possible to 'build in' to the machine the massive physical characteristics which would lend stability to the cutting process itself, and therefore 'bounce' between material to be cut and the cutting picks is not absorbed. It is on the contrary accentuated.

INITIAL WORK ON THE MECHANISATION OF RIPS

6. The Joy ripper (See Figure 2) was developed at the NCB Central Engineering Establishment as a test rig, and was later taken up by Joy Manufacturing Co. Ltd. as a production machine; it was first installed for operations in a colliery in the then East Midlands Division in 1960/61. For the reasons mentioned previously, it was a fairly light machine of about 16 tonnes and its installed horsepower was 45 kW. The rock was attacked by cutter picks mounted on three drums which in turn were carried on an arm that was caused to pivot about one end, thus striking an arc through the rock and creating a semicircular roadway. The slewing gear, motor and gearbox for the cutting arm were mounted on an inner carriage that was hydraulically advanced by lowering the roof anchors and moving it forward on a hydraulically operated walking base. The cutting arm was generally arranged to make a 3.6 m x 2.7 m or 4.3 m x 3 m arched roadway while taking a slice of rock varying in depth from 0.2 to 0.3 m. A set of transmission gears was available which gave linear pick speeds varying from 0.66 m/sec to 1.4 m/sec.

7. This machine had reasonable success where it was applied in soft to medium strata and some very good production performances were achieved. However, enthusiasm for this new-found method of mechanising the ripping operation also caused it to be installed in a number of places that were quite unsuitable (in very hard rock, in abrasive conditions, in very large roadways) and it was thus that many of the problems concerning production of excessive amounts of dust, heating, sparking and consequent ignition hazards, very rapid and uneconomic pick wear and loss arose, resulting in uneconomic rates of production. Despite this situation the ripper nevertheless showed the advantages of machine cutting a road, of producing suitable profiles for the quick setting of roadway supports and of obtaining better strata control. Had the Joy ripper been restricted to the conditions for which it was genuinely suitable, it might have had a longer productive life. However, at the same time that it demonstrated the desirability of machine cutting of rips, other possibilities appeared, mainly in the form of boom rippers; as a result the application of Joy rippers began to fall off. Much the same could be said for the Greenside ripper, although this was never used to the same extent as the Joy machine.

THE BEGINNING OF BOOM RIPPING

8. Shortly after the Joy ripper made its appearance, efforts were made to produce machines which would fully mechanise the drivage of complete main roadways for the development of districts etc. Central Engineering Establishment was engaged in this work and produced a variety of alternative proposals and design schemes. In the end, the favoured design approach was one that had already been exploited by Eastern European countries, Soviet Russia in particular. This was incorporated in a machine which employed a cutting head comprising picks carried and rotated at the end of a boom that was carried on a machine chassis. The boom was mounted on a stub shaft and bearing assembly so that it had horizontal swing, and on trunnions so that it had vertical swing. Both of these movements were effected by means of pairs of hydraulic rams. Drive to the cutting head was from an electric motor via a transmission shaft running through the centre of the boom. The cutting head was pressed forward into the rock and/or coal to the full depth required by urging the complete machine forward on caterpiller tracks. The debris produced as the cutting head traversed horizontally and vertically over the full face of the heading was gathered by a conveyor which passed around the front part of the machine and discharged the debris at the rear. This machine was known in Soviet Russia as the PK3 (see Figure 3). In 1961 two NCB engineers visited the USSR and saw these machines in operation. It was decided then that, although the machine was not directly applicable to coalmining in the United Kingdom, because it operated via six sets of electric motors and switchgear, which did not meet British FLP requirements, the quickest way of developing a machine on these lines was to buy a PK3, obtain operational experience with it and use that to provide design information and knowledge for a heavier, more robust machine suitable for British conditions.

9. This was done and the PK3 arrived in Great Britain to be tested in the north of England at the end of 1961. From these beginnings, further work was undertaken in the United Kingdom, and

and both Anderson Mavor and Dosco now make machines of this type. The NCB has about 350 of them. These machines were, and are, heading machines, but the benefits obtained from flexibility of operation, the ability to cut any shape of roadway and the advantage of concentration of cutting power into one single relatively small-diameter cutting head rather than over three or four drums were quickly appreciated. It was therefore not too long before it was decided that the same principle would have beneficial application at rippings. So in 1967 a roadheader, as they were known by then, was stripped down (i.e. the conveyor was removed) and was tried in conjunction with a suitable dirt-disposal device - in this case one known as the rampacker - at a colliery in the Midlands. The strata in which it was put to work was of medium hardness and the cutting operation was quite successful. Access to the face was good. It appeared possible to match the machine with any dirt-disposal device and the boom could be used to assist in setting the roadway supports.

10. Both of the firms that produce roadheaders in this country have since been encouraged to produce specifically designed boom rippers, and currently the NCB has over 50 of these machines in operation. A technical description and photographs of the Dosco and the Anderson Mavor boom rippers are included in Appendices 1 and 2.

DISCUSSION

11. From the comment made on requirements for successful rock cutting, it will have been noted that the boom ripper is not ideal in terms of pure rock-cutting requirement. It is a design and operational compromise between what is required at the cutting end and the operational characteristics necessary to allow it to be used successfully in a particular coalmining situation, i.e. at a ripping lip. The cutting head is not held rigidly to the rock and in this respect is not as good in theory as the Joy ripper mentioned in the preceeding section. It is carried at the end of a long boom, the boom itself being supported in any given position by hydraulic rams. The mountings for the boom and for the hydraulic rams are secured on the machine body, which is not anchored in any way in the roadway but relies for stability on its own weight and adhesion between the caterpiller tracks (or skid base) and the floor.

12. However, the compromise works, and shows certain advantages. The cutting potential of these machines is so high that they do not limit the rate of coalface advance; the cutting can be controlled at a rate facilitating disposal of dirt into a pack hole on the face, as opposed to drilling and firing, in which all debris is deposited on the floor in one explosion. Supports previously set under the rip need not be withdrawn before cutting. Compared with shotfiring, there is less shattering of the roof and surrounding strata. This leads to better roadway conditions and better strata control. There is generally a reduction in the labour force required to handle rippings.

13. Also, we can have 48 kW (and if necessary up to 67 kW), concentrated on providing torque for the picks carried on one small-diameter cutting head rather than distributed between three or four similar-sized cutting heads as used on the Joy ripper. Obviously the force available for individual picks is greater. Where in workable strata a very hard band of rock appears, and this is quite usual, a small-diameter head on a boom can be manoeuvred to cut out the support above and below the hard band and then worked to break through it, whereas the Joy-type machine might willy-nilly strike this hard band with all three drums at more or less the same time, with no possibility of previous over- and under-working. Difficult cutting can sometimes be avoided by changing the roadway shape, e.g. it is possible to produce a flat top to a roadway, thus preserving inherently strong 'beams' of strata rather than eroding them by cutting an arch.

14. Mechanically and hydraulically a large number of problems have been encountered and overcome. When cutting the harder rocks with picks at the end of a long boom, a good deal of vibration can occur and be transmitted throughout the machine; initially this had an effect on gears and bearings in the transmission system, and in particular on the mountings and securings for hydraulic rams.

15. We normally restrict operating pressures on our machines underground to 140 N/mm^2, with relief valves set at about 170 N/mm^2, because we operate on fire-resistant hydraulic fluids. The fluid the Industry has preferred for several years and that now most widely used is a 40/60 oil-and-water emulsion; although such fluids have been improved a good deal in that time, they are of course still not as inherently good as lubricants as mineral oil. These relatively low operating pressures mean the use of larger-diameter rams to provide hydraulically induced thrusts and it is a problem to accommodate these larger rams and mount them on machines which we are at the same time trying to minimise in physical size.

16. From the nature of rock cutting and, additionally, the process of traversing the cutting head through the rock on the end of a long boom, it will be readily seen that hydraulic pressures over and above that provided from the pump circuit will be induced in the lifting and traversing system. High transient pressures have been noted and this has caused such problems as destruction of oil seals in the rams, the breaking of cylinder mountings, both on the boom and on the machine body and bursting of hydraulic hoses. The problem has been partly alleviated by using relief valves in the circuit immediately adjacent to the cylinders, and doing such things as replacing cast-steel trunnion rings with rings manufactured from forged steel.

17. In the first prototypes the cutting head design used too few picks and this itself caused 'bounce' in the boom with amplitudes up to 12.7 cm. Relacing of the head reduced this problem and so long as the amplitude of bounce remains below about 5.08 cm the problems of impact breakage of picks are generally avoided, and the cutting action is not impaired. This tendency to bounce was also caused by the very simple hydraulic control system used on the prototypes. The exhaust side of the slewing and elevating rams went directly to tank, allowing rapid and uncontrolled movement in temporary open spaces. Pilot operated check valves and restrictions were used to cure this. Some hydraulic pressure recordings were made at this stage, with peak pressures of up to 245 N/mm^2 being felt right back to the pump, although the circuit relief valve was set at 130 N/mm^2. The recorder used was a Dobbie McInnes mechanical device, and the speed of response may not have been high enough to show the true maximum pressure. (Further tests with U.V. recorders will be undertaken later this year).

18. Partly arising from the use of fire-resistant fluids is the desire to use the simplest possible hydraulic circuit and controls. For this reason the oil supply to the traversing and lifting rams is normally from a simple gear pump. The capacity of the pump is matched to the best possible traversing speed that is likely to be achieved through the softer rocks and in coal. Since the harder rocks restrict speed, a proportion of the oil has to be returned to tank, normally through a pressure-relief valve rather than an unloader. When low traversing speeds are imposed, the large quantity of oil passed through the relief valve causes a rise in oil temperature. This is sometimes difficult to cope with in situations where the ambient temperature is already high - possibly in the high 80s - and the quantity of ventilating air is relatively restricted. Water cooling is used, of course, finned water tubes being led through the oil tank, and the heated cooling water is dispersed as dust-suppression sprays. This is not always a satisfactory solution, since the heat is still present in the ventilating air and may cause problems of humidity.

19. The machines will be assembled, operated and maintained in very dirty conditions, particularly since the ventilating air flow will normally be from the cutting head back over the machine, and a good standard of oil filtration is required. This will normally include 5-micron filters with magnets in the tank on the suction side, and additional 5- or 10-micron filters on the pressure side.

20. Every effort is made to avoid contamination when filling or topping up, and the oil barrel is normally connected to the machine tank via a hand pump and a coarse filter. However, acknowledging the difficulty in achieving high maintenance standards probably the best solution is the choice of hydraulic components which are least sensitive to dirt, e.g. simple gear pumps and motors etc.

21. Because the boom is a fairly large diameter and will normally have added to it a support-lifting device, the driver's view is a little restricted and attempts are now being made to seat him on the boom carriage assembly so that his fixed line of sight along the boom is always maintained whatever the position of the boom.

22. Summing up, the boom ripper is a good example of the successful adaptation of an apparently unsuitable design in circumstances where operational and geological considerations dictate a compromise between conflicting requirements.

APPENDIX I

ANDERSON MAVOR BOOM RIPPING MACHINE

DESCRIPTION

The machine consists of the centre platform, turret and telescopic cutter boom of the M & C Roadheader. This platform is carried on slides which permit the whole cutting unit to move a distance of 1 m relative to machine base.

The base unit to which the slides are attached is a substantial bridge unit, skid mounted, which spans the full width of the roadway. This gives an area under the machine which permits free safe access to the face for men, materials and ventilation. The unit can also span the

equipment normally found in main gates (e.g. stage loaders, cables, etc.).

Bridge Base

This base is carried on two broad skids to reduce ground pressure.

The machine is advanced by two hydraulic jacks incorporated in the base of each skid. These are coupled to a powered support under the ripping lip by chains, and the jacks are powered from the machine hydraulics.

The base also incorporates the longitudinal slides, along which the upper part of the machine is moved relative to the base.

Centre Platform

This carries the power pack, switchgear, turret and telescopic boom. The platform can be moved longitudinally relative to the base by two 1 m stroke jacks. This permits a 2 m advance to be taken with one move up of the frame (described later). Side staking jacks can be fitted but have not proved to be necessary to date.

Telescopic Boom

The telescopic boom carrying the 0.76 m diameter 0.5 m deep cutter head can be moved by hydraulic jacks to cut any part of the ripping. The cutter head which is powered by a 48 kW electric motor, is equipped with tungsten carbide tipped picks.

The telescopic movement available is 0.5 m.

Power Pack

This is mounted on the centre platform and comprises a single gear pump powered by a 15 kW motor. The machine can be operated on fire resistant fluids, (oil/water emulsions) and adequate cooling of the hydraulic oil is achieved by passing water at 36 l/min, 1.4 N/mm^2 through a cooling oil.

General

Dust suppression is by means of water sprays mounted behind the cutter head. These utilise the water which has been used to cool the hydraulic oil. The latest machines are fitted with a cutting head which is fed with water internally to provide pick face flushing. These have been working for six months and are proving reliable and successful in reducing dust counts.

The operator can be positioned within the side frame at the front, on either side, or on the centre platform behind the turret. The best positions are the side positions.

The whole machine can be easily dismantled for transport underground and rebuilding on site.

OPERATION

Stage 1

Following the completion of a 2 m advance, the complete machine is moved forward by two pulling jacks which are attached to two chocks under the ripping lip. For this move up the telescopic boom is fully retracted and the platform of the machine is located in the rear position on the sliding shaft. The unit is thus pulled forward 2 m.

Stage 2

During the last 0.5 m of the above movement, the cutter head is sumped into the ripping, thus enabling the first cut to be taken off at a depth of 0.5 m.

Stage 3

The telescopic boom is extended 0.5 m sumping into the ripping and the second cut of 0.5 m is taken off.

Stage 4

The telescopic boom is fully retracted and the machine platform advanced on the slide shafts a distance of 1 m. During the last 0.46 m of this travel, the cutter head is sumped into the ripping and a third cut of 0.46 m is taken off, once the sliding movement has been completed.

Stage 5

The last 0.5 m is removed by extending the telescopic boom to sump into the ripping and thus take off the fourth cut to give a total cut of 2 m.

Following the completion of the fourth cut, the complete machine is moved forward a total of 2 m, the last 0.5 m again giving the sump for the first cut, thus it is possible to obtain an advance of 2 m with one move up of the machine, but it should be noted that any increment up to a total of 2 m can be taken.

SPECIFICATION

Standard cutting head Type: Conical with sumping cutter. Maximum diameter 910 mm. Speed; 36.7 rpm, mean peripheral speed of picks: 1.56 m/sec. Normal depth of sump: 510 mm.

Electrical Supply 500 or 1100 volts 50 cycles 3 phase. Motors: Cutting Head 48 kW, continuously rated dual voltage, Flameproof Group 1 to BS229 and 741.

Double isolating 550/1100 volt switchbox with off/start/run switch controlling remote gate end box. Remote ammeters are also available as optional extras. Switchbox has removable handles for safety.

Lighting One FLP headlamp.

Safety Switches Two emergency stop switches are supplied. Oil level switch and oil temperature switch can be fitted as optional extras.

Cable entry Restrained type plug and socket fitted with locking and withdrawing bolt mechanism.

Ground pressure 0.64 N/mm^2

Overall Dimensions

    Length 7.62 m
    Height 2.286 m
    Width   2.896 m

    Weight 19.96 tonnes

Hydraulics

No of pumps - 1 gear pump
Capacity - 40 l/min
Motors - 0
Oil Capacity --
Working pressure - 13.79 N/mm^2
Hydraulic fluid - Mineral oil or oil/water
                                    emulsion.

Cylinders

Six pairs operate following motions:

    Cutter boom elevation
    Cutter boom slewing
    Cutter boom extension
    Platform traversing
    Chassis movement
    Deckplate elevation

Skid base

Two piece each 0.38 m width x 4.94 m length.

Ground pressure 0.64 N/mm^2

Water Circuit

Rate of flow - recommend 24 l/min
Working pressure 1.73 N/mm^2

Insert Figure 4
Neg. No. 2113/21

APPENDIX II

DOSCO UNIVERSAL TRACK-MOUNTED RIPPING MACHINE

DESCRIPTION

The Universal Track-mounted Ripping Machine is electro-hydraulically operated, and consists basically of cutting assembly, main frame, twin crawler assembly and components of electric and hydraulic systems.

A bridge formed by the main frame and twin crawler assemblies, affords space to allow the machine to be operated, straddling a stage loader in a Main Gate.

Carried on the main frame, at the forward end is the cutting trunk assembly, consisting of, arcing cylinders, lifting cylinders, cutting boom, cylindrical cutting head and cutting head motor.

Carried on the main frame, at the rear is a 635 litre capacity oil tank, a 48.5 kW air cooled electric motor, a 1 Four Section hydraulic pump and operating controls.

The basic design of the U.T.R. is such that a machine initially used in a Tail Gate can, with minor modification, be used in any Main Gate.

It is possible to offset the mounting of the cutting assembly to suit alternative gate conveyor positions. In this way the machine may be used wholly at the side of a conveyor positioned off roadway centre-line or straddling a centrally mounted conveyor.

To minimise support setting time, a lifting device and platform is mounted on the cutting boom. For general transportation the machine dismantles into conveniently sized components.

Electrical System

Power to the machine is supplied via a trailing cable to an electrical siwtch panel mounted upon the machine. This panel controls the aircooled electric motors, one of which drives the cutting head, and one of which energises the hydraulic system. Also incorporated in the panel is the control of the pilot circuits for the safety systems. The machine has an integral water system for dust suppression and also for cooling hydraulic oil.

Cutting Arrangement

The cutting trunk assembly is attached to the machine main frame and comprises, a cast trunk body, cutting head shaft, reduction gear box and electric motor. These components are bolted together to form a single rigid assembly. Connection between the gear box output shaft, and the cutting head shaft, is by means of a self-aligning, gear type coupling.

The cutting head shaft carries the cutting head, which is principally a cylindrical steel boss with cutting tool holders welded around it. Arcing of the cutting trunk in both horizontal and vertical planes is achieved by two pairs of hydraulic cylinders.

The machine has a flexible cutting action, and complete flexibility of movement, allowing freedom of choice of cutting pattern. Thus almost any shape of roadway profile may be excavated. The machine is capable of excavating strata of a compressive strength up to, and in certain cases in excess of 96.51 N/mm^2.

Crawler Arrangement

Maximum machine manoeuvrability is assured by the hydraulically powered, independently chain driven crawler assemblies.

Low contact pressure on the caterpiller tracks makes operation of the machine possible in wet and soft floor conditions.

The machine will operate on inclines.

OPERATION

The machine is moved forward on its caterpillar tracks, sumping the cutting head into the ripping at a controlled rate.

When the requisite depth of sump has been achieved (normally 0.4 to 0.5 m) the head is traversed over the rip to remove that depth of rock.

The machine will then be moved forward on its tracks in order to remove the sides and top from the concave section formed by the arcing motion of the boom, and to leave a straight faced rip.

The process is repeated as required.

U.T.R. SPECIFICATION WITH 314 LITRES/MIN POWER PACK

Cutting Head

Standard head	Single Mk IX cylindrical (Long boss)
Diameter of standard head	483 mm
Speed of cutter head	50 rpm or 75 rpm (depending on cutting conditions)
Peripheral pick speed	76-110.5 m/min
Normal depth of sump	381 mm

Electrical Equipment

Cutting head motor (air cooled) 1450 rpm 37 kW
Hydraulic pump motor (air cooled) 1475 rpm 48.5 kW
Total electrical power (air cooled) 85.5 kW
Voltage 550/1100 volts
Control panel Baldwin & Francis
Oil level switch Alan Cobham type
Trailing cable Type 7 50 mm^2 (3 power cores, 1 earth, 1 pilot)
Headlamps (two per M/C) Westair Dynamics 24V 70W
Pump motor cable Type 7-25 mm^2 x 3.05 m
Cutter motor cable Type 7-25 mm^2 x 5.33 m
Lighting & Pilot cable Type 62-4 mm^2 x 15.26 m
Hydraulic oil thermostat Maclaren Type 2/85°C

Overall Dimensions

Length	7.264 m
Height	2.337 m
Width – Standard	2.286 m
Maximum	2.591 m

Total Weight of Machine

17.8 tonnes
(includes Bulldozer and Platform or 15.24 tonnes Basic M/C)

Hydraulic Equipment

Number of pumps 1 Four Section
Total capacity of pumps 314 l/min
Number of Hydraulic motors 2
Oil capacity 635 litres
Working pressure 13.79 N/mm^2
Recommended hydraulic fluid - Walkers Aquacent 'Light' or 'Heavy' FRFs dependent on ambient temperature or Walkers P.W.L.C. Mineral Oil.

Cylinders

Two pairs operate following motions

Cutter boom elevation
Cutter boom slewing

Crawler Assembly

Details of chain 35 links at 251 pitch 251 mm
Length of track on floor 2.9 m
Width of track 406 mm
Ground pressure - Basic 0.064 N/mm^2
Ground pressure - With
  platform and bulldozer 0.074 N/mm^2
Track centres (standard) 1.88 m
Speed - working 6 m/min
  flitting (boost) 12 m/min
Type of motor Staffa Type MB 2 70s - 11.931 kW

<u>Water Circuit</u>

Rate of flow   15.9-21 l/min
Working pressure   1.24 N/mm^2

ACKNOWLEDGEMENTS

   I have consulted working papers available at
MRDE and from manufacturers, and wish to thank
those who have discussed boom ripping with me. I
also wish to thank Mr. Skidmore, the Director of
MRDE for permission to publish this paper. The
views expressed are my own and not necessarily
those of the National Coal Board.

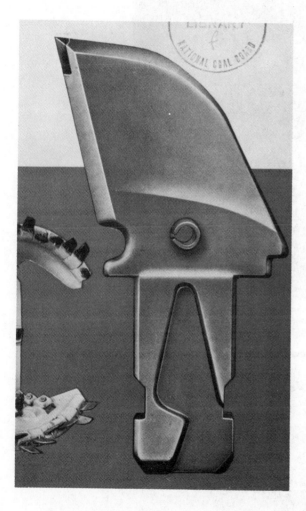

Fig.1

Fig.2

Fig.3

Fig.4

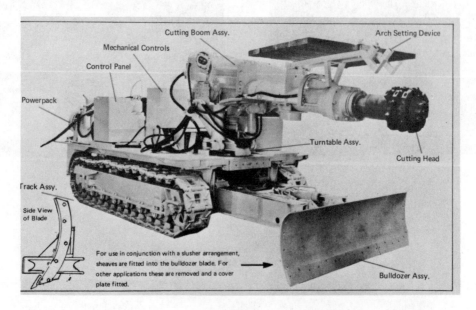

Fig.5

56

C24/74

EXPERIENCE WITH IMPACT UNITS

I. G. RODFORD, HNC(Mech)

Senior Development Engineer, Mining Research and Development Establishment,
National Coal Board, Stanhope Bretby, Burton-on-Trent, Staffordshire

The Ms. of this paper was received at the Institution on 25th July 1973 and accepted for publication on 23rd October 1973. 23

SYNOPSIS

In the 1960's much thought and effort were devoted by the NCB to the ever-increasing need to mechanise the drivage of roadways and by 1965 it had established that the operation of pick-type machines was restricted to strata of about 70 MN/m^2 compressive strength. The dust created by these machines was and still is a problem when forming roadways at the ends of a coalface. In 1966 the NCB's Central Engineering Establishment, now the Mining Research and Development Establishment, began surface and underground trials with hydraulic impact units, which have resulted in the development of impact rippers. These trials have been carried out with a variety of high-energy impact units in strata with compressive strengths ranging up to 200 MN/m^2.

INTRODUCTION

1.   The methods employed by the NCB in mining coal necessitate the removal of large quantities of rock in order to form and maintain the underground roadways required for transport and ventilation purposes. For example in 1966, when the NCB began experimental trials with hydraulic impact breakers, the volume of stone extracted amounted to about 10 million cubic metres, which was virtually 100 per cent hand-got by shotfiring, compared with 167 million tonnes (126 million m^3) of coal won with a coal face mechanisation level of 85 per cent.

2.   Nearly all underground roadways are made with the floor of the coal seam serving as the roadway floor, so that the roadway is formed by taking the rock from over the coal. In some cases, however, the whole section of roadway can be in rock, as when driving between coal seams at differing levels or when opening new districts of the mine. The roadways are mostly of arch section, the excavation varying in size from 3.0-m wide x 2.3-m high to 5.2-m wide x 4-m high; when rectangular roadways are taken the roadway is usually within the coal seam.

3.   With the present system of longwall mining, where the face length is usually about 180 m, a roadway is driven at each end of the face. When working an advancing longwall face the most common practice is to form the roadway immediately behind the face by what is generally known as the ripping operation. Normally the ripping stone is disposed of in the coal excavation, at the side or sides of the roadway, to form packs. These packs serve to support the strata around the roadway and obviate the need to transport stone.   See figures 1 and 2.

STONE CUTTING DEVELOPMENTS

4.   Since 1957 the NCB has been investigating methods of cutting coal-measure strata with the object of producing machines that can be worked continuously in order to eliminate the cyclic methods of working and safety hazards imposed by shotfiring. The strata can vary between soft laminated shales and mudstones, having a compressive strength of 40 MN/m^2, and the hard massive sandstones, with a compressive strength of up to 200 MN/m^2. Thin ironstone bands are also often associated with the rocks overlying the coal.

5.   By 1965 the use of heading and ripping machines, employing picks to cut the strata, had shown the advantages to be gained in advance rates and also in the condition of the finished roadway. These machines were restricted to operation in rocks of about 70 MN/m^2 compressive stress with low quartzitic content so as to minimise incendive sparking and pick wear. The dust created by pick-type machines was a problem, particularly where there was a cumulative effect from several machines in a face system. In consequence the machines were confined to operation in return air tailgates. After appraising different techniques for cutting hard rock in NCB mining conditions it appeared that the repeated impacting method warranted further investigation. Among the advantages foreseen was the possibility of designing equipment which would allow the impact unit to attack the weak points of the strata and enable it to produce lump debris with little dust make. As the NCB already possessed several hydraulically powered impact units[1], originally developed for coal ploughing, it was decided to undertake a series of trials to determine the types of rock that could be cut with the unit and the potential advance rates in these rocks. High energy pneumatic hammers were considered unsuitable owing to the cost and noise output of the compressors.

6.   Initially the trials were directed toward the application of impact units for ripping, rather than solid heading in order to take advantage of the free face provided by the bottom of the rip.

STONE BREAKING TRIALS

7.   The NCB unit had been designed to deliver a blow of approximately 1350 J at 120 blows/min from a hydraulic supply of 45 l/min at 9.3 MN/m^2. To put the value of the blow into perspective it should be realised that it is about 20 times more

powerful than that of a compressed-air roadbreaker.

8.   In order to achieve an efficient application of the impact unit against the rock face it was realised that a mounting similar to that used for rock drilling could be basically suitable, and a Secoma demonstration drill rig, incorporating a short robust boom, was purchased. This rig, figure 3, was used for surface trials in two quarries; at Bulwell in Nottinghamshire, where the laminated limestone had an average compressive strength of 40 MN/m^2, and at Middleton in Derbyshire, where the cleated limestone had an average compressive strength of 105 MN/m^2, and an average tensile strength of 15 MN/m^2. At both sites the rock was non-abrasive and a simulated ripping could be broken down at approximately 3.5 m^3 per hour.

9.   These trials were sufficiently encouraging to justify the manufacture of an experimental impact ripping machine for underground operation. This electrically powered, hydraulically operated machine incorporated 690-mm stroke walking bases, in preference to tracks or rubber tyred wheels, in order to minimise maintenance, as a maximum shift advance of only 3 m was envisaged. The Secoma boom was retained as the seven movements provided enabled the impact unit to be positioned on the rip at virtually any angle of attack and ensured good manoeuvrability. The 90° slew, 30° elevation, 360° rotation, and 1.02-m extension of the main boom allowed the impact unit to be positioned in the zone to be impacted. Then the 90° elevation and 90° slew of the cradle mounted at the front end of the main boom, plus the 450-mm extension of the impact unit slide in the cradle, enabled the impact unit tool to be accurately positioned. The operator was seated behind the boom, and hydraulic stakers were built-in to anchor the machine within the roadway profile when impacting. The 30-kW power pack utilised a Commercial Hydraulics gear pump for operation with fire-resistant fluid. As the Middleton trials had shown that the NCB impact unit was mechanically un-reliable when working in hard rock, the experimental machine was installed at a mudstone tailgate rip of a training face in Lea Hall Colliery for the sole purpose of assessing the practical mining problems of impact ripping. The 3.96-m wide x 3.05-m high arched roadway with a 1.22-m face extraction and rip area of 6.05 m^2 was ripped and mechanically packed for a 1.37-m advance in 2-2½ hours, of which the actual ripping time was approximately 45 mins. The ripper was withdrawn in July 1969 when it had been established that further development of impact ripping methods would be beneficial.

10.   Although the overall time for breaking down the Lea Hall rip was longer than that taken by other mechanical rippers the cutting rate was suitable for the mechanical packing methods available. By now it was evident that the use of pick-type ripping machines could be further restricted by pending regulations regarding approved dust levels and it was apparent there was a need for a method of cutting, other than by picks, in all types of strata. In consequence a world-wide search was made for hydraulic impact breakers that might be suitable for NCB application, so that further trials could be conducted to determine the optimum energy and frequency of blow and the types of tools necessary to break down all coal measure strata at a rate satisfactory for ripping installations, without the NCB having to carry out further development of an impact hammer. Three hammers of differing energy outputs within the range of

interest to the NCB were obtained:

i   Shand unit: blow energy 2440 J at up to 180 blows per minute. This unit was at the prototype stage.

ii   Ingersoll-Rand 'Hobgoblin' unit: blow energy 1356 J at up to 600 blows per minute. Had been marketed in the U.S.A., but was not available elsewhere.

iii   Krupp HM 400 unit: blow energy 542 J at up to 550 blows per minute. Several units had been sold in Germany and Holland, and was being marketed in the U.S.A.

Table 1 gives further details of these and other units. Data as supplied by manufacturers.

11.   The MRDE experimental impact ripper was re-installed in Lea Hall Colliery in 1970 after being extensively modified to provide operator positions on both sides of the machine to improve operator visibility, to provide a new power pack, and to remove the stakers. It had been found that with the ripping machine working to one side of the roadway it was more convenient to provide separate stakers for insertion between the machine and the roadway sides. The machine was part of a fully mechanised face-end system which was advanced 450 m. The 3.35-m x 2.74-m arched roadway had a rip area of 5 m^2 over a 1.37-m face extraction and the rip comprised a well laminated mudstone with thin ironstone bands. Most of the ripping was taken by the Krupp unit. Although the Hobgoblin was equally well suited to the conditions, the Shand unit proved too powerful for such laminated strata and the operator could not control the breaking down of the rip. Both the Krupp and Ingersoll-Rand unit were fitted with standard moil tools and produced little dust. The information obtained from this site was made available to the mining machinery manufacturers for the exploitation of the technique within the NCB.

12.   In the meantime MRDE produced another machine, figure 4, for installation at Bolsover Colliery. The 67-kW power pack was designed to provide sufficient power for the operation of both the impact ripper and any one of the hydraulically powered packing systems under development. The machine was used to advance a well cleated sideritic rock and siltstone rip, in a 3.66-m x 2.74-m arched tailgate excavation having a rip area of 5.5 m^2. Once again it was found that the Krupp and Ingersoll-Rand units gave the most satisfactory performance and the Krupp hammer was used for most of the 800-m advance. In the harder sections of the rip the rock had a compressive strength of up to 200 MN/m^2 and a maximum tensile strength of 19 MN/m^2, but due to the cleating they were not difficult to break with a moil tool. As at Lea Hall the shift advance was 1.83 m with an actual ripping time of approximately 1 hour. The dust produced when cutting dry was 13 g/m^3 of rock removed; most of this dust was released from the cleats as the rock was broken down rather than by the actual impact breakage of the rock.

13.   The main advantage of using a Krupp breaker rather than a Hobgoblin, in conditions suitable to either, related to the regulations covering the use of equipment underground. The Krupp unit contained no light alloy components and did not need charging with gas. The unit is basically a

rectangular steel shell incorporating a hydraulically actuated piston-hammer which strikes an anvil against a tool crowded into the rock. A control valve fitted on the outside of the unit reverses the hydraulic supply to either side of the piston-hammer. A high-pressure and a low-pressure accumulator are screwed to the unit and are guarded against accidental damage. The Ingersoll-Rand 'Hobgoblin' utilises the hydraulic supply to compress a nitrogen gas spring enclosed in the hammer-piston and the blow energy is achieved by expansion of the gas. The use of the Hobgoblin therefore required nitrogen gas bottles to be kept underground in the vicinity of the workplace, so that the unit could be recharged after a leak of gas or after the draining of oil from the gas chamber, which was considered an unsafe practice unless the cylinders were transported and stored in special containers. Both breakers were found to operate satisfactorily on Walkers Century Oils' 'Aquacent Light' fluid (60% oil and 40% water). The use of Aquacent fluid limits the maximum working pressure of the pumps to 13.8 MN/m^2 and the fluid temperature to 65°C.

14. The trials had revealed certain weaknesses in the Secoma boom and despite modifications carried out by MRDE the boom could not be recommended for commercially manufactured impact rippers for use in strata requiring more powerful impact breakers than the Krupp HM 400. In 1971 Secoma advised that they were producing a boom for the new range of impact units coming onto the market as the French coal and iron ore industries had expressed interest in the application of the impact technique using the Montabert BRH 500 breaker, to their mining methods. MRDE ordered three of these booms for mounting on their heavier-duty impact rippers, figure 5, required for the trials of impact breakers in tough rock conditions. This 67-kW machine has the operator seated alongside the boom, so that he slews but does not elevate with the boom movement. The operator position has a good field of vision and minimises fatigue when impacting for long periods. The ripper has a maximum overall length of 8.23 m, width of 1.52 m, height of 1.83 m and weight of approximately 15 tonnes. The 780-1 capacity oil tank has a large surface area to assist oil cooling. Also in 1971 Gullick Dobson produced the first of their impact rippers, incorporating their high-energy hammer which is capable of impacting at 600 blows per minute with a blow energy of 4070 J, for installation in Fryston Colliery where it has advanced a friable shale rip more than 1000 m. By July 1972 six Gullick Dobson machines were working in tailgates, one of which was an air intake roadway.

15. During 1972 and 1973 MRDE conducted further trials at five collieries with strong rock rips, using Krupp HM 600, Ingersoll-Rand 'Hobgoblin', Shand, and Gullick Dobson impact units. It was quickly established that the standard moil and chisel tools, produced for use with these breakers in civil engineering applications, were unsuitable for ripping massive rock and that other shapes were required. A moil tool tends to form deep holes without inducing breakage of the rock surrounding the hole and leads to jamming of the tool; wide chisel tools are difficult to accurately locate on an irregular rock face and are prone to skid across the rock when impacting commences. It is also difficult with a chisel to control the debris sizing in non-friable strata. Two tools, figure 6, were developed for different hard rock conditions; the narrow-nosed chisel for use in laminated rock and for profiling the roadway in massive rock, and the 'cruciform' for massive stone. The advantage

of the cruciform is that it can be located by either the nose or one of the corners penetrating the rock and can create breaks around the point of impact by virtue of the chisel edged cruciform. The flutes of the cruciform allow the fines produced at the bottom of the hole to be released from the impact area and provide passages for the dust suppression water directed along the tool to reach the dust before it becomes airborne. With breakers such as the Krupp and Ingersoll-Rand, which have the facility for quick tool changing, both tools can be used on the same rip: the cruciform for general breakage and the chisel for profiling. The use of the cruciform has also been extended to soft rock ripping where debris sizing is important. At Desford colliery a Krupp HM 600 and cruciform tool have advanced an excavation, for 3.35-m x 2.44-m flat-topped arches, over 400 m. The ripping, over a 1.07-m coal extraction, comprises a fine-grained siltstone overlain with a massive band of fine-grained sandstone, and method studies show that a 1.07-m advance, removing 6.14 m^3, can be achieved with an impacting time of 26 min and a boom manipulating time of 27 min for 160 impacting positions. When ripping in a solid sandstone (compressive strength 55.6 MN/m^2: tensile strength 4.7 MN/m^2) an overall time of 2 h is required. A Hobgoblin with cruciform tool has achieved approximately the same advance rate. Figure 7 shows a 5.5-m wide x 4-m high rectangular excavation made for a junction in the sandstone. Ripping in a tough massive siltstone (average compressive strength 78 MN/m^2: average tensile strength 20 MN/m^2) at Hapton Valley Colliery showed the advantage of the high-energy output of the Gullick Dobson impact unit fitted with a cruciform tool: its cutting rate of 2.5 m^3/h was approximately 50% better than that achieved with a Krupp HM 600 and cruciform tool. A 1.22-m advance with the Gullick Dobson hammer could be achieved with an impacting time of 32 min and a boom positioning time of 76 min. A machine installed at a sandstone (compressive strength 30-75 MN/m^2: tensile strength 4-10 MN/m^2) rip in Monktonhall Colliery was also equipped with Krupp HM 600 and Gullick Dobson impact units. The rip had a cross-section of 7.5 m^2 and included large sections of massive rock. In the sections of fragmented sandstone the Krupp HM 600 and a cruciform tool effectively broke down the rock, but in the massive areas the cruciform tool was ineffective and it was necessary to revert to a moil to form holes as break-out points for subsequent impacting. The Gullick Dobson unit with a cruciform had an advance rate of about 50% more than the Krupp-moil assembly and was capable of advancing the rip 1.22 m in 2-2½ hours. A Shand hammer on a Lemand machine at Horden Colliery, figure 8, has successfully broken down a laminated sandstone with a compressive strength of 96 MN/m^2.

16. In July 1973 there were thirteen impact rippers working in NCB mines with a further six installations pending.

17. As a move toward the introduction of machines utilising impact breakers into solid drivages the NCB have installed, at Whitwell Colliery, an Eimco loader fitted with a Krupp HM 600 unit, figure 9. This prototype machine is breaking out the stone and coal in a half-gate system. In this method of mining, at a maingate, the coal is extracted only sufficiently far across the roadway to enable the coal discharge conveyor to be installed and the remaining coal is left across the roadhead to be removed with the overlying stone. Spade-type blades have been developed for impacting down the shale and coal. Anderson Mavor have also, in

liaison with MRDE, manufactured a prototype impact-loader based on their existing MC3A loader. The prototype machine incorporates a Secoma boom and Ingersoll-Rand G1100 impact unit (has superseded the Hobgoblin), and will be tested underground at Lea Hall Colliery on completion of surface trials.

FURTHER INFORMATION FROM THE TRIALS

18. Impacting technique - When impacting down a rip, in other than very friable stone, the preferred method is to impact with the breaker in an up-hand position, i.e. with the impact unit rolled onto the underside of the boom and the cradle elevated, as opposed to the down-hand operation of a breaker mounted on an excavator for civil engineering purposes. The advantages are that the operator has better control of debris sizing by smashing the rock on the rip and that he can see the tool above the impact unit-boom cradle assembly. When impacting with the unit positioned on the top of the boom and angled downwards there is a tendency for oversize debris to break away, particularly in well laminated strata. The usual method of ripping is to take out the centre of the rip to provide manoeuvring space for the impact unit when profiling. The provision on ripping machines for crowding the impact unit into the rock along the axis of the unit minimises the number of occasions when the tool binds in its bearing and stalls the unit. Although the 'pick and pry' method of rock breakage is used by ripping machine operators in soft, friable strata , and on some rips with minimal use of the impact unit other than for profiling, the use of such a technique in hard rock invariably results in a loss of effective blow energy because of tool binding.

19. Impact unit dimensions - One factor determining the possible application of a hydraulic impact breaker for roadway making is the overall length of the impact unit-cradle assembly, as the assembly has to be manipulated within the roadway. When profiling it may be necessary to attack the rock virtually at right-angles to the line of advance, especially when the foremost roadway support has been set close to the rock face. Similarly the secondary breakage of debris on the floor or on top of the disposal system can dictate the minimum height of the roadway for a specific impact unit. The cross-section of the breaker can affect the operator's view of the tool in certain impacting positions.

20. Use of water for dust suppression - Because dust control is of great importance, water jets are mounted at the front of the impact unit slide to provide water suppression of the dust during impacting. This water combines with the dust to form a slurry, which can be very abrasive, that runs down the tool shank and will enter the front bearing unless it is effectively sealed. The slurry can also cause rapid wear of the slides used when crowding the unit against the rock.

21. Sparking - In only a few instances, mostly at Hapton Valley Colliery, did sparking occur during impacting. Where ironstone nodules and bands have been encountered it was possible to remove these by undercutting, and overcutting to minimise the amount of impacting directly onto the ironstone.

22. Noise - The noise levels recorded at the operator position have exceeded, in the majority of cases, the limits stipulated by the Department of Employment's Code of Practice, Ref: HMSO (1972).

This limit is time-dependent and therefore the equivalent continuous noise level when impacting in hard rock will almost certainly always be above the limit. It is recommended therefore that all operators are provided with ear protectors.

23. Support setting - The impact unit assembly can be utilised for the lifting into position of the roadway supports. At Desford Colliery when forming the high junction the roof beams were raised in a clamp fitted into the tool holder of the Krupp HM 600.

24. Impact unit breakdowns - Most of the breakdowns encountered with the units have occurred when impacting in hard rock.

   i. Gullick Dobson unit - Units have operated reliably in the less arduous ripping conditions. In tough rips the locking arrangements of the bolts and screws were found to be inadequate and modified units are now being assessed.

   ii. Krupp HM 600 unit - The MK 3 accumulators, both high and low pressure, have given an unsatisfactory service life. MK 4 accumulators are being obtained for life tests.

   iii. Shand unit - In the hard rock rip at Horden the unit has been undergoing development trials and modifications have been made as failures occur.

   iv. Ingersoll-Rand 'Hobgoblin' - The 'Goblin' range (G500 and G1100) has been introduced to improve on the performance of the Hobgoblin. Forthcoming trials will determine the reliability of the G1100. The sealing of the gas chamber of the Hobgoblin had been unsatisfactory when operating on Aquacent. Metal erosion of the spool had also occurred.

25. Impact unit mounting - The Secoma booms are of insufficient strength for mounting the higher-energy impact units to be used in hard strata, but the Gullick Dobson boom and other booms under development should provide for the use of all types of impact unit. The Secoma and Gullick Dobson booms provide excellent manipulation of the impact unit and the 'yield' in the hydraulic motions allows the tool to follow, within limitations, the break formed in the rock.

26. Vibration - The boom hydraulics, in particular the crowd ram, dampen virtually all the vibrations set up when impacting and there is no discomfort at the seated operator position.

27. Machine rigidity - With the boom mounted close to the centre of gravity of the walking bases the machine is stable when impacting, except when profiling the roadway sides in hard rock with the impact unit at right-angles to the line of advance. Where movement has been encountered the machine has been staked at floor level. The Gullick Dobson machine has hydraulic stakers built-in.

CONCLUSION

28. The underground trials have established that hydraulically powered high-energy impact units can provide the basis of machines eminently suitable for NCB ripping operations and it is already evident that the use of impact rippers will steadily

increase, as manufacturers' machines are introduced, to supplement the boom rippers already in use, provided the faults on the impact units are corrected. It is unlikely that the impact ripper will supersede the boom ripper, as the higher cutting rate of the boom ripper can be an advantage in operating conditions suitable for pick cutting. The current price of around £22,000 for an impact ripper is dependent upon the type of boom, impact unit, and ancillary equipment required. This price is about 75% that of a boom ripper.

29. The use of impact rippers has the advantage that not only are there impact units available with sufficient energy outputs to break all types of coal measure strata, but also that the machine requires a relatively small motive power in comparison to other hard rock cutting machines. The majority of rips could be broken down at acceptable advance rates by impact rippers requiring no more than 50 kW to power all the machine services. The Gullick Dobson impact ripper is fitted with a 90-kW motor. These two motor sizes are the most favoured, as a large number are used to drive the face conveyors installed by the NCB.

30. Although tests on unconfined rock core samples produce useful data relating to the compressive and tensile strengths, hardness, specific energy, and abrasivity of the rock, such data can only be used as a general guide when determining the type of impact unit required to break the rock in situ. The massiveness, or lamination, or cleating of the rock on site is of prime importance when selecting both the impact unit and tool shape. The tool shape can also determine the blow energy required to achieve rock breakage. For instance at Hapton Valley, where it was necessary to shatter the rock on the solid rip, the prototype Krupp HM 600, (designated HM 500) with a blow energy of 1356 J at 450 blows per minute, had difficulty in driving a cruciform tool into the rock in order to induce breakage; but a short test with a Shand hammer and similar sized cruciform tool achieved a better penetration rate. The energy output of the Krupp unit was approximately 44% more than that of the Shand, but the blow energy of the Shand was 73% more than that of the Krupp.

31. The mounting of impact units on booms, similar in principle to the heavy-duty versions produced for tunnel drilling, has proved most successful.

REFERENCES

1. BRIDEN H. The design of a heavy impact unit for use in coal mining.

   Colliery Engineering, 1965.1.

The author wishes to thank Mr. D.J. Skidmore, the NCB's Director of Research and Development (Mining), for permission to publish this paper. The views expressed are those of the author and not necessarily those of the NCB or other interested parties.

TABLE 1 - DETAILS OF PROPRIETARY IMPACT UNITS

Manufacturer	Type	Approx Max Blow Energy J	Blows per min	Overall Dimensions without tool - mm			Approx Weight without Tool Kg	Hydraulic Supply		Nitrogen Gas Pressure
				Length	Width	Depth		Flow 1/min	Pressure MN/m^2	
Ingersoll-Rand	G 500	680	135-600	1041	178	222	220	Up to 94.5	13.8	Gas pressure = ½ Fluid pressure
	G 1100	1900	60-600	1076	280	330	339	Up to 163	13.8	Max 9.6 MN/m^2
Krupp	HM 200	540	700	1066	200	336	240	55	12-15	Sealed external accumulators for pressure and return
	HM 600	1830	450	1272	220	426	550	70-90	13-16	
Shand		2350	180	1880	317	356	500	60	11-14	Requires charging at 6.9 MN/m^2
Montabert	BRH 500	2000	320-450	1546	512	310	415	60-170	6.5-13	Internal sealed accumulator
Gullick Dobson		4070	600	1600	381	430	703	185	16.55	Requires charging at 0.41-0.55 MN/m^2

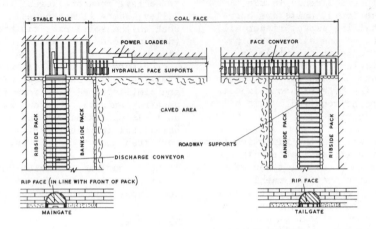

Figure 1: Neg. No. 2174/1 - Typical Coal Face layout.

Figure 2: Neg. No. 2124/5 - Sandstone Rip at Monktonhall Colliery.

Figure 3: Neg. No. 7877 - Test rig with Secoma boom, type JTHS 1030, and NCB impact unit at Bulwell quarry.

Figure 4: Neg. No. RD623/14 - MRDE experimental impact ripper with Secoma boom, modified type JTHS 1030, and Ingersoll-Rand 'Hobgoblin' impact unit.

Figure 5: Neg. No. RD1745/11 - MRDE Impact Ripper with Secoma boom,
type 1950: C1100, and Krupp HM 600
impact unit.

Figure 6: Neg. No. RD21181/1 - Cruciform and chisel tools manufactured
for the Krupp HM 600

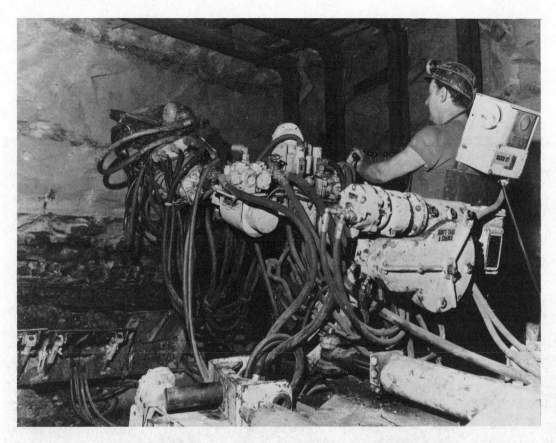

Figure 7: Neg. No. RD1922/2 - Junction formed with Krupp HM 600 hammer and cruciform tool in sandstone at Desford Colliery.

Figure 8: Neg. No. RD1715/3 - Shand impact unit, mounted on a Lemand Impact Ripper, on trial at a simulated rip in sandstone at Horden Colliery.

Figure 9: Neg. No. RD1348/1 - Prototype Eimco Impactor on test in limestone at Middleton Mine.

C25/74

COMPLETELY HYDRAULIC ROTARY-PERCUSSIVE ROCK DRILLS

F. B. LEVETUS

Director and General Manager, Keelavite Hydraulics Limited, Allesley,
Coventry, Warwickshire CV5 9AX

G. CAGNIONCLE, Ing

Directeur Général, Sécoma, 274 Cours Emile Zola, Lyon, France 69

The Ms. of this paper was received at the Institution on 2nd August 1973 and accepted for publication on 26th October 1973. 2

SYNOPSIS   The need for a fully hydraulic rotary percussive drill is indicated by the low efficiency and consequent high power input required by air operated impactors. The fact that manipulators for drill units are normally hydraulically operated means that basically the same power source, whether electrically or diesel operated, can be used for manipulation, rotation and impact.

The paper describes some of the problems to be overcome, and the methods selected to solve them, in a type of rotary percussive drill developed as a joint product between a French and a British firm. The performance of the machine is examined vis-a-vis compressed air machines, and some conclusions drawn regarding the utility of this type of machine in particular, and of hydraulic impact devices in general.

1.   The classical method of driving galleries in mines or for tunnelling for public works requires the drilling of holes varying between 20 and 70mm in diameter and from 2 to 7 metres in depth. These holes are made either by using purely rotary drills or by drills rotated by percussion, or more recently by rotary percussive drills. The choice of drilling tool is obviously dependent upon the type of rock, i.e.,on the degree of hardness and of abrasiveness. Rotary drills are normally used where the rocks are relatively soft and not too abrasive, the other percussive types being used for harder and more abrasive stone.

2.   During the last ten years designs by different manufacturers of these categories of machines have become stabilised. The rotary drills are usually either electrically or hydraulically operated: they call for output torques of the order of 15-70 m.kg. with a speed range of 150 to 1300 r.p.m. and a feed force of 500 to 1800 kg. On the other hand the machines rotated by percussive means have normally used compressed air as the fluid power medium; the speed of rotation is very low and the thrusts generally less than 300 kg.   The more recent rotary percussive machines have generally used two sources of energy: hydraulic for manipulation and for the rotary drive, and pneumatic only for the impact device.

3.   The rotary percussive principle is intended to apply to hard rocks the same principle of chip formation as applies to rotary drilling, the effect is simply to accelerate the formation of chips by blows which add a crushing force to the steady pressure that characterises rotary drilling.   When using this method it is important to be able to control separately the essential parameters, i.e., the speed of rotation, the thrust, and the energy of each blow. If this can be achieved, the rotary percussive machine can then operate so as to give the best possible performance in all kinds

of rock. Many types of machine and many tests have been made by constructors and users during some ten years, and it can now be said that the rotary percussive machine has step by step overtaken the type with rotation by percussion. However, these machines at first always used compressed air as a source of energy for the blows, involving as a result the major inconvenience of noise, of mist, and of excessive power consumption.

4.   For these reasons Secoma in 1965 decided to develop a fully hydraulic rotary percussive machine which would at least equal the specified performance of the best available air hammer, but would only demand about one fifth of the power: this last factor is most important in mining since it reduces the cost of exploitation to a marked extent. The roadway construction of a mine using compressed air is very expensive: on the other hand, a low energy level will make the use of diesel driven "Jumbos" feasible. By way of example, a "Jumbo" carrying two rotary-percussive drills can be driven by a diesel engine of about 100 h.p:equivalent compressed air machines would require between 400 and 500 h.p. which would be quite unacceptable for diesel engines in an enclosed atmosphere.   This reduction in power must be regarded as extremely important since the mobility of drilling equipment in a mine is an essential factor in productivity.

5.   Using as a starting point a reciprocating mechanism developed by Keelavite, Secoma began by 1968 to make a number of prototype machines and to carry out tests in order to perfect the machine which has now been commercially launched(See Figure 1)

This machine consists of :-

A rotary drive unit comprising a
hydraulic gear motor with a reduction
gear

A hydraulic hammer

The accessory devices to give the necessary

thrust and feed, comprising a slide, a feed unit, a tension device to position the flexible pipes, and a control unit to give the necessary automatic feed and return motion.

A suitable dual hydraulic power supply.

The rotary drive is operated by a hydraulic motor, capacity 52 cm^3/revolution, and enables the speed of rotation to be adjusted within the range of 200-600 r.p.m. The speed setting is most import-ant, since according to the soil concerned, the machine can be used either as a purely rotary drill, or for mainly percussive drilling, where the shock from the blows is of major importance.

The hammer unit consists essentially of a variable stroke piston, the chosen stroke and pressure being functions of the required impact energy, always having regard to the maximum that the drill bar can transmit. The piston actuates the main valve, by which it is controlled, by pilot means, the piston itself opening pilot ports to operate the valve as required.

A diagrammatic arrangement of the main impactor piston and of the valve which controls its motion is shown in Figure 2. As will be seen, pilot ports x, y which are connected to pressure, or blanked or exhausted by the main piston as it travels from end to end are used to operate the valve as required at each successive reversal by applying pressure to either area (c) or (d); when either of these is connected to pressure the valve travels to the opposite position since the detent areas (a) and (b) are respectively smaller than (c) or (d). When the valve travels, the area (a), which is larger than the contin-uously pressurized area (b), is connected to either pressure or exhaust as appropriate, thus ensuring that the valve is held positively in one position or the other during the corresponding travel of the main piston. This is necessary as it is impracticable so to position the ports and to proportion the piston so that there is a positive pilot signal at all stages of the cycle. The drained space (e) is of course in fact connected internally to the drained space (f) which always connects to the return line. To reach speeds of up to 10m/second, the drive circuit includes a diaphragm type accumulator at the drive port of the cylinder; a second similar type of accumulator is provided at the valve outlet to control shocks in the return line. The piston is hollow, to accommodate an injector for air or for water, according to the preferred method for removing the debris from the tool.

The rotary percussive unit is carried on a slide of variable stroke, generally from 2-5m, consist-ing of a U frame and a sliding cylinder which drives a drill through a 1½'' pitch chain and pulley block (see Figure 3). When the drill reaches the end of its travel, the hammer is automatically stopped and the drill is returned in fast traverse. Only rotation occurs during the return stroke, so as to prevent the drill bit from sticking: the high torque available to drive the drill is sufficient for this purpose. By this means it is possible to avoid the hammer striking against no resistance; this would not cause damage due to the internal damping provided in the hammer cylinder, but would cause unnecess--ary waste of power and so heating of the oil.

6. Many bench and field trials have enabled a precise determination of the range of variation of the various parameters which enable the machine to operate at optimum efficiency when drilling holes in the range 20-70 mm diameter.

These may be summarized as follows:-

Frequency	2,000-3,000 blows/min
Speed of rotation	200 - 600 revolutions/min
Energy per blow	150-200 N.m
Oil input to Hammer	60 l/min at 180 bars
Oil input to Rotation	60 l/min at 50 to 150 bars
Total input power	35 hp allowing for efficiencies.

7. This rotary percussive machine enables appreciably better results to be obtained than with classical machines. By way of example, a 50mm hole can be drilled in the hardest granite at speeds up to 1.2m/min. The SECOMA/KEELAVITE rotary percussive drill has been designed to use wherever possible commercial boring bars, since for a mining concern one of the essential require-ments for economic operation is both availability and a low consumption of cutting edges and of the boring bars, the cost of which expressed per metre of penetration is important. The actual speed of penetration should not be regarded as the only criterion: it is important to obtain a steady rate of penetration, at the lowest possible overall cost per hole, including also manoeuvering time.

A rotary percussive machine poses the problem of the Jumbo to carry it. One advantage of this type of unit is to permit the use of a completely self-contained equipment with a low power input. The chassis carrying it should be compact,mobile, and carry the complete source of fluid to feed the boring unit: it may be driven by either an electric motor or diesel, or perhaps even by a diesel electric drive, if the user is looking for high manoeuverability, but prefers a completely clean prime mover to operate at the face.

By way of example, the Jumbo shown in Figure 4 shows an integrated machine with the drills, arms and mobile chassis: it has a completely hydraulic unit driven by a diesel engine, with four powered wheels operated by hydrostatic motors. Similar machines are made with from two to six arms.

8. CONCLUSION.

Fully hydraulic rotary percussive drills open up new possibilities to mining and to public works engineers. These are highly reliable machines which greatly improve conditions of work, both by reducing the volume of noise, and by giving perfect visibility due to the elimination of mist. Control is much simplified, and one man can operate two or three drills without difficulty. Due to the relatively low power input and to the improvement in overall manoeuverability, operat-ing costs are also significantly reduced.

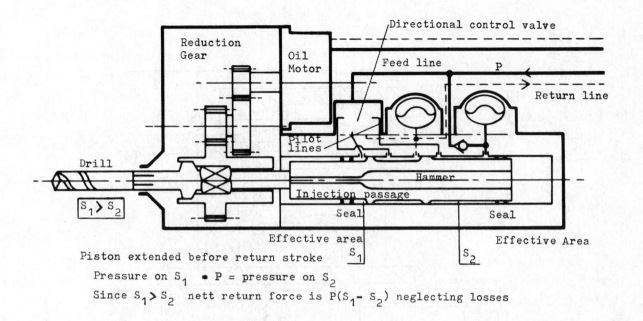

Piston extended before return stroke

  Pressure on S_1 • P = pressure on S_2

  Since $S_1 > S_2$ nett return force is $P(S_1 - S_2)$ neglecting losses

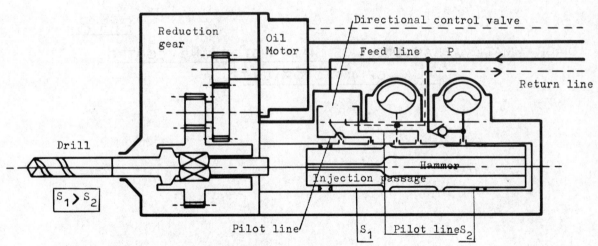

Piston retracted before working stroke

  Pressure on S_1 = 0, Pressure on S_2 = P

  Nett driving force for impact = $S_2 \times P$, neglecting losses

Figure 1 Principle of operation of the SECOMA/
KEELAVITE Rotary Percussive Drill.

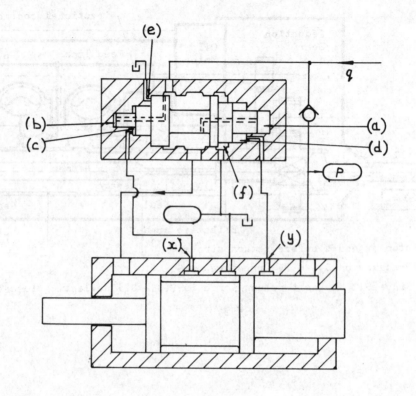

FIG 2

DIAGRAMMATIC ARRANGEMENT OF MAIN PISTON AND CONTROL
VALVE OF IMPACTOR UNIT

Figure 3 Photograph   of the type CC 2000
            slide and of the type R.P. drilling head.

Figure 4   Rotary   percussive Jumbo type PEC

C26/74

THE GULLICK DOBSON IMPACT RIPPER

J. GASKELL, CEng, MIMechE
Manager, Industrial Products, Gullick Dobson Limited, Seaman Works,
Ince, Wigan, Lancashire

R. A. PHILLIPS
Manager, Research and Development, Gullick Dobson Limited, Seaman Works,
Ince, Wigan, Lancashire

The Ms. of this paper was received at the Institution on 30th August 1973 and accepted for publication on 23rd October 1973. 2

SYNOPSIS   This paper describes a self-contained hydraulically powered and controlled Impact Ripping Machine which was designed and built primarily for ripping and profile trimming of underground roadways in coal mines.

The authors outline the stages of early experimental work, design, tests and subsequent development leading up to the stage of "Production Model".

INTRODUCTION

1.   In June of 1968, the Company, being aware of the increasing need for a mechanical means of breaking hard rock, began the design and development of an Impact Ripper Machine. The choice of an impacted chisel device was influenced by previous work carried out in the United Kingdom and by a careful study of other rock cutting and breaking principles. Cutter life, versatility of application, an ability to break hard rocks and a low level of dust creation were considered to be of prime importance.

2.   From the outset, it was decided to produce a machine primarily for gate road ripping in coal mines, which would be capable of cutting hard as well as soft rocks. Except for a trailing cable for an electric power supply, the machine was to be self-contained, fully manoeuvrable and as small as possible, but capable of ripping all normal sized roads.

Early Experimental Work

3.   It was felt that the most logical way to begin design work on a project such as rock breaking was to carry out field experiments in an attempt to establish what the problems would be. To this end, a diesel powered JCB excavator was fitted with a proprietary impact breaker, and put to work in quarries. This machine, operated by members of the Research and Development staff, enabled first-hand experience to be gained which later proved to be of great value.

4.   In all, four weeks of quarry work were carried out in this particular year: 1 week in a quarry of fine-grained Sandstone of 17,500 p.s.i. (1230 Kg/cm^2) and 3 weeks in a quarry of Greywacke of up to 50,000 p.s.i. (3,515 Kg/cm^2) crushing strength.

5.   The quarry tests, even though of only 4 weeks duration, served to point out problems and, more important, gave sufficient information to enable the first design specification to be drawn up. The prime features of this specification were based on the following:-

5a. Control System

Generally speaking, approximately 17% of the working time of the machine was spent in breaking rock.

The remaining time was spent in manipulating the impact breaker. Therefore, the control system for an efficient machine would have to be such that manipulation was speedy and simple to operate, thus allowing more time to be spent on impacting.

5b. Impact Unit Power

Whilst the power of blow obviously would have to be sufficient to break most rocks, there was, in fact, a second   consideration. When presented angularly to a rock face, a low powered impact unit's chisel had a tendency to strike glancing blows which resulted in a very precise positioning being necessary. It was felt that a heavier blow must inevitably result in the chisel travelling along the line on which it was aimed, thus cutting down the necessary number of manipulation operations.

5c. Manipulation

The restricted manipulation of the excavator mounting very quickly made itself apparent. To efficiently break rock in a pre-determined manner (as required in tunnelling and underground ripping work), the manipulator must be capable of presenting the impact chisel at any position and at any angle.

5d. General Design

It was realised at a very early stage that whilst the impact unit's energy did a very useful job in breaking rock, it also had a harmful effect on its mounting vehicle, which suffered badly from vibration. This of course, had to be catered for in the machine to be designed.

5e. Reliability and Servicing

From the location and lack of workshops facilities at various working sites, and the demands likely to be made by the user of a Ripping Machine, it was decided that reliability was to be the keynote, coupled with a minimum amount of servicing being necessary.

6.   The initial quarry trials ended in December of 1968, with a substantial amount of experience having been acquired in addition to the above-mentioned. Such items as chisel metallurgy,

hydraulic circuitry, manipulator design, etc., each became studies in their own right and it was at this stage that a concentrated effort began in the Research and Development Department on the business of designing a machine particularly for ripping work in coal mines.

An Outline of the Design

7. The machine may be best described as a "walking" base carrying an electrically driven hydraulic power pack and an impact unit mounted at the end of a manipulator boom. Except for the trailing electric power cable, the machine is completely self-contained. Figure 1 shows a diagrammatic arrangement. Figure 2 shows an actual photograph.

8. For the sake of clarity, the machine is described under the following headings:-

    1) Machine Base
    2) Power Pack
    3) Control System
    4) Manipulator Boom
    5) Impact Unit

Machine Base

9. The base structure comprises five basic units. A deck plate mounted on two base tanks, (hydraulic fluid reservoirs), which are in turn mounted on two "walking" feet.

10. The deck plate, measuring 10 ft. x 6 ft. (3.05m x 1.83m), is the main part of the construction and is designed to carry the power pack, control system and boom anchorage. For ease of transport during underground installation, the deck plate is split into three pieces, with the largest piece being 6 ft. x 3' 9" (1.83m x 1.14m)

11. The base tanks, having a capacity of 60 gallons (273 litres) each, act as hydraulic fluid coolers by allowing heat from the fluid to dissipate through the complete machine. In addition, these tanks serve as spacers to provide additional ground clearance of up to 24 inches (0.61m), for the machine when straddling a conveyor.

12. The "walking" feet advance the machine 18 inches (0.46m) when a full stride is taken, and steering is accomplished merely by walking one foot further than the other. Alternatively, one foot can be walked forward and the other backward, thus turning the machine about its own centre. Ground contact pressure is around 20 p.s.i. (1.41 Kg/cm^2).

Power Pack

13. A 120 H.P. (89.5 KW) motor, a header tank and a hydraulic pump form the nucleus of the power pack. The header tank is fitted with thermal and float switches which cut out the motor and pump should the temperature rise too high or the level fall too low.

14. Filling of the header tank is by means of a hand pump which fills via the return line filters.

Control System

14. For the sake of good visibility for the operator, dual controls are provided; one set at each front corner of the machine. Each set comprises of four joy-stick levers, with the position and direction of

movement of each lever being related to the position and movement of the boom. Thus, as a lever is moved in a particular direction, the boom moves in that same direction. A change-over valve is provided to enable the operator to control the boom from whichever side of the machine he chooses. This valve, in addition to providing a power supply to the chosen controls, serves to isolate the duplicate set of controls, thus preventing their accidental operation. A further safety feature built into the boom control system, ensures that in the event of a hose-burst or a pump failure, the boom will not fall, as a drop in fluid pressure causes the boom to hydraulically lock in position.

15. The "walking" controls are situated at the rear left-hand corner of the machine. In this position, the operator is behind the machine as it advances which gives him good visibility whilst keeping him in a position of safety.

16. All controls, (boom, impacting and walking) are "Dead Man's Handle" type.

Manipulator Boom

17. The boom is capable of seven distinct movements. This allows the impact chisel to be presented at any height and at any angle chosen by the operator. The movements are illustrated in Figure 3. As the boom can "telescope" to increase its reach by more than 36 inches (0.915m), manoeuvring of the complete machine is only occasionally necessary.

18. There is sufficient angular movement of the boom to provide a coverage (measured at the impact chisel tip) of 16' 6" wide x 16' 6" high (5.03m x 5.03m). These figures should be treated as a minimum, as they are measured with the telescopic section and crowd ram both fully retracted, and the impact unit angled no more than is enough to allow the chisel to touch roof and walls. In practice, the telescope and crowd rams will always be extended a little and the impact unit at a rather coarse angle. The stated 16' 6" square area therefore, will be increased by a substantial amount. Coverage is illustrated in Figure 4.

Impact Unit

19. This is a hydraulically powered unit designed to deliver blows of up to 3,000 ft. lbs. (4070 J.). The frequency is variable up to 14 blows per second. The principle of operation is that a heavy piston is hydraulically bounced backwards against a gas spring. From this position, it is released (hydraulically) and blown forward by the gas to strike the rear end of the chisel. Full power is developed only when the chisel is pressed against the rock face. When firing in free air, the chisel remains for most of the time in the forward position out of reach of the piston which is then stopped at the end of its travel by a hydraulic damper. The cycle of operations is automatic and continues for as long as the operator holds the trigger handle in the firing position.

20. A feature of the design of the impact unit is that, with the exception of the chisel, there is only one moving part within the unit. The two valves for automatically controlling firing are bolted to the unit to facilitate simple replacement should that ever be necessary.

The Hydraulic System

21. General Description

The hydraulic system (see Figure 6) is split into three parts, each driven by its own section of a triple bank gear pump. The first bank, $17\frac{1}{2}$ g.p.m. (79.5 l/min.) with automatic unloading feeds a constant pressure hydraulic main and 4 gallon (18 l) accumulator supplying all manipulator and walking functions; the second bank delivering 23 g.p.m. (104.5 l/min.) supplements the first to supply the impacting head and the third, $11\frac{1}{2}$ g.p.m. (52 l/min.) is for auxiliary attachments.

22. Manipulation and walking services are mostly actuated by double acting rams controlled by manually operated closed centre spool valves fed from the hydraulic main.

23. Supply to the head for impacting is by connecting it to the hydraulic main via a P.O. check valve while piloting on-load both pumps.

Power Supply

24. Choice of Pump

The maximum fluid power requirement was determined by the hammer demand which was more than twice that needed for manipulation and walking.

25. At the time of designing the ripping machine, the head itself was still in design, intended for a 40 g.p.m. supply at 2000 p.s.i.

26. For use in coal mines in the U.K., the 60/40 water in oil invert emulsion aquacent in one of its earlier forms was coming into use as the preferred fire resistant fluid (where 95/5 water/oil emulsion could not be used). Pump manufacturers were generally rather non-committal or at best, vague about usage on these fluids, but early tests by MRDE at Bretby, absence of negative instructions from the pump manufacturers and our own hope for future product improvement led us to choose 2000 p.s.i. as the highest realistic working pressure. Later experience increased this to 2100 p.s.i. for general service use and 2400 p.s.i. for impacting.

27. Only two pumps showed at the time much promise in the Bretby tests; one a gear pump, the other an axial piston type. Despite the attraction of the automatic delivery control of the latter, cost and installation considerations and our uncertainty regarding the effects of dirt and the water in the fluid led us to choose the former.

28. To keep pump bearing loads to a minimum, two narrowgears were used instead of a single wide one, giving us the opportunity of dividing the supply system as previously described.

29. Pump Unloading

Of the two traditional methods of unloading fixed displacement pumps, we adopted the automatic unloading valve and ballasting accumulator for the general services pump (see Figure 7), rather than the perhaps more widely used open centre selector approach. Our reasoning here hinged on the size and type of manual valve available for our particular control arrangement, a more favourable heat balance and the availability in the circuit of the accumulator which assists in smoothing the effects of the impact head. Being already fully charged as impacting is selected, there is not the delay there otherwise would be if the accumulator had first to be filled.

30. The second pump runs normally off load, dumping through a vented pilot relief valve and coming on load in response to the same pilot signal that opens the P.O. check valve connecting the hydraulic main to the impact head. A modification to the automatic unloading valve allows the impact trigger pilot signal to inhibit its action during impacting, thus preventing any unloading. The aim here is to generate a flow surplus to guarantee a sustained pressure. With the exception of the trigger valve, which is sited with the manipulation controls, all the power control valves are grouped onto a common manifold for compactness, ease of replacement and minimisation of leakage points. For safety, on stopping the machine, the accumulator is discharged by venting the general services pump relief valve. On early machines, this is done manually. A valve has now been developed which detects a pump stopping and automatically discharges the accumulator.

31. Fluid Cleanliness

Supply and return line filters are rated at 10 micron. With the low tank head available and the need to keep suction line losses lower with emulsion than with mineral oils, suction lines were left unfiltered apart from a coarse strainer. Instead a clean tank approach was pursued, with a fixed lid and air filter, both made difficult to remove. The hand pump for filling feeds into the return line, just before the filters.

32. Fluid Reservoirs

Fluid heating, minimised by attention to off load flow losses is contained by utilising a large portion of the machine surface area for dissipation. Return flow divides between the two base tanks, extensively baffled to promote turbulence before entering the header tank where again circulation is promoted around all the outside faces. Further baffles also guard against suction vortex formation. Low level and fluid temperature switches are fitted.

33. Manual Controls

Essentially, the same basic control valve is used for all manual controls on the machine; a closed centre, 4-way spool valve with 2 spool types and 3 spring/detent variations. While rather undersized for good hydraulic efficiency at our power levels, it still allows adequate speeds for all movements and reasonable inching control.

34. Manifolded into groups of 4, each pair of valves controlled by a bi-directional handle permitting simultaneous or separate operation of the two valves, there are eight valves to a set for controlling the boom. Right and left hand sets are fitted with a changeover supply valve to give preference to one and disable the other not in use. Shuttle valves in the ram service lines prevent supply fluid exhausting via the opposite hand, non-working selectors.

35. Boom Rams

These are of Gullick Dobson construction and designed to fail safe. Because of the versatility of the boom and its controls, most of the rams can experience following loads in either direction due to gravity or the effect of operating another movement. For safety, with men likely to be working beneath and close to the boom for much of its life, it was also necessary to provide protection against collapse due to accidental hose damage.

36. To meet the combined safety, following load control and overload yield protection requirements, built into the ram end blocks are dual cartridge valves which combine the functions of P.O. check and relief valve (see Figure 8).

37. The relief valves are set at 2500 p.s.i. and act on the exhausting fluid when supply pressure to the ram falls below $\frac{1}{3}$ of this value, i.e. on impending following loads. When raising a load, supply pressure pilots the exhaust relief valve wide open so as not to restrict raising. Used with a control valve having a spring centred spool connecting both service parts to return in neutral, the cartridge valves cannot then be unlocked by supply leakage into the service lines, and a passage is allowed for fluid exhausted by a ram forced to yield.

38. The Impact Head crowd ram alone of the boom rams, is without cartridge valves and is controlled by a spring centred spool valve having service lines blanked in neutral. A similar valve controls the hydraulic motor for 'roll'.

39. Walking Feet

Each of the two feet contains a pair of single acting lift rams and a double acting advance ram. The four raise rams are controlled by a single detent spool control. A P.O. check valve prevents lowering when hydraulic power is off.

40. Left and right advance rams are individually controlled by spring centred valves as used for boom crowd and roll function.

41. Impact Head

Hydraulically, the head is simply a gas spring loaded hammer piston and a pilot operated valve for switching fluid to or from the hammer piston. Life expectancy, in terms of operating cycles is high and every attempt is made either to eliminate or ease the duty of the hydraulic seals. The hammer piston relies for sealing on the closeness of its fit in its bearings to limit leakage, outboard seals being only to contain drain fluid at the front or gas leakage at the rear. Valves are close fitting spools. (see Figure 9)

42. Originally designed for working at 2000 p.s.i., the head has been developed for use on the ripping machine at 2400 p.s.i. and is in fact tunable to supplies ranging from 2800 p.s.i. to 1600 p.s.i., blow energy being related to supply pressure and flow.

Development of the Machine

43. By the end of 1970, the prototype machine was completed up to the stage of being able to carry out demonstrations. In parallel to this, a second prototype impact unit, of our own design, was fitted to a manipulator boom mounted on the back of a wheeled excavator for surface trials in a local quarry. Impacting trials began in the quarry in December 1970, where the impact unit and chisel were generally abused with the object of proving the design. Unfortunately, the rock being cut (sandstone of 17,500 p.s.i. crushing strength - 1,230 Kg/cm^2), did not prove to be hard enough to test either the maximum power of blow or the chisel edge. It did serve, however, to test the internal bearings of the impact unit and also its triggering valves.

44. In March 1971, the completed prototype Ripping Machine was put on surface trial at the National Coal Board's Swadlincote test site. The test consisted of cutting a 12 ft. x 9 ft. (3.66m x 2.74m) roadway through a 24 ft. long (7.31m) block of fly-ash concrete with a pre-cut slot underneath to represent the space left by extracted coal (see Figure 5). As with the quarry test, this material did not prove to be a test for the chisel, but owing to the plastic, homogeneous and tough nature of fly-ash, it was possible to demonstrate the versatility of the machine and its control system, as with each series of blows, the chisel removed only a little more than its own swept volume. Thus, to rip and profile the roadway, a great number of manipulations had to be carried out in as short a time as possible.

45. A timed trial at the Swadlincote site showed the machine to be capable of advancing the ripping 1 yard (0.91m), including trimming, in 55 minutes. This involved 400 manipulations, which suggested that a considerably better performance would be achieved underground in a natural rock. The ability of the operator to choose 400 positions in 55 minutes was considered a good indication of the speed with which the control system could be operated.

46. Throughout the Swadlincote trial, the machine was equipped with a prototype impact unit mounted on a proprietary drill boom. The general findings at the end of this particular trial were that:-

1. The basic concept behind the overall machine was good and the walking mechanism gave all that was desired.

2. The prototype impact unit, whilst very effective had external piping which was prone to damage. Also, the chisel mounting did not readily lend itself to quick changing of chisels.

3. The manipulator boom was not robust enough for an impacting application and a new boom would have to be designed and built.

47. Development of the impact unit design continued with the object of producing one which would be more streamlined and without external pipework. In addition, emphasis was placed on the need for facilitating the carrying out of any servicing underground, rather than in the manufacturer's workshop.

48. In anticipation of the proprietary boom not being suitable, design work had been started at the beginning of the year on a completely new manipulator.

49. At the conclusion of the Swadlincote trials, it was generally agreed that simulated surface trials could never be considered a true substitute for underground tests under actual working conditions. The policy adopted therefore, was to continue development to overcome all known problems and to take the machine underground as quickly as possible to determine what other problems would come to light.

Underground Trials

50. In October 1971, the machine commenced underground trials at Fryston Colliery. At this stage, it was still fitted with a drill boom, as its

manipulator, and the prototype impact unit.

51.   Ripping began in a Tail Gate of a production coal face on three shifts per day. The machine immediately proved that it could cut a rip easily and quickly. For quite some time, the required advance rate was only 5' 5" (1.65m) per shift which, including the trimming operation and occasional stoppages for the disposal of debris, usually took approximately 30 to 40 minutes. It was interesting to note that after the first few yards of advance, the rip hardened, thus illustrating how impact ripping was much kinder to the surrounding strata than the previously used explosives.

52.   As anticipated, trials under actual working conditions brought some problems to light for the first time. The most important of such problems was in the valvegear responsible for automatically cycling the hammer. This valvegear, comprising four small hydraulic units interconnected by mechanical means, performed remarkably well when properly adjusted, but unfortunately needed a highly qualified technician to carry out such adjustments. The obvious course of action was, therefore, taken and a single new valve was made to replace the four valves with mechanical connections. From this stage, regular adjustment was no longer necessary, but could, when desired, be done as a driver/maintenance task.

53.   In May 1972, the newly-designed Gullick Dobson manipulator boom was fitted, together with the corresponding new deck mounting. Being a completely new design, it was possible to incorporate all requirements determined by the experience of using a drill boom as a manipulator. Telescoping was by means of hydraulic rams rather than the original lead-screw and thus cushioning against shock loading was provided. Safety isolator valves were built into rams rather than being connected by external hoses which were too easily damaged. The design was generally considerably more robust than the original.

54.   The first production model impact unit was subsequently fitted to bring the machine up to standard.

55.   In all, five complete machines were built to production standards by the Gullick Dobson Development Department. The object being to fully record all workshop activities and determine manufacturing procedures for the future.

56.   A summary of the five machines is as follows:-

No. 1	Despatched to Fryston Colliery	August 1971
No. 2	Despatched to Acton Hall Colliery	June 1972
No. 3	Despatched to Snowdown Colliery	May 1972
No. 4	Despatched to France for demonstration	June 1972
No. 5	Despatched to London for exhibition	August 1972

Production Machines

57.   Manufacture under normal "production" conditions began with machine number 6, from which time, the following have been produced:-

No. 6	(Feb. 1973)	A Boom and Hammer Assembly to the N.C.B. at Bretby for mounting on their own base unit.
No. 7	(Mar. 1973)	Complete machine – Hapton Valley Colliery.
No. 8	(Mar. 1973)	Complete machine – Ackton Hall Colliery.
No. 9	(Mar. 1973)	Complete machine – Hickleton Colliery.
No.10	(Apr. 1973)	Complete machine – Monktonhall Colliery.
No.11	(May 1973)	A Boom and Hammer Assembly to Germany for mounting on an existing crawler chassis.
No.12	(May 1973)	Complete machine – Exhibition in Poland.
No.13	(June 1973)	Complete machine – Brodsworth Colliery.

58.   As one would expect with a new product, there has had to be a systematic ironing out of teething troubles in development and the early stages of production, but problems which will probably never be solved are those of choosing chisel profile, power of blow and frequency. Chisel profile is dictated by the characteristics of the rock to be cut, and to some extent, by the method of mining adopted. The required power of blow and frequency are also determined by experiment, but as a means of simple on-site adjustment is provided, the impact unit is usually delivered with the power output set at maximum, and if necessary, de-tuned after being put to work.

Recent Activities

59.   A relatively recent development has been to adapt the existing impact unit to enable it to be attached to dipper arms of excavators in place of digging buckets. In this way, the impact unit, being powered from the excavator's own hydraulic system, provides a fully mobile means of breaking rock and concrete without the use of explosives. It also has the advantage of providing more power and less noise than the more widely-known pneumatic breakers.

60.   In order to prevent damage from vibration to the excavator, a mounting cradle with a built-in recoil device is provided. Power output at the impact unit is dependent on the hydraulic supply from the excavator.

61.   Whilst it is intended that a standard impact unit and recoil cradle be maintained, the vast number of variations of excavators demands that sets of hydraulic hoses and connections, together with mounting brackets, will have to be individually made to order.

ACKNOWLEDGEMENTS

The authors wish to express thanks to the National Coal Board for co-operation and facilities provided in testing at the Swadlincote Test Site.

Thanks are also due to the directors of Gullick Dobson Ltd., for permission to use subject material needed in the preparation of this paper.

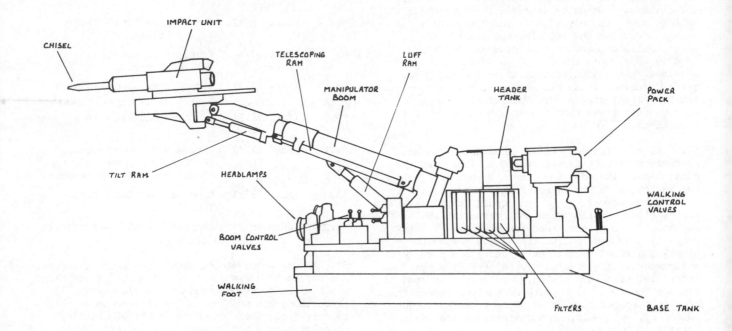

CHISEL

IMPACT UNIT

TELESCOPING RAM

LUFF RAM

MANIPULATOR BOOM

HEADER TANK

POWER PACK

TILT RAM

HEADLAMPS

BOOM CONTROL VALVES

WALKING CONTROL VALVES

WALKING FOOT

FILTERS

BASE TANK

Fig. 1   Diagrammatic arrangement of the Ripping Machine.

Fig. 2   Photograph of the Ripping Machine

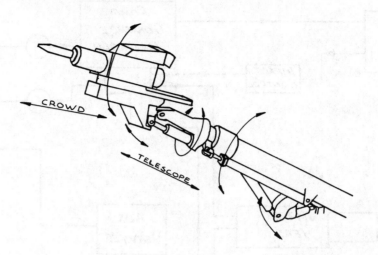

Fig. 3   Diagram showing boom movements.

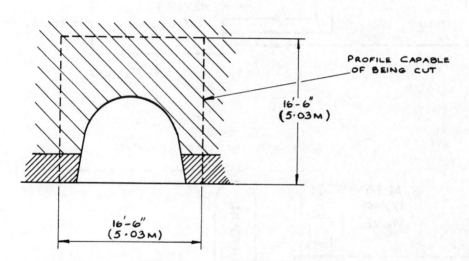

Fig. 4   Illustration of profile of coverage.

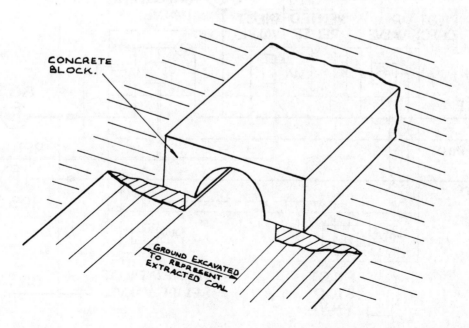

Fig. 5   Illustration of fly-ash concrete cut during surface trials.

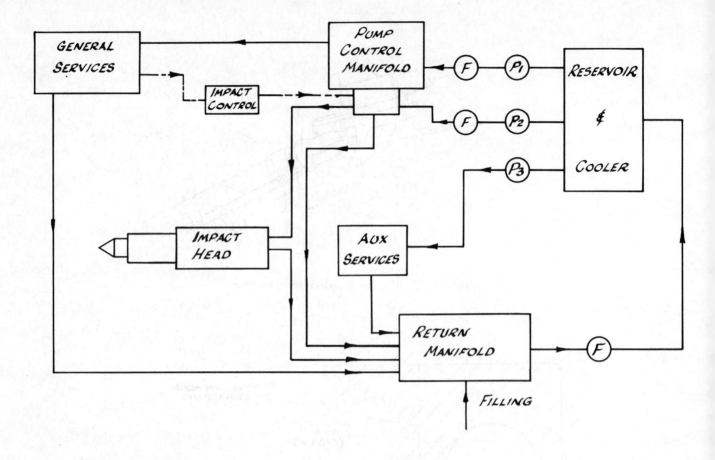

Fig. 6   Block diagram of hydraulic system.

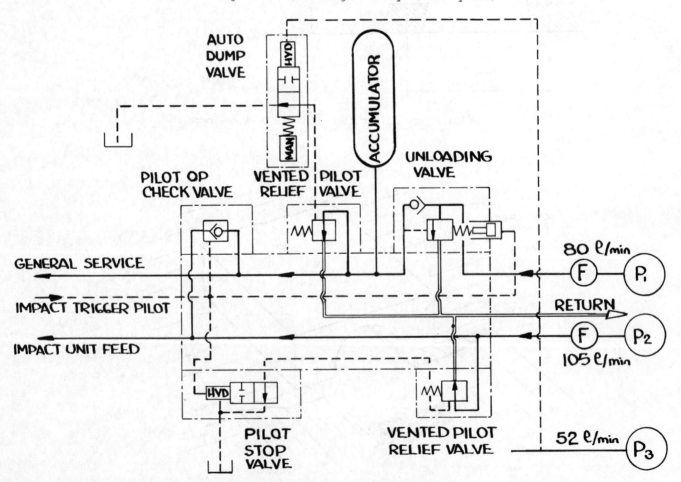

Fig. 7   Circuit diagram of pump unloading control manifold.

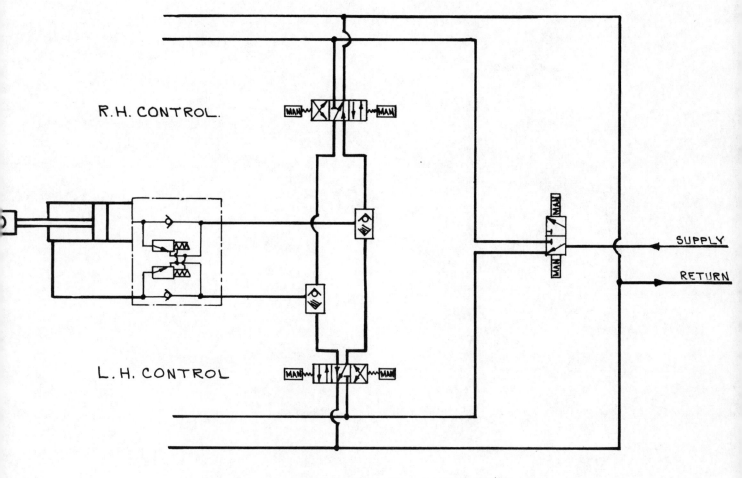

R.H. CONTROL.

L.H. CONTROL

SUPPLY

RETURN

Fig. 8   Circuit diagram of ram control system.

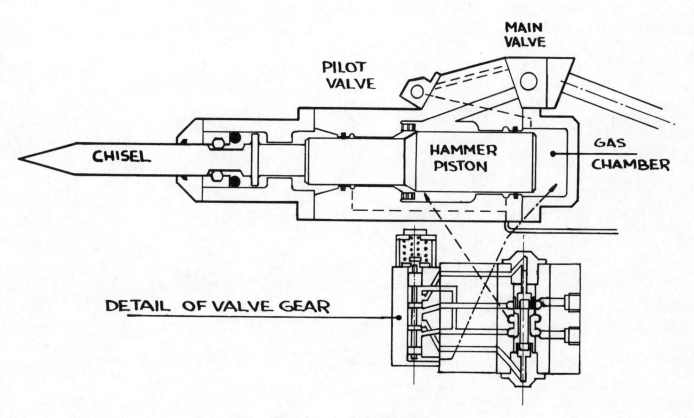

PILOT
VALVE

MAIN
VALVE

CHISEL

HAMMER
PISTON

GAS
CHAMBER

DETAIL OF VALVE GEAR

Fig. 9   Impact Head

81

C27/74

THE HYDRAULIC HAMMER IN COAL MINING

H. M. HUGHES, MA(Cantab)

Head of Production Design Branch, Mining Research and Development Establishment,
National Coal Board, Stanhope Bretby, Burton-on-Trent, Staffordshire

The Ms. of this paper was received at the Institution on 7th August 1973 and accepted for publication on 23rd October 1973. 13

SYNOPSIS

   Percussion and impact machines represent two steps forward in engineering separated by one hundred years. The first enable small diameter holes to be drilled so that rock can be broken with explosive and the second can break rock without explosive. These developments are reviewed, both historically and numerically, from the point of view of British coal-mines. The relatively low speed of the hydraulic hammer is shown to be significant in both cases.

INTRODUCTION

1.   In British coal-mines, there is a need for an electrically powered hydraulic jackhammer: i.e. a manually operated drill either hand-held or feed-leg mounted. A formula for the performance of percussive drills is developed and is utilised to illustrate the critical inverse dependence of their weight on the ultimate hammer speed. A hand tool is limited to a weight of around 25 kg and the relatively low speeds which the hydraulic hammer can readily achieve make this difficult to realise.

2.   Percussive breakers weigh up to 50 kg and the energy of their blow ranges up to 135 J. In 1956, the National Coal Board commenced experiments with the higher order of impact of 1355 J. Such tools weigh 500 kg.These have shown that rock can be broken off to a free face in large pieces without the assistance of explosive. But a critical expression is derived which indicates that the range of rock which will shatter on breaking, and so increase the dust, is also governed by the ultimate hammer speed. Dust confers an objectionable environment and, in the case of breaking, its reduction is assisted by a relatively low hammer speed at impact.

DRILLING

3.   Small hole drilling such as for shotfiring was originally carried out manually utilising a rod with a chisel shaped blade at one end. A blow with a sledge hammer caused it to penetrate the rock: and the rod was turned a few degrees between blows both to chip the rock off between the indentations and to make a circular hole. In 1861, in the Mont Cenis (or Fréjus) rail tunnel between France and Italy, Germain Sommeiller mechanised the process by introducing compressed air operated machines. They were rig mounted drifters weighing around 200 kg each (Ref.1.).They had a reciprocating action (giving under 5 blows/s) and indexing and feed motions. This was one of the great steps forward in engineering; it foreshadowed most of today's techniques of drilling in important tunnelling contracts.

The dependence on compressed air

4. Pneumatic percussive drilling remains the normal method of making shot-holes in hard rock and has meant that virtually all such operations are based on compressed air. Electric percussive drills have been manufactured for some time but they give only one fifth of the blow and cannot rival pneumatic drills for major works.

5. In the United States, in 1890, C.H. Shaw separated the rod from the piston by introducing the hammer, and, in 1897, J.G. Leyner invented the flushing drill utilising first air and then water. The reciprocating motion of the rod was no longer required for evacuating the debris and the rate of blow could be increased reducing the weight of the drill. Moreover, there is little torque to be reacted since the rod is indexed on the return stroke of the hammer. Since 1912, the hand-held drill, or jackhammer, has appeared weighing around 25 kg and giving some 40 blows/s of 70 J about. It was supplemented around 1930 by a pneumatic feedleg so that the operator does not have to react the drill after setting it up. To avoid bending the drill steel, however, owing to the angle at which the feedleg pushes, thrust is limited to the order of 500 N. Nevertheless, penetration force is generated by the hammer so this is adequate for addressing the drill to its work.

6. Water hydraulic rotary drills were introduced in the Arlberg tunnel in Austria by Alfred Brandt in 1880 and were also utilised in the Simplon tunnel but they needed 120 kN thrust. In today's coal-mines, electric, oil hydraulic, and pneumatic, hand-held rotary drills are available for shot-holes but are limited to coal and other rock of low strength. Strata in the British coal measures generally comprise seatearth, shale, mudstone, siltstone and sandstone. Sandstone, the strongest, has an unconfined compressive strength of up to 170 MN/m^2. They are far from being the hardest rocks in the earth's crust but a thrust of up to 20 kN is needed to give a reasonable performance with a rotary drill throughout the range. Moreover, a correspondingly high torque is required from the motor to overcome the proportionate

resistance to turning which the thrust generates. A thrust of this order needs a mechanically braced anchorage both to react the thrust itself and the torque; so the performance of hand-held or feedleg rotary equipment cannot be improved in this way. The years since the last war saw the introduction of rotary drills with percussion but their weight and torque are too great for hand-held or pusher leg operation and they serve as drifters on mechanised booms. Moreover, the percussion still required compressed air.

The need for hydraulics

7.   Generally speaking, enlarged openings have to be ripped in stone at the ends of long wall coal faces in British coal-mines. Face heights are kept within the seam and average around 1.4 m. Arched roadways about 3 m high by 4 m wide are needed each end to allow access and egress for men, machines, mineral, and ventilation. A main method of making these gates is by shot-firing the stone above and behind the coal excavation. As the gate end has also to house the portable substation, electric distribution gear and control boxes, the loading and main conveyors, and to provide mechanical handling facilities for incoming supplies and for packing the shotfired debris into the waste to one side, it is a congested locality. Particularly at the main gate (where the coal is loaded out) there is no room for a mobile drilling rig and hand-held drilling is usual. Moreover, even when driving full headings or tunnels, the roadway size is seldom conducive to the utilisation of mobile drilling rigs as the mechanical loaders have to pass them for mucking out. Thus, hand-held or feedleg drilling is normal.

8.   Compressed air has been available in British coal-mines since 1840 and electricity underground since 1882. As the latter is five times more efficient, modern collieries tend to be all-electric although a number have considerable compressor installations. The present position is that all normal operations can be powered by electricity except drilling in the harder rocks which requires compressed air. Inbye compressors are utilised but they need rooms to be excavated for them; moreover, they have to be carefully supervised as they comprise heat engines in an environment where heat is a source of danger. There is a demand for hand-held drills powered from an electric source capable of making shot-holes in all strata encountered in British coal-mines.

9.   The answer is a hydraulic jackhammer operating on fire resistant fluid. Hydraulic picks have appeared on the market in recent years: but a drill, of course, requires an indexing mechanism in addition if the rod is to penetrate any distance. Drifters have been developed and effort is currently being directed at producing commercial hydraulic jackhammers.

Rate of penetration

10.   At the optimum, around 75% of the energy of the blow (W) is transferred to the rock (Ref. 2). The rest goes in the return of the hammer, indexing, flexing of the rod, hysteresis, and sound, etc. The work done on the rock per blade of the bit is the area under the force (F)/penetration (u) diagram which can be idealised as in Figure 1 (Ref. 2). Two further assumptions can also be made which accord with experience. Firstly, the sides of the indentation fracture, owing to

the brittle nature of the rock, so that the area of contact between the blade and the rock tends to become constant. Thus this area is proportional to the diameter of the hole (D) but is independent of the blade angle for the range commercially utilised. Secondly, F for a given penetration is proportional to the unconfined compressive strength of the rock (f_c). Accordingly, the equation for the penetration of the blade approximates to the following:

$$F = k_1 u f_c D \qquad (1)$$

where k_1 is a constant.

11.   If the energy returned to the drill rod (W_E) is ignored, a is the number of blades (i.e. 1 for a chisel bit, 2 for a cross bit, etc.) and u_o the penetration per blow, then

$$.75W = a k_1 \frac{u_o^2}{2} f_c D$$

$$u_o = (1.5W/a k_1 f_c D)^{\frac{1}{2}} . \qquad (2)$$

12.   If v is the rate of penetration, N the rate of blow, and n the number of blows per revolution of the rod, then

$$v = \beta \frac{N}{n} 2 a u_o \qquad (3)$$

where β is a factor less than one when indentations are not superimposed in successive revolutions so that the advance of the hole per revolution is less than $2 a u_o$. Thus,

$$v = k_2 (Wa/f_c D)^{\frac{1}{2}} N/n \qquad (4)$$

where k_2 is a constant.

13.   If v is in cm/s, W in J, f_c in MN/m^2, D in cm, and N in blows/s, then k_2 is of the order of 0.725 for integral steels so that the model becomes

$$v = 0.725 (Wa/f_c D)^{\frac{1}{2}} N/n . \qquad (5)$$

With detachable bits, although the joint may be tight, some of the stress wave is reflected at the change in section (Ref. 3) reducing k_2 to the order of 0.6 so that the model becomes

$$v = 0.6 (Wa/f_c D)^{\frac{1}{2}} N/n . \qquad (6)$$

It is known that these joints sometimes become hot. In British coal-mines, detachable bits are usually cross bits and integral bits chisel bits so that the above formulae give a 17% increase in the rate of penetration for the former. For a button bit, a may be taken as equal to 4/3; which gives an integral button bit a performance similar to a detachable cross bit.

Drill weight

14.   One difference between compressed air and a pressurised liquid is that the former expands in the tool mechanism with two consequences. Firstly, the air loses internal energy so that its temperature falls. As almost all the energy of the tool ultimately reappears as heat (Ref. 4) the refrigeration of the pneumatic drill can be beneficial. With a hydraulic drill, the temperature of the liquid rises as it passes through small orifices so that it is not a good coolant while the energy lost in friction directly heats the tool. To some extent, the flushing water can provide an additional coolant.

15. A second consequence is that higher piston speeds are more easily generated with a pneumatic tool. A typical ultimate hammer speed for a pneumatic jackhammer is 11 m/s; a hydraulic jackhammer may not do more than 7.5 m/s. If M is the mass of the hammer, V_u its ultimate speed, and its stroke is constant, then $W \propto MV_u^2$ and $N \propto V_u$. From equation (4), for the same performance, $W^{\frac{1}{2}}N$ has to be the same. Thus, $M^{\frac{1}{2}}V_u^2$ has to be constant so that $M \propto V^{-4}$. With the above speeds, the hydraulic hammer would need a mass 4.5 times greater than the pneumatic hammer. Currently, a typical pneumatic jackhammer weighs 24 kg and a prototype hydraulic jackhammer 29 kg. The performance of the former is susceptible in practice to the frequent condition of a fall in the pressure of the air supply. But it does seem that this weight gap will be difficult to close entirely if a reasonable performance is to be obtained from the latter. Some hydraulic manufacturers, however, are claiming comparable ultimate hammer speeds.

16. Nevertheless, in coal-mines at this time, where compressed air is not installed, the only machine available for drilling ripping lips is the hand-held rotary drill. In rock of any strength, as many as three men push it in an attempt to make progress. This is not a satisfactory method of working; a hand-held drill which could improve on it without requiring compressed air or a high thrust or torque, would be welcome.

BREAKING

17. In 1956, a 1355 J pneumatic impulsive experimental rig was tried underground by the National Coal Board in the Garw coal seam at Cwmtillery Colliery. It was utilised against a buttock prepared at right angles to the face and enabled experiments to be carried out with a blow ten times greater than a drifter could apply. It showed coal could be hammered off in bulk without the energy of explosives; and other work indicated that the blows of pneumatic mechanisms of 40 J and 110 J and hydraulic mechanisms of 50 J were insufficient for this purpose in coal and stone. The pneumatic impulsive rig comprised a steel piston rod of 0.05 m diameter striking a steel tool on a 0.1 m by 0.045 m rectangular section shank which had a 0.216 m blade of 0.7 rad angle integral with it. The ultimate piston rod speed was 10.45 m/s.

Impulsive force

18. From Figure 1,

$$\frac{aF_u}{2} = .75W$$

$$F = \frac{1.5W}{au} .$$

$$\text{(7)}$$

At a point on the buttock 0.2 m from the face, under a 50 kN continuously sustained thrust, the blade took eleven 1355 J blows to fracture the coal, penetrating around 0.05 m. Assuming the elastic rebound portion of Figure 1 is retraced upon reloading and the original F/u line continued (Ref. 2) the ultimate value of F would be

$$F = \frac{1.5 \times 1355 \times 11}{1 \times 0.05} = 447,000 \text{ N} . \quad \text{(8)}$$

Thus, the total force would have been about 500 kN. The coal under the blade pulverised and the projected bearing area of the wedge was around 0.008 m² so the final stress could have been not less than

62.5 MN/m². The unconfined compressive strength of the coal is 18 MN/m² perpendicular, and 12 MN/m² parallel, to the bedding planes respectively. This would indicate that up to failure the coal under the blade was being progressively confined (increasing its compressive strength) and that the work was being expended in its plastic deformation (Ref. 4).

Stress waves

19. The impact put a compressive stress wave into the tool and the coal. For simplicity, let it be assumed that plane sections remained plane; and that, as long as there was compression between interfaces, they remained together so that their particle velocities were the same and the forces on them equal and opposite. The sectional area of the rod was 0.002 m², of the tool 0.0045 m², and the projected area of the tool in the coal at 0.05 m penetration was 0.008 m². If V is particle velocity, C compressive wave velocity, σ compressive wave stress, P interface force, A face area, ρ density, G modulus of rigidity, λ Lame's parameter, E Young's modulus, ν Poisson's ratio, then for the steel rod and tool (Ref. 5)

$$C = (E/\rho)^{\frac{1}{2}}$$

$$\sigma = \rho CV = V(E\rho)^{\frac{1}{2}}$$

$$P = \sigma A = VA(E\rho)^{\frac{1}{2}}. \quad \text{(9)}$$

If V_r and V_t are the particle velocities of the rod and tool, respectively, owing to their collision, then

$$V_t = 10.45 - V_r \quad \text{(10)}$$

and, from equation (9)

$$0.002V_r = 0.0045V_t \quad \text{(11)}$$

so that

$$V_t = 3.22 \text{ m/s.} \quad \text{(12)}$$

20. Similarly (Ref. 5) for unbounded coal

$$C = \left[(\lambda + 2G)/\rho \right]^{\frac{1}{2}}. \quad \text{(13)}$$

If ν for coal is taken as 0.3, then (Ref. 5)

$$\lambda = \frac{E\nu}{(1+\nu)(1-2\nu)} = .577E$$

$$G = \frac{E}{2(1+\nu)} = .385E$$

so that $C = 1.16(E/\rho)^{\frac{1}{2}}$

$$\sigma = \rho CV = 1.16V(E\rho)^{\frac{1}{2}} \quad \text{(14)}$$

and $P = \sigma A = 1.16VA(E\rho)^{\frac{1}{2}}. \quad \text{(15)}$

For this coal, the dynamic Young's modulus parallel to the bedding planes and perpendicular to the main cleats*(which made only a small angle with the face) is 1570 MN/m² and ρ is 1342 kg/m³ (Ref. 6). For the steel, let E be taken as 210,000 MN/m² and ρ as 7850 kg/m³. If V_b and V_c are the particle velocities of the blade and the coal, respectively, owing to the impact between them, then using equation (12)

$$V_c = 3.22 - V_b \quad \text{(16)}$$

*"Cleats" are the joint planes in a seam of coal.

85

and, from equations (9) and (15) approximately

$$0.0045(210,000 \times 7850)^{\frac{1}{2}}V_b = 1.16 \times 0.008(1570 \times 1342)^{\frac{1}{2}}V_c \quad (17)$$

so

$$V_b = .0735V_c$$

and

$$V_c = 3_m/s . \quad (18)$$

21. Therefore, from equation (14) the intensity of the stress wave in the coal is given by

$$\sigma = 1.16 \times 3(1570 \times 1342)^{\frac{1}{2}} = 5,040 \text{kN/m}^2 = 5.040 \text{ MN/m}^2. \quad (19)$$

The static tensile strength of the coal parallel to the bedding planes and perpendicular to the main cleats is .55 MN/m^2 (Ref. 6). Allowing the dynamic tensile strength to be five times this figure (Ref. 7) owing to the transient nature of dynamic stresses and the lag in the strain, it would be 2.75 MN/m^2 which is about one half of the stress given by equation (19). The coal shattered on breaking and the distance the tool was positioned from the face made no material difference to its sizing.

Impact stone work

22. Since 1965, the National Coal Board has successfully utilised hydraulic impact mechanisms for underground stone excavation without explosive (Ref. 8) and such machines have become commercially available. This represents another step forward in technology. Typically, the mechanisms have a steel hammer of 0.15 m diameter weighing 80 kg with an ultimate speed (V_u) of 6 m/s giving a blow of 1440 J. The hammer strikes a tool comprising a 0.1 m diameter steel cylinder terminating in a 0.525 rad cone with a 1.575 rad tip. When the tool penetrates the rock 0.0125 m the projected area of contact is a circle of around 0.025 m diameter. Thus, the sectional area of the hammer is 0.0177 m^2, of the tool 0.00786 m^2, and the projected area of contact in the rock is 0.000491 m^2.

23. A penetration of the rock of 0.0125 m would give a force of

$$F = \frac{1.5W}{u} = \frac{1.5 \times 1440}{0.0125} = 173,000 \text{ N}. \quad (20)$$

The corresponding stress on the rock is 352 MN/m^2. This is more than twice the unconfined compressive strength of the strongest coal measure rock.

24. If V_h and V_t are the particle velocities of the hammer and the tool, respectively, owing to their striking, then

$$V_t = V_u - V_h = 6 - V_h \quad (21)$$

and, from equation (9)

$$0.0177V_h = 0.00786V_t \quad (22)$$

so that

$$V_t = 4.16 \text{ m/s}. \quad (23)$$

Poisson's ratio is about 0.25 for rock so that (Ref. 5)

$$\lambda = \frac{E\nu}{(1+\nu)(1-2\nu)} = 2E/5$$

and

$$G = \frac{E}{2(1+\nu)} = 2E/5.$$

The velocity of the compressive wave in unbounded rock, as equation (13), is given by

$$C = \left(\frac{6E}{5\rho}\right)^{\frac{1}{2}} = 1.095(E/\rho)^{\frac{1}{2}}.$$

So $\sigma = \rho CV = 1.095V(E\rho)^{\frac{1}{2}} \quad (24)$

and $P = \sigma A = 1.095VA(E\rho)^{\frac{1}{2}}. \quad (25)$

The density of coal measure rock is 2600 kg/m^3 about. The static Young's modulus for rock is around 350 times its unconfined compressive strength (f_c) (Ref. 7) and the dynamic modulus some 25% greater (Ref. 7). If V_p and V_s are the particle velocities of the tool point and the stone, respectively, owing to their impact, then using equation (23)

$$V_s = 4.16 - V_p$$

and, from equations (9) and (25)

$$0.00786(210,000 \times 7850)^{\frac{1}{2}}V_p =$$

$$1.095 \times 0.000491(1.25 \times 350 \times f_c \times 2600)^{\frac{1}{2}}V_s$$

so $V_p = 0.0018 f_c^{\frac{1}{2}}V_s$

so that $V_s = \dfrac{4.16}{1 + 0.0018 f_c^{\frac{1}{2}}}. \quad (26)$

Therefore, from equation (24) the intensity of the stress wave in the rock is given by

$$\sigma = \frac{1.095 \times 4.16}{1 + 0.0018 f_c^{\frac{1}{2}}}(1.25 \times 350 \times f_c \times 2600)^{\frac{1}{2}} \text{ kN/m}^2$$

$$= \frac{4.86 f_c^{\frac{1}{2}}}{1 + 0.0018 f_c^{\frac{1}{2}}} \text{ MN/m}^2. \quad (27)$$

25. The static tensile strength of rock is about one fifth of its unconfined compressive strength. But its dynamic tensile strength is five times the static (Ref. 7) and thus about equal to f_c. So, if the wave approaches a free face, it can expect to propogate microscopic cracks if

$$f_c < \frac{4.86 f_c^{\frac{1}{2}}}{1 + 0.0018 f_c^{\frac{1}{2}}}$$

or $f_c < \left(\dfrac{4.86}{1 + 0.0018 f_c^{\frac{1}{2}}}\right)^2.$

This gives the following critical condition for f_c

$$f_c + 3.6 f_c^{3/2} \times 10^{-3} + 3.24 f_c^2 \times 10^{-6} < 23.6. \quad (28)$$

A solution is

$$f_c < 23 \text{ MN/m}^2 \text{ approximately}. \quad (29)$$

Dust

26. Thus, an impact tool can be expected to strike the rock with considerable force. As u in equation (20) is proportional to F, the force increases with the square root of the blow. At a ripping lip, pieces of around 0.3 m size can be broken off to a free face after a few blows. But little stone in the British coal measures has an unconfined compressive strength of less than 23 MN/m^2. In practice, there is little shatter of the rock and the make of respirable dust is small.

27. If no substitution is made for the ultimate hammer speed (V_u) in equation (21) the critical condition for f_c (as expression (28)) becomes more generally,

$$f_c + 3.6 f_c^{3/2} \times 10^{-3} + 3.24 f_c^2 \times 10^{-6} < 0.66 V_u^2. \qquad (30)$$

If a pneumatic impact tool were utilised with an ultimate hammer speed the same as that of the original pneumatic impulsive rig described in paragraph 17, then $V_u = 10.45$ m/s. From expression (30) the limiting strength of rock which would shatter is given by

$$f_c + 3.6 f_c^{3/2} \times 10^{-3} + 3.24 f_c^2 \times 10^{-6} < 72.$$

A solution is

$$f_c < 70 \text{MN/m}^2 \text{ approximately.} \qquad (31)$$

About one half of the rocks in the British coal measures have an unconfined compressive strength less than this limit.

28. Young's modulus for steel, the densities of steel and of coal measure stone, and Poisson's ratio for coal measure stone, respectively, do not vary greatly. Assuming plane sections remain plane after striking, increasing the diameter of the tool relative to that of the hammer reduces the velocity and the intensity of stress of the waves. The utilisation of a less pointed tool has a similar effect. It is suggested that the impact equipment described in paragraph 22 gives the greatest practical multiplication so that, to a first approximation, expression (30) can be reduced simply to

$$f_c < 0.66 V_u^2. \qquad (32)$$

The conclusion may be drawn that the unconfined compressive strength below which the rock will shatter on breaking, and so create more dust, depends on the square of the ultimate hammer speed. It is independent of the energy of the blow. Such an impact tool would weigh around 500kg and would have to be mounted on a mechanised rig. Thus, considerations of its weight are not critical and the advantage in this case appears to be with the hydraulic mechanism.

CONCLUSIONS

29. In British coal-mines both hand operated percussive drills and rig mounted impact tools are currently utilised. Both comprise mechanisms in which a hammer strikes a tool arranged to chip rock off to a free face. But the energy of the blow is at least twenty times greater in the case of the impact tool; and the force exerted on the rock depends on the square root of this energy. This enables the impact tool to break off large pieces for excavation. The work is chiefly absorbed in the plastic deformation of the rock and the greater its confinement the more the work required. It is also submitted that whether the pieces of rock fragmentate further depends on the amplitude of the stress waves induced; and that this is independent of the energy of the blow but does depend on the ultimate hammer speed.

30. When drilling, the holes are flushed by water (slurrifying the debris before it leaves) so that dust is less of a problem. During excavation, however, dust enters the ventilation stream and its augmentation by fragmentation is to be avoided.

When reviewing the utilisation of these equipments in British coal-mines, the following further conclusions may also be drawn.

Drilling

31. Traditionally, percussive drills have been powered by compressed air and these equipments are exceptionally reliable. But power is distributed in British coal-mines in the form of electricity. And the percussive tool constitutes the only currently available means of drilling hard rock. Accordingly, there is a need for electro-hydraulic machines. Moreover, while powerful rig mounted drills, or drifters, are favoured in major civil engineering tunnels, the confined spaces in British coal-mines call for the hand-held or feedleg mounted drills known as jackhammers.

32. Compared with pneumatic drills, oil-hydraulic jackhammers have a relatively heavier hammer working at a relatively slower speed. Thus, they tend to weigh more which is significant for manual tools. They also tend to heat while the pneumatic drill works cold. Nevertheless, the latter is the noisiest equipment in a coal-mine - around 80% of the noise deriving from its exhaust. The hydraulic percussive drill has no exhaust (returning its oil to the power pack) and is, therefore, less noisy. It is also less likely to suffer from a lack of pressure in the supply. Neither is a problem from the point of view of dust so long as water is available for flushing.

Breaking

33. High energy impact breaking provides a means of excavating rock without the disturbance associated with explosive. It can also be utilised for other forms of demolition. The pollution of its working environment by dust can be kept to a low level without loss of efficiency by employing a relatively heavy hammer at a relatively slow speed to agitate the rock less. This style of operation is more characteristic of a hydraulic tool than a pneumatic one.

ACKNOWLEDGEMENT

34. The author wishes to thank the Director of the N.C.B. Research and Development Establishment for permission to publish this paper and colleagues for the provision of information. The views expressed are, however, the author's and not necessarily those of the National Coal Board.

REFERENCES

1. SANDSTROM G.E. The history of tunnelling. Barrie and Rockliff, 1963.

2. HUSTRULID W.A. and FAIRHURST C. A theoretical and experimental study of the percussive drilling of rock. Int. J. Rock Mech. Min. Sci. 1971, 8, 311-356 and 1972, 9, 417-449.

3. FISCHER H.C. Stress pulses in percussive drilling. International symposium on mining research, 2, Pergamon Press, 1962.

4. HUGHES H.M. Some aspects of rock machining. Int. J. Rock Mech. Min. Sci. 1972, 9, 205-211.

5. LOVE A.E.H. The mathematical theory of elasticity. Cambridge University Press, 1927.

6.   EVANS I. and POMEROY C.D. Strength, fracture
and workability of coal. Pergamon Press, 1966.

7.   FARMER I.W. Engineering properties of rocks.
Spon, 1968.

8.   RCDFORD I.G. The application of impact
cutting to underground roadway formation by the
N.C.B. National Engineering Laboratory Report 434,
1969.

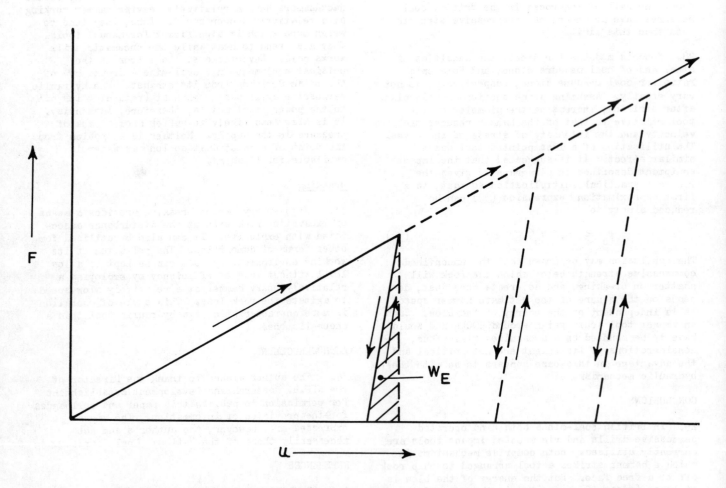

Figure I. Idealised Force/Penetration Diagram for Multiple Loading

C28/74

SOME BACKGROUND AND SOME TRENDS IN HYDRAULIC EQUIPMENT DESIGN FOR MINING ROOF SUPPORTS

A. D. ALLEN, HNC, CEng

Chief Design Engineer, Gullick Dobson Limited, P.O. Box 12, Kirkless Street, Wigan, Lancashire

The Ms. of this paper was received at the Institution on 21st August 1973 and accepted for publication on 23rd October 1973. 34

SYNOPSIS   The application of powered roof supports in longwall mining systems has increased rapidly over the past twenty years. This has stimulated the development of both the hydraulic and structural components from the quite rudimentary equipment used in the early days to the more advanced designs of today.

INTRODUCTION

1.   There are approximately 900 installations of powered roof supports in use in Great Britain and a further 150 installations of British made or designed supports in use in other mining countries throughout the world. This includes installations which may at present be being overhauled and repaired in preparation for re-installation underground or new installations awaiting installation.

2.   With approximately 165 supports per installation and assuming an average of five support props per support unit, this represents a total usage of 866,250 support props, 173,250 conveyor rams and 173,250 sets of quite involved valve gear equipment.

3.   It is obvious from these figures that a huge market has existed and still exists for hydraulic equipment in the mining industries of the world and that an environment has been maintained which has stimulated continuous design and development of the hydraulic equipment involved.

4.   It is the purpose of this paper to trace the development of this hydraulic equipment and to instance some current trends. It is of necessity that the information given will mainly reflect the hydraulic equipment design and experience of the author's Company, Gullick Dobson Ltd., rather than that of the other companies involved in the supply of powered roof supports.

Early Days

5.   The operational details and some historical facts concerning longwall mining systems have been given in other papers presented at this conference.

6.   It is of importance, however, to say that early roof supports were operated with either a mineral oil or a 95/5 water/soluble oil solution, although the former has now been completely superseded because of the cost and the possible fire risk.

7.   My Company adopted the use of the water / soluble oil solution from the beginning and this determined the design of the hydraulic equipment used in the early days and has largely influenced the development since, particularly with regard to

the valve gear.

8.. An early four leg chock design is shown in figure 1. The hydraulic equipment used consisted of four 2.7/8" (73 mm) bore support props or legs, a horizontal mounted conveyor ram with a 2.82" (71.6 mm) dia. cylinder, a 1.5/8" (41.27 mm) dia. thrust bar and the necessary valve gear to operate the unit and to isolate the legs and control roof convergence.

9.   The vertical support legs were single acting and each gave a yield load of 30 tons (299 KN) with a yield pressure of 10,400 psi (71.7 MN/m^2) applying in the 2.7/8" (73 mm) bore and the main pressure seal being a leather cup seal mounted at the bottom of the inner member as illustrated in figure 2. The design of the support legs was determined by the availability of materials and the component costs which were then considered compatible. With the best tubing available in those days in the 'as drawn' condition having a bore tolerance of $\pm$ .012" ($\pm$ .3 mm) and a bore finish of 250 micro inches (6.4μ), the leather seal was the best one available with which to cope with these conditions and also consistently seal water pressures of up to 10,400 p.s.i. (71.7 MN/m^2).

10. The horizontally mounted conveyor ram, which performs the dual tasks of advancing the conveyor and of then advancing the support, was designed with similar factors in mind, although in this case a double acting design was necessary. Back to back leather cup seals on the piston and a leather hat gland seal were used to achieve this.

11. The valve gear used in the early days is shown in figure 3 and consisted of a flat faced rotary control valve to give the basic operations of conveyor push, chock advance and legs raise and manually operated isolating valves to isolate each pair of legs once they were set to the roof, with convergence then controlled by a ball and spring yield valve set at the desired pressure.

12. The flat faced rotary control valve was generally found to be the best approach with water based solutions and consisted of a brass body with a lapped face and a lapped stainless steel rotor which was held in contact with the brass face by the pump pressure of 1200 p.s.i. (8.27 MN/m^2) to

1500 p.s.i. (10.3 MN/m^2) applied to its top surface. The various operating positions were achieved by turning the rotor to the desired position and hence mating the feed port with the desired service port in the brass body.

13. The isolating valves were operated manually to open them to allow the support to lower and close by screwing the stainless steel plunger on to the brass sealing surface in the isolating valve body. The yield valves were screwed into the isolating valve body and bled to atmosphere when yielding of the support occurred.

14. With three levers to operate, it can be seen that chock operators in those days had to be fairly dexterous to operate the chock in the desired time.

15. These early designs were operated from a single three throw piston type pump with the maximum pressure and reduced flow conditions being controlled by a simple pressure relief valve. A 10 H.P. (7.46 KW) motor was used to give a delivery of 9 g.p.m. (41 L/M) at pressures up to 1200 p.s.i. (8.27 MN/m^2) with a crankshaft speed of 165 r.p.m.

16. The pump suction came from quite a rudimentary reservoir and the pump delivery was delivered to the face line by approximately 300 yards (274 M) of 3/4" (19 mm) bore hosing. The pumping pressures and delivery hoses involved obviously gave limitations to the flow which could be delivered to any one roof support unit, but the speeds of operation achieved were generally compatible with the general tempo of face operation and presented no great difficulty at the time.

17. In concluding this section of the paper, a brief mention of the structures may be of interest. These were generally welded fabrications and were even then designed to quite small factors of safety so as to limit the weight and initial production costs. Standards of testing were not very severe in those days, although the structures stood up to their job pretty well in service.

Development of the Theme

18. From 1959 to 1967, most design work so far as Gullick Dobson were concerned was directed towards developing the chock type of support for wider and wider application.

19. The most important change so far as the basic support configuration was concerned was the introduction of forward legs, flexibly connected to the rear four-leg base unit, and an additional roof bar between the rear base unit and forward legs extending over the conveyor area. This formed roof support units of either 5 or 6-leg configuration with a walkway for the operators behind the front legs and a non-bendable roof bar over the walkway and conveyor.

20. Whilst a great deal of thought was given to different support designs during this period, with anything from 2 to 8 support leg configurations being considered, the 5 and 6 leg types have survived to this day and form the bulk of the equipment used in this country.

21. A 5-leg support of the 1967/68 era is shown in figure 4. This has 3 1/4" (82.5 mm) bore double acting legs of 30 tons (299 KN) yield each, a 3 1/4" (82.5 mm) bore conveyor ram and manually operated valve gear with four operating levers.

22. The change to 3 1/4" (82.5 mm) bore legs was made early in the period, about 1961, but they were still of the single acting type with leather seals until about 1966. The change to 3 1/4" (82.5 mm) bore was primarily made to increase bending strength but also had the benefit of reducing yield pressures to 8100 p.s.i. (55.8 MN/m^2).

23. The availability of leg tubing with closer bore tolerances and improved finishes was getting progressively better and a great deal of both laboratory and field testing took place with synthetic cup seals to replace the well known leather cups. These attempts were usually defeated, however, by the single acting design which did not limit in any way the upper cylinder corrosion which quickly wore out synthetic cup seals if they had to operate in such an area.

24. Even the early double acting cylinders used a leather seal in the high pressure area, but with bore tolerances of $\pm$ .006" ($\pm$ .152 mm) and finishes of 60 micro inches (1.64) now becoming available in the 'as drawn' condition, synthetic ring seals were eventually introduced to replace the leather seals and to start a new era of reliability. A 3 1/4" (82.5 mm) bore leg of the 1967/68 era is shown in figure 5.

25. The conveyor ram underwent the same progression to 3 1/4" (82.5 mm) bore and synthetic piston seals, although the leather hat seal in this particular ram is still retained to this day because of its ability to cater for slightly bent thrust bars and still seal adequately.

26. The standard chock valve gear remained more or less the same as previously up to 1967, but with an additional manually operated isolating valve being added to control the front legs. Progressive development did, of course, take place to improve the reliability of the basic valves and considerable improvement was gained in yield valve performance by the introduction of the pad type valve.

27. A drawing of the mark VII yield valve, standard from 1963 to 1970 is shown in figure 6. This had a pad type seal and the yield pressure was set by pre-charging the upper chamber with oil at the desired pressure.

28. Hydraulic reservoirs also underwent the same improvement during the period up to 1967, with properly sealed tanks, adequate filtration, temperature switches and low level switches being progressively introduced.

29. The pump units, still of the three throw piston type, progressed to 25 H.P. (18.6 KW) pumps capable of up to 16 g.p.m. (89 L.P.M.) delivery at a maximum of 1750 p.s.i. (12.06 MN/m^2). Unloading valves were also introduced which would give the full or partial flow conditions necessary with this type of equipment, but which would unload fully during periods when no support operation was required.

30. The factors of safety on the support structures remained at about 1.1 on yield stress, but obviously improved greatly in both design and performance. The general standard of acceptance testing towards the end of this period was for up to 200 cycles of loading with any of the loading conditions then specified.

Valve Gear Development up to 1967

31. As discussed previously, the standard valve gear remained the manually operated type up to late 1967, but a great deal of design and development took place towards the more advanced systems of today and limited production of several systems took place for certain areas of the National Coal Board and for Export purposes.

32. So far as my Company was concerned most of this development took place as a result of the R.O.L.F. (Remotely Operated Longwall Face) programme initiated by the then Mining Research Establishment at Isleworth. This programme was directed towards operating both the coal cutter and roof supports from a central control station, usually situated at the end of the longwall face.

33. Regarding the supports, each one was equipped with the necessary hydraulic equipment and circuits to carry out the functions of pushing the conveyor forward, lowering and advancing the support and then resetting it once the desired advance had been achieved.

34. The hydraulic circuits were initiated by electrically operated solenoid valves which in turn were energised and monitored from the central control console.

35. The R.O.L.F. system achieved considerable success at several collieries in Great Britain, but came up against several problems of machine steerage and in any event was probably in advance of its time in terms of capital investment.

36. The main benefit gained from participation in the programme, however, came from the experience gained with pilot operated valves which would seal a water/soluble oil solution at pressures of up to 10,000 p.s.i. (68.9 MN/m^2) and which offered scope for introducing single lever systems of control to replace the older manual valve gear.

37. The basic M.R.E. valve, as it was and still is known, is shown in figure 7. It consists of a central spool which can be operated to two positions using the three pilot ports available and sealing is achieved by seating the stainless steel spool on the nylon seats provided.

38. Developments using the basic M.R.E. valve were Phase II and Phase III valve gears. Phase II had a modified flat faced rotary control valve known as a 'shear seal' valve. This had a small pad spring mounted in the rotor through which the operating fluid passed when it was rotated to mate with the appropriate service port. The 'shear seal' valve had much less area subject to pressure than previous types and hence was easier to turn at higher pump pressures.

39. The isolating valve system consisted of six non-return valves, two per circuit, to allow the different yield pressures to exist in each circuit, and a single M.R.E. valve to act as the main isolating medium.

40. Phase III employed more or less the same system except   that the control valve became the 'Deadman's Handle' type, with the handle being rotated to the appropriate position and then pulled outwards to allow fluid to pass through the D.M.H. poppet and hence to the shear seal pad. This type of valve was mainly introduced to allow operation at higher pressures and to meet the need for better standards of safety.

41. Phase II and Phase III systems were applied in limited quantities in this country and also created interest in adaptations suitable for partial remote operation. These are known as 'bank control' systems and give several of the benefits of R.O.L.F. without the complication of using electronic equipment. Each chock was equipped with the necessary hydraulic circuits to lower, advance and reset it automatically and the sequence was passed from chock to chock by a trip valve which monitored the setting pressure in each chock as it was reset and then passed the sequence onwards. The number of chocks in each bank was normally limited to eight or ten.

42. Because only one main isolating valve was used in the phase two and three systems, operational flexibility was limited as compared to the older manual systems and it was eventually decided to combine the best features of both the manual and single lever systems.

43. The outcome of this was Phase IV valve gear which consisted of an eight port Deadman's Handle control valve and an isolating valve block which housed three separate isolating valves. This system gave most of the flexibility of operation required underground and all the operations could be carried out by using a single lever.

44. The control valve is shown in figure 8 and the isolating valve in figure 9. The design of the control valve is fairly self-explanatory and the isolating valves were of the two stage type with the small poppet releasing first with a release piston pressure between 450/750 p.s.i. (3.1/5.2 MN/m^2) and then the bigger poppet lifting to allow full flow conditions. The bigger poppet also acted as a non-return valve during legs setting.

45. The D.M.H. poppet arrangement and the isolating valves all employed one nylon surface in effecting the desired sealing and this use of soft seats was considered the only effective way of consistently sealing high pressure water at this time.

46. Both Phase III and IV have since been developed for operating pressures of up to 4500 p.s.i. (31 MN/m^2) and whilst they were not standard in this country until 1968, they helped considerably in expanding the export market for powered supports and there were several installations in both Europe and the United States before the end of 1967 operating at higher pressures than those normally used in this country.

47. These export installations also generally required bigger yield loads and larger diameter support legs than those used in Great Britain and the general standard abroad up to 1967 was for five or six leg units of 250 tons (2490 KN) or 300 tons (2990 KN) total yield load. The support legs used in these were generally 3 3/4" (95.2 mm) bore and in some cases 5" (127 mm) bore.

The Modern Era

48. From early 1968 to the present time has been one of consolidation rather than one of rapid innovation, with the British market staying at a fairly consistent level but with the export possibilities increasing rapidly.

49. In dealing with the home market first, supports have generally settled down at total

yields between 150 tons (1495 KN) and 250 tons (2490 KN) maximum with pump operating pressure only rising slightly to 2300 p.s.i. (15.85 MN/m²) maximum.

50. The main progress has been in general support design, the design of pumping systems and general coal face system engineering.

51. In the face supports, rigid based chocks are taking over from the semi-flexible base configurations previously used, especially in the thicker seams, and support prop bore diameters have generally increased to 3 3/4" (95.2 mm) bore for 30 tons (299 KN) yield, 4 1/4" (108 mm) bore for 40 tons (399 KN) yield and 127 mm bore for up to 75 tons (747 KN) yield loads.

52. Figure 10 shows a typical 6 leg 240 tons (2391 KN) yield support which was introduced in 1968 and has enjoyed considerable success in increasing both bulk output and productivity on many modern British coal faces.

53. The base is a one piece fabrication which is rigid in both the lateral and longitudinal planes. The main advantages in this concept is that the legs are maintained square to the roof in soft floor or thicker seam conditions and that the catamaran type base allows better dirt clearance both through and around the base structure. The roof members still consist of a four leg rear canopy and articulated forward bars as in older types of supports.

54. The legs are of 4 1/4" (108 mm) bore with a 3 3/4" (95.2 mm) diameter inner member and to the general standard of the modern 3 1/4" (82.5 mm) bore double acting leg mentioned previously. The main reasons for the bigger legs are the higher yield loads, greater bending strength and to give greater setting loads without undue increases in pump pressure.

55. The conveyor ram is 4" (101.6 mm) bore with a 2" (50.8 mm) thrust bar and the ram is reverse mounted with the cylinder attached to the conveyor. The advantage of this is to help push dirt through the central tunnel and of necessity the push and pull flows are fed through the thrust bar to the appropriate part of the cylinder.

56. Phase IV valve gear is used on this support and this has changed little in principle since 1968 but some changes have been made to improve resistance to dirt and to increase operating pressures up to the current maximum of 4500 p.s.i. (31 MN/m²).

57. There has been less interest in the period under review than formerly in bank control systems, although there has been an increase in the use of adjacent control systems over the past few years. There has, however, been an increase in the complexity of the hydraulic equipment on each support with hydraulically operated extension bars, and hydraulically operated leg aligning circuits being common. There has also been a considerable increase in the application of powered supports in the packhole and roadend areas of the coal face and these all require additional hydraulic features such as additional legs, rams and valve gear.

58. The most popular pump in use in this country is now a 30 H.P. (22.4 KW) three throw piston type with a crankshaft speed of 286 r.p.m. This gives a flow of 16 g.p.m. (71.5 L/M) at up to 2150 p.s.i. (14.8 MN/m²). In addition there are a limited number of pumps with 50 H.P. (37.3 KW) motors which are capable of delivering 16 g.p.m. (71.5 L/M) at up to 3600 p.s.i. (24.8 (MN/m²).

59. Some considerable improvements in supply line systems have been made during recent years, with 1" (25.4 mm) bore feed and 1 1/4" (31.75 mm) exhaust hoses being common. Ringmain systems of feeding a face are also quite common and much better attention is now paid to pump suction filters, filtration internal to the reservoir or tank, and to main line filtration on the outlet from the pump.

60. In turning to the present day export market, this has stimulated the main developments in supports exceeding 250 tons (2491 KN) total yield and in support configurations other than 5 or 6 leg designs.

61. Many installations of 5 or 6 leg chocks have, of course, been sold abroad and there are several installations of 6-leg 450 ton (4484 KN) supports working very successfully in the U.S.A. These are very similar in principle to the support shown in figure 10 but have 5" (127 mm) bore legs of 75 tons (747 KN) yield loading each.

62. The main call, however, is for 4 leg supports working on the I.F.S. principle (Immediate Forward Support) with the conveyor rams being extended during the cutting run and then the supports being advanced immediately the coal cutter has passed to support the newly exposed roof.

63. Supports in this category are the 4-leg 300 ton (2990 KN) support with 125 mm bore legs, the 4-leg 450 ton (4484 KN) support with 170 mm legs and the 4-leg 710 ton (7075 KN) support with 8" bore (203 mm) legs.

64. The support legs in all these supports are all double acting with synthetic seals. In the higher loadings a compromise has to be reached between tube deflection and burst strength. The burst strength is generally twice the rated yield and the tube deflection generally needs to be limited to .008" (.202 mm) so that no seal by-passing is experienced before the rated burst pressure is reached.

65. In the bigger diameter legs this generally leads to cylinders with relatively low yield materials but with quite thick walls. In the 8" bore (203 mm) leg for instance the yield of the tube material is 18 ton/sq.in. (278 MN/m²) and the wall thickness is 1 1/8" (28.6 mm).

66. There is also a demand in all of these basic supports for double telescopic support legs and a constant yield double telescopic leg is shown in figure 11. This leg will yield on both stages at a constant load of 101 tons (1006 KN) or 145 tons (1445 KN) in some cases. To achieve this a valve is added at the bottom of the inner tube assembly so that the big stage yields first and only when it has completed its travel does the valve open and allow the small inner member to converge. As the small stage converges, however, there is a loading situation which must raise the inner tube and a state of equilibrium is reached with a higher pressure existing in the smaller tube than that actually set by the yield valve. Thus the small stage yields at the same loading as did the larger stage.

67. A photograph of a 4-leg 800 ton (7971 KN) support is shown in figure 12. This has 8" (203 mm) bore legs, a 4 1/4" (108 mm) bore ram and will generally be supplied with phase IV valve gear adapted for adjacent control.

68. Operating pressures tend to be higher in export countries, both to give the higher setting loads desired and to give the best possible speeds of support operation.

69. The sizes of hoses it is possible to use are limited by both bulk and maximum pressure ratings and although ringmain systems are common, the only way of increasing the flow to any one support is by using higher pump pressures.

70. Pumps of 16 g.p.m. (71.5 L/M) delivery and 3600 p.s.i. (25.4 MN/m^2) maximum pressure, requiring a 50 H.P. (31.75 KW) motor, are common and some use of 12 g.p.m. (53.4 L/M) pumps at pressures of up to 4500 p.s.i. (31 MN/m^2) has been made.

71. In closing this section, it should be briefly mentioned that fabrications are now generally tested to 500 cycles with any three point loading which can be applied to the support structures under environmental conditions.

72. This does not automatically lead to heavier structures for any particular loading, but weld design becomes especially critical and pre-heating becomes a necessity on most of the heavier fabrications, especially on the highly loaded supports developed for export.

Future Trends

73. With world energy demands increasing and most industrial nations either maintaining or increasing their coal output, there is obvious scope for still further development of hydraulic roof supports. This possibility is highlighted by the recent considerable export orders won by British companies for the supply of powered supports to the Chinese Republic, following exhibition of British products at the 1973 Peking Fair.

74. In Great Britain the current generation of supports is well established and the main emphasis in the future will be on greater flexibility of application and in even further increases in productivity and reliability.

75. In the former context there is a trend towards double telescopic supports and most British companies are offering these for both thin and medium seam application. These are generally of the constant yield design previously described and are available in bore sizes up to 8" dia. (203 mm).

76. Increased productivity can come from increased speeds of support operation and both higher capacity pumps and improved pumping systems are under constant review. Improved unloading valves are also becoming available which give increased reliability and better characteristics than formerly.

77. To match the increased flows possible from improved pumping systems, valve gear has been developed to allow a bigger flow to be utilised at each support and in my Company's case our Phase V valve gear system is now fully proved and offers scope for increased speed and greater reliability.

78. The basic control valve is illustrated in figure 13 and is similar in principle to the phase IV control valve. The main improvements are in better resistance to external dirt, improvements in the D.M.H. valve seating loads and in the use of bigger ports to give up to a 50% better flow on each service for any given pressure availability at the inlet to each support unit.

79. The basic isolating valve is shown in figure 14. This is a complete change from phase IV with a hard seat arrangement being used and many less components. The steel seat is very finely machined, hardened, lapped and coined with a carbide ball. The 16 mm non-corrodable ball, then forms a perfect seal and the arrangement exhibits increased reliability as compared to soft seat configurations, mainly due to resistance to dirt and metal particles which could quickly cut soft seats.

80. The problem of dirt is always with us in the mining industry and there has been a considerable increase in recent years in the use of individual filters on every support. This trend is bound to continue with the complexity of support hydraulic systems increasing. Phase V valve incorporates an additional block which incorporates a sintered filter for each support, plus isolating valves to enable any support to be maintained whilst the pump is still running.

81. In export countries the trend is also to constant yield double telescopic legs and an installation of supports with 170 mm bore version of this is already at work in the Gateway Mine in the U.S.A.

82. Higher and higher seam chocks are currently being quoted and another international trend is towards shortwall mining systems. This system utilizes the coal cutters formerly used for room and pillar working, which take a 10 foot (2.54 m) web over a 60 yard (54.9 m) length of face. The supports are generally 4 leg units of 450 (4484 KN) to 800 tons (7971 KN) yield and these advance in two 5 ft. (1.52 m) increments, with a 4 ft. (1.21 m) hydraulically operated extension bar playing an important part in the cycle.

83. Speeds of operation will become increasingly important and the new valve gear designs mentioned will obviously play their part. Whether there will be any trend back to full or partially remote operation is unknown, but modern equipment is fully adaptable to these systems and no particular difficulties should be experienced in fulfilling any customers requirements.

Conclusion

84. During this paper I have tried to trace the development of powered support hydraulic equipment from the quite rudimentary designs of the early 1950's to the more comprehensive but more productive machines of today.

85. Whilst some of the changes have been quite small, each one has played its part in overcoming operating and environmental problems underground and the modern support is very much different to its early predecessors when all the changes are taken in total.

86. The basic design and reliability of modern supports has created a considerable export market for British equipment manufacturers and this has only been possible because of the healthy home market created by the National Coal Board.

Fig 1 - Early four leg chock design.

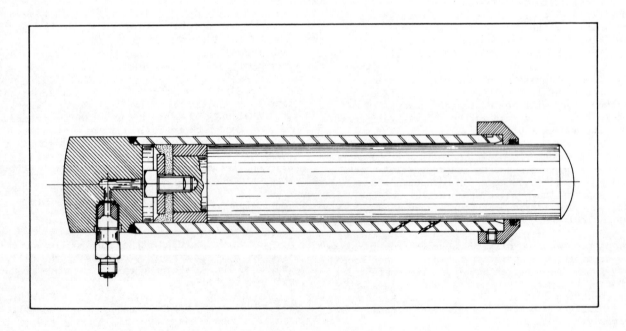

Fig 2 - Early 2.7/8" bore support leg.

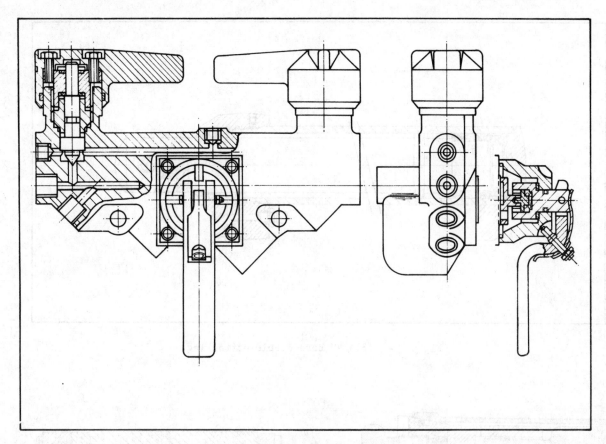

Fig 3   -   Early manually operated valve gear.

Fig 4   -   5 leg support of the 1967/68 era.

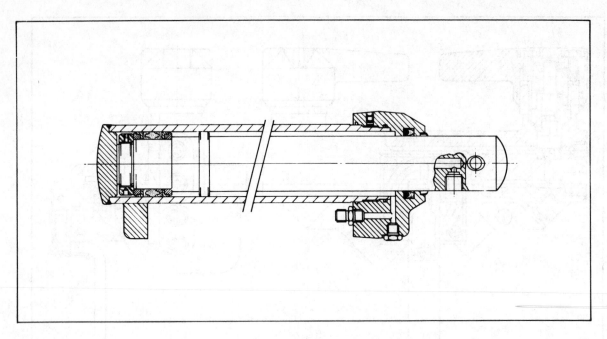

Fig 5 - 3.1/4" bore double acting leg.

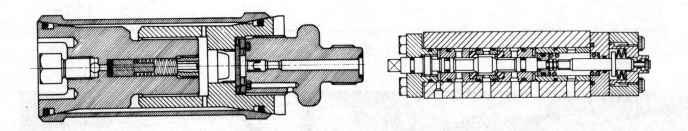

Fig 6 - Mark VII bleed valve.   Fig 7 - M.R.E. valve

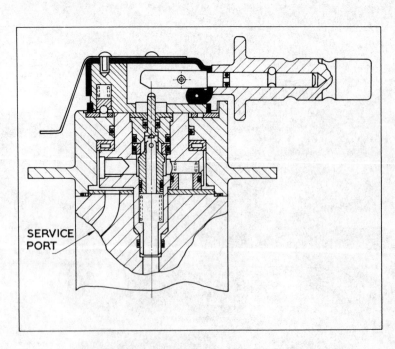

SERVICE
PORT

Fig 8 - Phase IV control valve

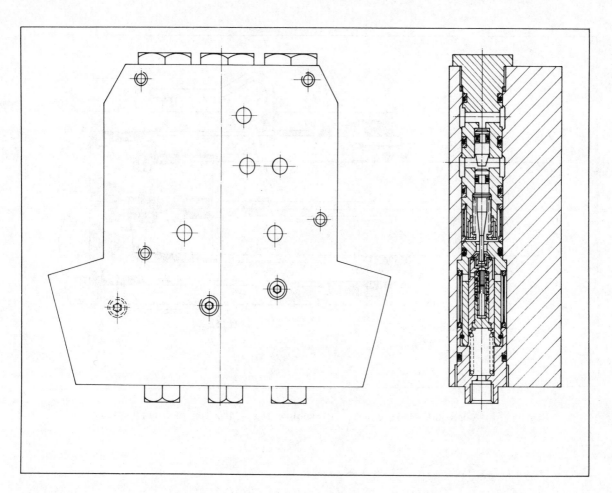

Fig 9 – Phase IV isolating valve manifold.

Fig 10 – 6 leg 240 ton yield support.

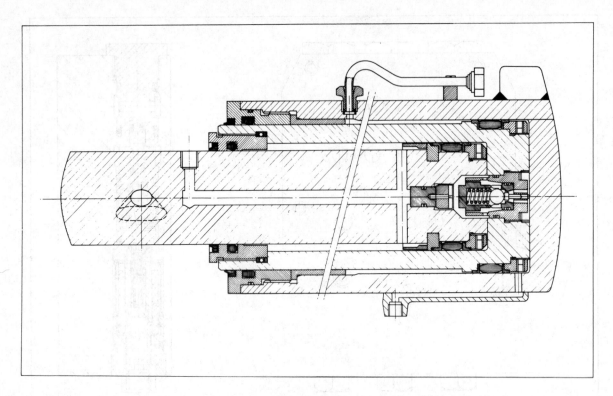

Fig 11 - Constant yield double telescopic leg - 145 ton maximum rating.

Fig 12 - 4 x 800 ton support.

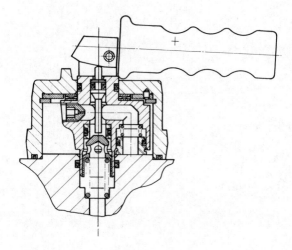

Fig 13 - Phase V control valve.

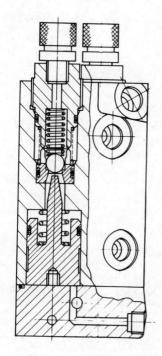

Fig 14 - Phase V isolating valve manifold.

C29/74

DEVELOPMENT OF HYDRAULIC EQUIPMENT FOR CONTROL OF ROOF SUPPORTS AT THE COAL FACE

A. PEACOCK, CEng

Chief Products Engineer, Dowty Mining Equipment Limited, Ashchurch,
Tewkesbury, Gloucestershire GL20 8JR

SYNOPSIS   The mechanisation of longwall coal faces, which accelerated rapidly in the 1950's, saw the development of high output production systems using continuous cutting machines and conveying systems in conjunction with hydraulic powered, self advancing roof supports. This paper reviews the developments in roof supports which took place and describes current equipment, manufactured by Dowty Mining Equipment Limited, being used throughout the world. Emphasis is given to the hydraulic components and systems used to control the supports, and current valve construction is explained. A description is given of a new valve system being introduced to improve existing roof support performance by giving faster operation and shorter down time for maintenance. Future developments in underground roof support equipment for improving safety and productivity are outlined.

INTRODUCTION

1. There are many different methods employed to extract coal throughout the world, both above and below ground. This paper is confined to describing the equipment used for deep mining operations; in particular the "longwall" system of coal extraction. With this system, the coal seam is worked between two roadways 100m/250m apart. Prior to the introduction of self advancing, hydraulic powered roof supports, the roof in the vicinity of the working area, known as the coal face, was supported by wooden props holding steel girders against the roof. As the coal was taken, the props and bars were extended to cover the newly exposed roof and permanent packs built behind to support the excavated area.

2. Hydraulic power for roof support was first introduced by Dowty in 1945 in the form of a hydraulic prop which was hand pumped to the roof (Figure 1). Incorporated in the prop was a relief valve which allowed it to yield at a preset load to control the rate of roof convergence. Thousands of these hand set props are still supplied annually.

3. In the 1950's, mechanisation at the coal face was accelerated, resulting in the development of machines which traversed the length of the face cutting coal continuously and loading it on to an adjacent conveyor, which transported it quickly away from the face. This encouraged the development of roof support systems which were able to keep up with the rate of face extraction and realise the potential of rapid face advance. The grouping of hydraulic props into assemblies of two or three props with floor and roof beams, which were attached to the conveyor, made it possible to automate support advance. The conveyor was pushed forward by a ram attached to the base beam with the unit set to the roof, and then the support itself was advanced by lowering it from the roof and retracting the ram.

4. Continuous development since that time has led to a range of self advancing, hydraulically powered roof supports with load carrying capacities from

150 tons up to 625 tons. Figure 2 shows a 5-leg 150 ton support for thin seams down to 600mm and Figure 3 a 4-leg 625 ton spring base support designed for operation under massive sandstone. Supports have been supplied for working seams 3m thick. The differences in prop layout, support size and load carrying capacity have been evolved to cater for the diverse environmental conditions in which supports are required to work. Despite these differences, all types of support must perform the same basic operations in order to achieve efficient roof support and rapid advance.

BASIC ROOF SUPPORT OPERATIONS

5. Figure 4 shows a typical face layout. 150/200 supports, or "chocks", are installed along the face between the roadways, or "gate roads". The armoured face conveyor (A.F.C.) lies between the face and the chocks and the coal cutting and loading machine rides astride the A.F.C. Each chock is attached to the A.F.C. by a double acting ram in the base structure. Four, five or six hydraulic props are located in the base structure and support a canopy which is set to the roof by extending the props. A travelling way along the face is provided for the machine and support operators between the front and rear props (Figure 5).

Sequence of operations

6. Initially, the chocks are positioned up to the A.F.C. and the canopy set to the roof. The coal cutting machine traverses the face, taking a "web" of coal 600mm/750mm wide over the seam thickness and loading it on to the A.F.C.

7. Following in the wake of the machine, a support operator travels along the face operating the rams to push the A.F.C. and "snaking" it behind the machine back up to the face line.

8. Following behind, a second operator lowers each support in turn, then closes the ram which pulls the support back up to the A.F.C. The canopy is then reset to the roof by extending the props.

Each support is lowered, advanced and set in sequence along the face to complete the cycle of operation.

9. When the cutting machine has reached the gate road, and all supports have been advanced, it works back in the other direction, with the A.F.C. and supports being advanced as before.

10. There are variations to this basic system of operation to meet particular requirements.

Immediate roof support (I.F.S.)

11. This system allows the supports to be advanced to catch the newly exposed roof as soon as possible after the cutting machine has passed. This is necessary in some instances in order properly to control the roof strata.

12. In this instance, the supports are initially set back from the A.F.C. one web width. The first operation, once the cutting machine has passed, is to lower, advance and set the support in sequence, thereby giving immediate support to the roof. The A.F.C. is then snaked across to complete the cycle of operations. Specially designed roof supports are required with an extended front roof canopy. Figure 6 shows a 4-leg 400 ton support for this type of operation, fitted with double telescopic props to cater for wide variations in seam thickness.

Plough Operation

13. The systems described above are designed to work with shearer type cutting machines where the cutting picks are fixed to a rotating drum. Ploughing machines use picks mounted on a static head which is pulled along the face at speeds of 55m/min., taking a depth of cut of 50mm/75mm, compared with the shearer machine moving at 3m/min., taking 600mm/750mm depth of cut.

14. For this operation, the advancing rams are always pressurised to push the conveyor against the face. Snaking is, therefore, automatic. The chocks are advanced only when the ram stroke is used up. Variations in coal hardness can deflect the plough and cause malalignment of the face line. To overcome this, the push rams are hydraulically locked as the machine traverses the face. When the cut is completed, the A.F.C. is advanced bodily by feeding a metered amount of fluid simultaneously into each ram to give the required amount of conveyor advance. This is generally known as fixed incremental ploughing (F.I.P.).

15. All the support operations described above are achieved hydraulically and a range of equipment has been developed efficiently to control the performance of the supports in all types of seam conditions.

HYDRAULIC EQUIPMENT FOR POWERED ROOF SUPPORTS

Legs

16. The function of the props, or legs, as they are more commonly called when used in roof supports, is to control the vertical movement of the roof beams and take the load exerted by the roof via the structures. Legs are set at a pump delivery pressure of 2,000 lb./in.^{2}. As the roof converges

on the floor, the leg pressure builds up until it reaches a preset maximum, at which point a "yield" valve connected to the full area side of the props opens to allow the pressure to relieve and destress the roof. This yield valve determines the load carrying capacity of the support and designs are available from 150 tons to 625 tons.

Advancing ram

17. This is positioned in the base structure and is double acting to enable the conveyor to be pushed over when extended and the support to be advanced when retracted. Thin seam supports use a "relay bar" between ram and conveyor to minimise restriction of the travelling way. This can be seen on the support shown in Figure 5.

Valves

18. The support operations are controlled by two basic valves; a rotary selector valve and a release/yield valve. All valve parts are designed in materials resistant to corrosion in water. Valve bodies are either brass or cadmium plated steel and internal parts are either brass, stainless steel or plastic.

19. Rotary selector valve

This valve is illustrated in Figure 7. One of four services may be selected by rotating the handle and then, by a push of the handle, high pressure is connected to the selected service. Release of the handle immediately shuts off the flow. The four services provided cater for push (conveyor), lower (legs), advance (chock) and set (legs).

20. This valve, therefore, combines two valves in one body; an inlet valve to isolate high pressure from the valve until the handle is depressed and a disc valve operated by rotating the handle to connect service ports to the high pressure port. The inlet valve is a simple poppet and seat arrangement sprung loaded shut. The poppet is made from "Delrin" and is held on a stainless steel seat. Since this valve isolates high pressure from the rotary parts of the valve, the load required on the handle to rotate the disc is kept to a minimum. As the handle is rotated, a slot in the disc connects the high pressure port to one of four service ports. Depressing the handle opens the inlet valve to connect high pressure to the selected service. The back of the disc is also subjected to high pressure fluid at this time to effect a metal to metal face seal and prevent leakage across ports. The housing, or "gate ring", in which the handle rotates may be slotted in a particular service position to allow the handle to be slid into the slot which locks it in position. This enables the operator to leave the valve whilst it is working, and is often used for the conveyor push operation. Conversely, the absence of a slot prevents the valve being left locked on where this is unsafe, i.e. support lowering and advance.

21. Release/yield valve

This valve is piped into the hydraulic circuit between the legs and the rotary selector valve, and its function is to control the lowering of the legs and also the pressure at which the legs yield. Individual leg lowering, for maintenance purposes, is effected by operating handles on this valve, shown in Figure 8.

22. Normally, a pair of legs is controlled from one release/yield valve. Twin valves are, therefore, available for four leg supports and triple banked valves for five and six leg supports. Each pair of legs is, therefore, controlled by two separate valves and all valves for the legs are assembled into a single valve block. The release valve is again a poppet and seat arrangement, since leakage from the legs would cause inadvertent lowering from the roof. Normally, this valve is sprung loaded closed to lock fluid into the legs. Manual operation opens the valve to pass fluid to return and lower the legs. The legs are also connected to a low flow relief or "yield" valve, which is designed to control pressures generated in the legs by roof loading up to 10,000 lb./in.^{2}, depending on the leg rating, which varies from 30 tons to 158 tons per leg. This valve is the most important part of the overall valve arrangement, since it is the ability of the seats to function for long periods at high pressures without leakage that determines the effective control of roof movement, without which the safety of the operators would be at risk and efficient, rapid face advance unobtainable.

23. For manual chock operation the rotary selector valve (R.S.V.) "leg" service ports are connected to the P/R port on the release/yield (R/Y) valve and the legs to the L ports (Figure 8). With the R.S.V. handle at "lower", operation of any or all the R/Y valve handles causes the legs to lower off. Setting of the legs is effected when the R.S.V. handle is put to "set" and the R/Y valve handle(s) operated.

24. To allow faster operation of the support during normal advancing, the release valves can be pilot operated from the R.S.V. to open simultaneously to connect all legs to return. This is known as "auto-release". The addition of an isolating and non-return valve bank to the basic R/Y valve (Figure 8), pilot operated from the R.S.V., enables high pressure fluid to by-pass the release valve and feed all legs, which set simultaneously. This latter operation is designated "auto-set" on the R.S.V. Manual operation of individual pairs of legs is still retained for maintenance or advancing in difficult roof conditions, when more flexibility of leg control is required.

VALVE SYSTEMS

25. The two valves described above, the rotary selector and release/yield valves, can be used in a variety of ways to give different types of support control.

In-chock control

26. This is the simplest form of chock operation, where both valves are situated in the chock they control. The operator must, therefore, be in the chock being manipulated or reach into it from an adjacent chock. Time to advance a chock averages 16 seconds.

Adjacent control

27. The rotary selector valve is positioned in an adjacent chock, with hoses between chocks connecting it to the release/yield valve in the chock being controlled. The operator, therefore, controls movement of chocks from a position of safety under the canopy of a chock set to the roof. An additional feature is to connect the leg lower control on the rotary selector valve in with advancing ram pull which causes the chock to advance immediately it is free from the roof. Time to advance a chock is thereby reduced to 12 seconds.

Batch control

28. In thin seam workings, where individually advancing 250 chocks along the face is particularly arduous, supports may be hydraulically interconnected in batches of five or six to give automated control. The first chock in a batch is a master and controls the operation of the rest in the batch. Additional valves are required to those previously described, including master adjacent control, slave control and auto-main control valves. The advancing ram also requires an integral valve to sense and signal when full ram stroke is achieved. The master chock starts the sequence of lower, advance and set. As soon as the first chock has completed the cycle and leg setting pressure is sensed, a signal to the adjacent chock sets it in motion. This is repeated in sequence for the batch. The operator then travels to the next master chock to start up the next batch. Average chock advance is reduced to 9 seconds.

Auto-adjacent control

29. This is similar to the batch control system, except that each chock is a master, thus providing adjacent control to chocks either side of the operator. This system is, therefore, fully bi-directional. Chock advance is achieved in 9 seconds.

Remote control

30. The ultimate in automatic control is where all chock operations are controlled in sequence along the face from a console at the face end. Two systems have been developed; R.O.L.F. (remote operation of longwall face) and R.O.B. (remotely operated batch), with either hydro-electric or all-hydraulic control systems. The success of fully automated control depends on good face conditions where there is a high degree of certainty that chocks will be allowed to advance fully and set without being impeded by the floor and/or roof conditions. These systems are, therefore, limited in application.

ANCILLIARY HYDRAULIC EQUIPMENT

31. In addition to the hydraulic equipment necessary to achieve the basic chock functions, particular face conditions require further equipment to enable the supports to work effectively.

Steep seams

32. Most coal seams are inclined to some extent. Basic equipment can operate satisfactorily on faces inclined between gates up to 1:7. Above this, and especially in thick seams, it is necessary to incorporate stabilising equipment to prevent the chocks falling sideways when lowered from the roof. This is achieved by connecting rams between pairs of supports, in conjunction with a guide bar between bases at ground level, attached to the conveyor and also to each base member by claws. As the conveyor is pushed forward, the guide bar slides through the claws. When a chock is lowered off, the stabilising

rams are actuated to keep it upright in the seam. During advance, the guide bars prevent slewing of the base whilst the stabilising rams keep the chock upright, until fully advanced, when it is reset to the roof. The next chock of the pair can then be advanced, again stabilising it off the chock set to the roof.

Soft floor conditions

33. When the floor strata is soft, the chocks can bed into the ground, preventing advance. Extra wide base plates are provided, along with a ram to lift the base out of the ground when actuated. This type of arrangement can be seen fitted to the chock in Figure 6. The ram is attached to the front of the base between the main beams. A roller fixed to the end of the lifting ram rod runs on a guard over the advancing ram as the chock is advanced. Actuation is usually automatic with selection of chock advance.

Forward roof support

34. An extensible cantilever blade is often fitted inside the front canopy, which is extended and set by a ram to give support to newly exposed roof, prior to chock advance. This is particularly useful with friable roofs liable to local collapse. Retraction of the cantilever blade is automatic during chock advance.

MODULAR VALVE SYSTEM

35. In an era where the costs of providing raw materials are rapidly increasing, coal being no exception, it is important that consistent and efficient production are maintained. Fast chock operation and minimum down time required for maintenance are, therefore, important contributions towards achieving this situation, and Dowty Mining Equipment Limited have responded by developing a new valve system for the future which meets these requirements.

36. Fast chock operation is limited with existing systems by the flow restriction in the valves themselves, and also by the complex of pipes and fittings required between the various hydraulic components to construct a system. The trend towards higher capacity chocks of 500 tons and 625 tons, where leg bore diamters of up to 240mm are used, obviously aggravates the situation by having to deal with large volumes of fluid flow. Increasing pump flow only gives a marginal increase in performance, since the system is soon saturated and the introduction of dump valves to by-pass the rotary selector valve during chock lowering and advance increases the cost and complexity of the hydraulics. The size of the valves themselves is, of necessity, limited by the space available on the structures to mount them.

General arrangement

37. The principle of the Dowty modular valve, shown in Figure 9, is to divorce the control function from that required for flow. Each service is, therefore, connected direct to the service and return lines by a high flow capacity valve. These valve modules are normally pilot operated to connect pressure to service or service to return, but can also be manually operated. The pilot signals come from a rotary selector valve, and because the

flow through it is small, more services can be incorporated into a valve similar in size to the four port R.S.V. previously described. Ten pilot signals are, therefore, possible, and these are used to signal sets of modules in both adjacent chocks, giving bi-directional, adjacent control. The modules are mounted on to a manifold block with the pressure, return and pilot ports located at the interface and sealed by a special gasket which is described more fully later. A module can be removed in seconds by slackening two bolts and sliding sideways. The service port is external and accepts a quick release staple fitted hose, which connects up with the ram or leg being served. The leg modules incorporate the release/yield valve which controls the maximum leg pressure. The pressure and return hoses between chocks are also staple fitted into a connection block, which in turn is bolted to the main manifold block. Drillings connect these supplies direct to each module and the rotary selector valve.

38. The general arrangement so far described is typical of most manifold mounted valve systems, and the internal parts are similar in design to those used in the valves previously described. The Dowty modular valve is, however, unique in the technology used to transmit the pilot signals from the rotary selector valve to the remote module banks in both adjacent chocks.

39. Pilot signal transmission between chocks

Signals are passed along small bore hoses, which are grouped together, ten at a time, and encased in one large diameter hose to form a loom. This is shown in Figure 10. The pilot hoses terminate at each end in a pin which is arranged, along with the others, into a circle of pins at the hose ends. This enables the multi-cored hose to be plugged into a connecting block on the main manifold like an electric cable, to connect up all pilot lines simultaneously. The hose is then staple retained. This arrangement significantly reduced the number of hoses between chocks, making for a less vulnerable inter-chock connection and, should replacement be necessary, this is rapidly achieved.

40. Pilot signal transmission through valve pack

As previously described, the rotary selector valve, the banks of modules (usually six) and pressure, return and multi-cored hose connecting blocks are all mounted on to the main manifold block. Many of the complicated drilled connections are avoided by routing the hydraulic pilot signals at the interfaces of the components with the manifold block, using "printed gaskets". Examples of these are shown in Figure 10. Stainless steel plates, fitted between the manifold block and the valves, are slotted to make the connections between drillings out of line at the interface. Leakage between slots is prevented by surrounding each one with a bead of rubber on both sides of the plate. As the components are bolted up, the beads are compressed to form a high pressure seal. Pilot signal pressure from the rotary selector valve is thereby routed along the multi-cored hose via the drillings in the manifold block and the slots in the printed gasket to the valve being controlled.

41. The rotary selector valve can be separated from the manifold block and mounted remotely by connecting the two together with a second multi-cored hose.

42. The printed gasket principle enables variations in chock control to be achieved by substituting different gaskets programmed to connect the valves in the desired manner.

43. An intensive test programme in the laboratory and on trials underground has proved the feasibility of this valve system and the first full face is scheduled to be delivered at the end of 1973.

FUTURE DEVELOPMENTS

44. The potential of the modular valve system will be further developed with the probability of providing a cheap form of automated control.

45. Other equipment in the early stages of development includes a rapid yield prop for use in rock burst conditions. A rate of prop closure of 3m/sec. without damage to the components is planned for this application. In conjunction with this, a portable, pneumatically driven water pump and an injection gun to set the props to the roof are also being developed.

46. New powered supports are also being investigated for use with roadway cutting machines working on the face, taking a web of coal up to 3.3m wide. This technique, known as "shortwall" mining, is currently being developed in Australia and the U.S.A. and could lead to high production figures. Trial sites are planned in this country.

47. The worst kind of roof to support is one which breaks up and moves rapidly. Existing chock designs working under these friable roofs are prone to leg bending when the canopies are racked badly out of position. A chock with built-in resistance to roof movement, taken through the structure, leaving the legs unloaded, is the only type of support which will work successfully in these conditions.

48. Dust emission on the face is a serious environmental problem. When chocks are lowered and advanced, dust and debris which has collected on the top of the canopies falls into the travelling way and contaminates the air flow through the face. Some faces where the coal is dry and hard are particularly notorious in this respect. One possible method of combating this problem is to advance the chocks in contact with the roof, minimising roof breakage in the first instance, preventing build up of debris on top of the canopies and not allowing it to fall out until at the back of the chocks. Water sprays injected into the waste area behind the chocks automatically as they are advanced and resilient sealing pads between canopies should also contribute towards minimising this environmental hazard.

49. Finally, in countries on the continent, where very thick coal seams in excess of 5m are not uncommon, the method of extraction is to take the seam in two layers, one above the other. This is not an easy technique and involves a lot of time and expense either stowing the extracted area behind the chocks with sand to form a floor for when the upper layer is taken or working the two layers simultaneously, one just ahead and in phase with the other, with two sets of equipment. This second method has the disadvantages of having two faces at a standstill if either has to be shut down for maintenance and is particularly prone to delays for reheading in seams where the coal thickness varies widely. A stable, thick seam support, capable of working 2.5m/5m on inclines of up to 25°, is required to overcome these difficulties and improve productivity.

50. The hydraulic powered roof supports and associated systems developed over the last two decades have improved safety and productivity tremendously. There are still many problems to be solved to improve existing and develop new mining techniques. The right equipment must be developed for the Mining Engineer, if the rate of coal production is to be still further increased to meet the ever growing power demand, and the working conditions at the coal face are to be improved.

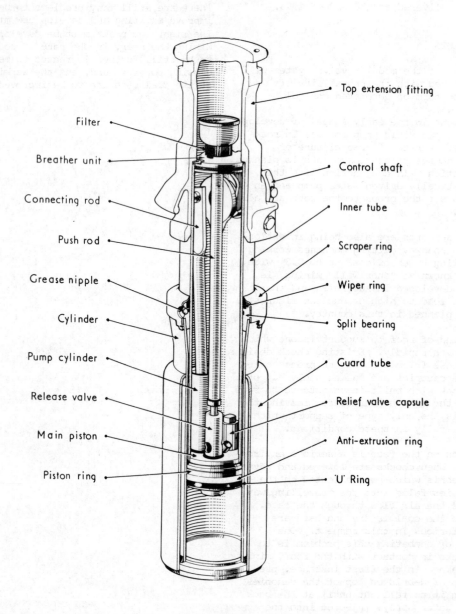

Top extension fitting

Filter

Breather unit

Connecting rod

Push rod

Grease nipple

Cylinder

Pump cylinder

Release valve

Main piston

Piston ring

Control shaft

Inner tube

Scraper ring

Wiper ring

Split bearing

Guard tube

Relief valve capsule

Anti-extrusion ring

'U' Ring

FIG. 1 DUKE PROP

FIG. 2. 5 LEG 150 TON THIN SEAM SUPPORT

FIG. 3. 4 LEG 625 TON HEAVY DUTY SUPPORT

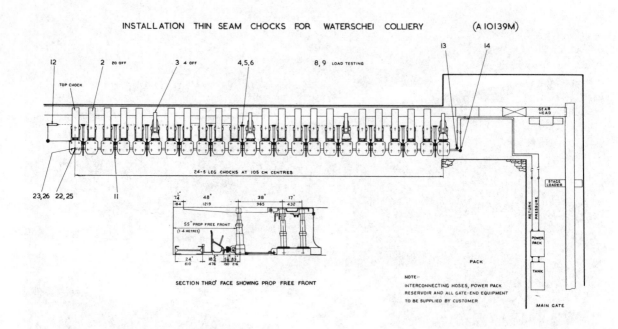

INSTALLATION THIN SEAM CHOCKS FOR WATERSCHEI COLLIERY   (A 10139M)

SECTION THRO' FACE SHOWING PROP FREE FRONT

NOTE:-
INTERCONNECTING HOSES, POWER PACK
RESERVOIR AND ALL GATE-END EQUIPMENT
TO BE SUPPLIED BY CUSTOMER

FIG. 4

FIG. 5

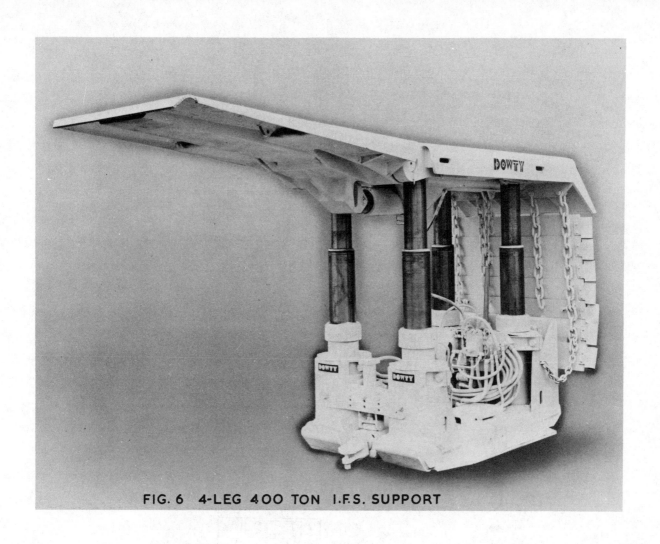

FIG. 6 4-LEG 400 TON I.F.S. SUPPORT

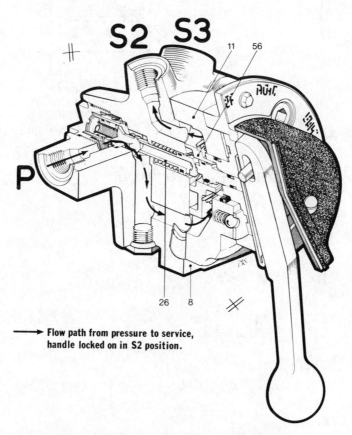

→ Flow path from pressure to service,
handle locked on in S2 position.

FIG. 7 ROTARY SELECTOR VALVE

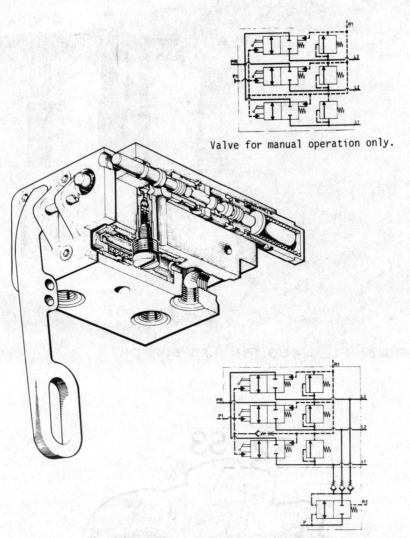

Valve for manual operation only.

Valve fitted for pilot operation and Auto Set.

Fig. 8 RELEASE/YIELD VALVE

FIG 9   MODULAR VALVE PACK

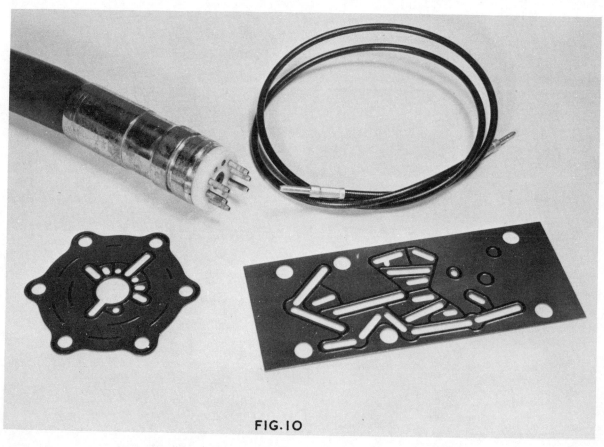

FIG.10

C30/74

HYDRAULIC SUPPLY SYSTEMS FOR POWERED ROOF SUPPORTS

J. D. KIBBLE, MA(Cantab), MIMechE
Head Engineering Principles Branch, National Coal Board, Mining Research and Development Establishment,
Stanhope Bretby, Burton-on-Trent, Staffordshire

The Ms. of this paper was received at the Institution on 25th July 1973 and accepted for publication on 23rd October 1973. 22

SYNOPSIS   The rate of operation and the effectiveness of setting of powered supports depend on the hydraulic supply. This takes the form, unusual for the present day, of supply and return mains for dilute emulsion fluid.

The principal factors in the design of such systems are outlined. These include the features of the power pack and the control of maximum pressure by means of an unloader valve, the effect of a number of operators working at the same time, and the hose arrangement. Testing and possible trends for the future are also mentioned.

INTRODUCTION

1.   When powered supports were introduced, now nearly twenty years ago, there were three largely independent streams of development, namely:

- the mining engineering approach, exemplified by Gullick and Desford chocks; in this the working fluid was either plain water from the pit range, discharged to waste after use on an open circuit basis, or water with soluble oil rust inhibitor, in which case return hoses and a tank were needed.

- the approach deriving from aircraft and industrial hydraulics, led by Dowty's, using mineral oil and thus having available a wide selection of existing pumps and valves. From the start quite sophisticated power packs with variable-delivery pumps were used.

- certain Continental designs in which compressed-air driven pumps on the face itself powered indivudual units or small groups of them.

2.   Gradually the first of these became universal, chiefly because of the cheapness and fire-resistance of the fluid. It was not a case of any technical superiority: in fact, to provide water valves for complex functions much new technology has been needed. A big impetus was given to this by the programme of work on remote control of supports, although this has unfortunately borne little direct fruit as yet. The use of hydraulics as power supply mains was another novel feature, or, strictly speaking, a revived one, since this was first done in Victorian times.

3.   The present large number of faces with powered supports and the extreme importance, for production, of good strata control, justify considerable technical effort. Whilst satisfactory design of the support units themselves is clearly a pre-requisite, their setting load and speed of movement depend largely on the hydraulic supply system. This paper is a brief summary of the various aspects of the design of these systems, with particular reference to the contribution of the N.C.B. Establishments.

PUMPS AND PRESSURE LIMITATION

4.   Several years ago the author (Ref. 1) described the standard type of low-speed three-throw plunger pump with its oil-lubricated crankshaft and alluded to the possibility of more compact types, perhaps with pressure-controlled variable delivery, wholly lubricated by the dilute emulsion being pumped. There has been regrettably little change since that time. The efforts to produce a water-lubricated pump have so far had only limited success. Though good results were obtained from testing above ground, in service in the pit mining pumps may be called upon to handle water without the correct proportion of soluble oil but with dirt, constituting very different conditions. A style of pump retaining oil lubrication for the working parts, but with high speed and variable delivery, seems feasible, but at present manufacturers do not see a large enough market to warrant the cost of development.

5.   Early installations used relief valves to limit the pressure, but these had many predictable disadvantages such as that of causing the water to boil! The application of unloader valves to coal face systems, however, presented some unexpected problems. First it had to be realised that when the demand is only a portion of the output of the pump, as commonly happens if there is leakage, the unloader can only respond by continuously cutting in and out at a rate dependent on the storage capacity of the system over the operating pressure range, or 'scan', of the valve. Cycling of this kind may be seen in a portion of Figure 1, which is a time-base recording of pressure. Fortunately the dilation of hose (about 1% of its internal volume per 6.8 MN/m^2 (1000 lb/in^2) pressure change, see Figure 2, also Ref. 2) proved to be enough to cope with many instances, although an accumulator is needed for systems with only short lengths of hose or if the valve scan is narrowed down in an endeavour to obtain closer control of pressure.

6.   However, another effect sets a lower limit to the valve scan. Whenever flow in a pipe is stopped or started a pressure surge results, the magnitude of which, for hose containing water, is given in

Figure 3. Surges are in fact often clearly visible in pressure recordings, being reflected from each end of the hose but soon damped out in a stable manner. But if the unloader valve scan is less than twice the pressure surge, the latter can itself make the valve switch, causing repeated oscillation (Ref 3). The solution to this is to prevent the valve from 'chopping' the whole of the flow, instead making it open gradually like a relief valve as cut-out pressure is approached. This causes a 'droop' in the pressure/flow characteristic (Figure 4 is typical), the actual flow diverted on unloading, Q_u, being only perhaps one-third of the pump output. Yet again, if leakage on the face becomes greater than Q_u, the valve will not unload at all but will remain acting as a relief valve with the attendant ill-effects. Successful application of unloader valves depends upon remaining within the practicable zone created by these opposing factors, and can be difficult, particularly with valves of which the scan and the unload flow tend to vary as adjustments are made.

CHOICE OF PUMP CAPACITY IN MAINS SYSTEMS WITH MULTIPLE DEMANDS

7. The N.C.B. is currently proposing to standardise on 0.6, 0.8, and 1.2 1/sec (8, 10, and 16 gallons per minute) capacities for water-hydraulic pumps, normally to be used in pairs to give continuity of supply in case of failure. This provides a reasonable selection, and, given the maximum number of chocks per minute which it is required to advance and re-set, it is simple to calculate the volume of fluid that must be supplied in that time. This is the mean demand and the pump need be only just large enough to meet it (together with allowance for leakage and any ancillary demands) provided that all operations occur in exact sequence without overlapping in time. This may be so on an installation with automatic control, but normally there are several men in the chock team and as a consequence it is possible that a number of hydraulic movements can be initiated simultaneously causing erratic movement.

8. Freedom from this mutual interference can of course be obtained by providing sufficient pump capacity for all the men present to move chocks at full speed at the same time, but, as indicated by Figure 5, this may call for a very large pump. For an economic design, it is important to find out what is really required in between these two extremes. Chiefly one must judge this from practical experience, of course, but in order to be more objective the following procedure is being suggested.

9. A pump will keep up the mains pressure except for such periods as the demand exceeds the capacity of the pump, and the proportion of the working time for which an arbitrary 'Required Pressure' is maintained is taken as a measure of the performance of the system. For example, during the face operations of which a recording is shown in Figure 1 the level of 7.9 MN/m² (1150 lb/in²) (the unloader valve cut-in pressure) was maintained during support advancing operations for about 90% of the time. This means that a similar proportion of the chocks are not set to the roof at their rated load, but it is clear that this, to a certain extent, is tolerable. Now whilst two or three chock men may perhaps work in a co-ordinated manner, a greater team than this is not likely to

keep in synchronism. If it is assumed that the demand is a truly random one, it is possible to base calculations on the Poisson Distribution. The pump sizes required to maintain pressure for 70, 80, and 90% of the time, derived in this way, are shown in Figure 5 and it is very interesting to note that for a wide range of conditions a capacity of about twice the mean demand will suffice.

10. Similar calculations indicate the benefit to be obtained from adding an accumulator to the system: smoothing out an uneven demand is in fact one of the classic cases for which this component is put forward. A good many are already in use in mines and they do perform as expected, though much larger units (at least 37 l (8 gal) shell size) are needed than for damping unloader valve operation. Also, they are not without their requirements for care and attention, so that it is sometimes preferred to use a pump of larger size instead.

HOSE

11. There is usually well over 1000 m of hose in the supply and return lines of a powered support installation, quite apart from the internal chock hoses. The cost of this, though substantial, is only a small proportion of the total, but it is nevertheless very desirable for the hose to be correctly sized: too many or too large hoses on the face are clumsy. On the other hand, it is still quite often found that the use of inadequate hoses is impairing results.

12. Hose size is best discussed in terms of the pressure loss that would result if the full output of the pump(s) were directed along the supply line and back through the return via an interconnection at the extreme end, this loss being expressed as a percentage of the maximum system pressure. A recent German paper (Ref. 4) advocated a hose loss not exceeding 10%. This is lower than most present installations and 20% would probably be a more reasonable maximum figure. (Incidentally, use of a standard flow velocity, such as the customary 5 m/s or 15 ft/sec, would give far too much pressure loss in such long hose lengths.) Unless an installation is to be identical with what has previously proved successful, some attempt should certainly be made to work out the hose loss. Where this has not been done, it has several times been found that large pumps have been used with hoses of such a small size as to prevent the full output ever being available at points far along the face.

13. For water flowing in, for example, a 25 mm (1 in) bore pipe or hose, the critical Reynolds Number is reached at a flow of 0.04 - 0.08 1/sec (½ - 1 gal/min). Almost all flows in a coal face system are therefore turbulent. The equations giving the pressure loss in pipes are very well known but rather tedious to use. Convenient charts exist for various oils but nothing of the kind relevant to water was available, and so it was necessary to draw up the chart reproduced in Figure 6. As a matter of interest, the flow at similar rates of a typical hydraulic oil (viscosity 5×10^{-5} m²/s (50 cS)) would be mainly laminar, so that the much lower viscosity of water brings only a slight advantage. Very approximately, for a given flow rate the same pressure loss per unit length will be obtained if a hose is one size larger with oil than it is for water.

14. These pressure loss figures were obtained theoretically and on the surface, but correspond closely with underground measurements. Large discrepancies are found, though, if the flow resistance of the hose end fittings is not taken into account. This is negligible in many industrial hydraulic circuits, but it is very significant in a face main hose that may contain several hundred Tee-pieces in series. It was found that the resistance of two end-fittings and a Tee-piece, of typical design with a bore 75% of that of the hose, was equivalent to that of about 1.5 m (5 ft) of hose. A rule of thumb is that the hydraulic equivalent length of an interchock hose is twice its true length.

15. If a face main hose is found to be inadequate when it is actually in situ, rather than replacing the whole harness it is much more convenient to install a supplementary or by-pass hose, connected to the original at each end of the face so as to form a ring-main. Here again it is desirable to know what one is doing and the pressure losses and flows in such rings can be determined from the chart of Figure 6 by using the fact that the pressure drop between the pump and the point of offtake must be the same for both limbs. A common case would be that of an interchock hose supplemented by another hose of the same size but with a negligible number of fittings. The fittings in the original hose double its equivalent length, as seen above. It can be shown that, for the same total flow, the pressure loss in the ring is then about 20% of that in the single hose. In this case, interconnections between the two hoses at additional points on the face are not recommended. They improve the flow very little but would confuse the issue when maintenance was required.

16. Recordings of back pressure in return lines do not, of course, show the variations found in the supply line due to the operation of the pump and unloader valve. Instead, the pressure rises as chock operation starts, but only in a very gradual and damped manner. (See Figure 1). Pressure surges can sometimes be seen, as in the supply line, but these are damped out a short distance from the chock from which the fluid is being ejected. Presumably the hose is working under the conditions of the initial portion of the curve of Figure 2, giving a very large effective capacitance, no doubt aided by the presence of a good many pockets of air.

17. Therefore, on installations of powered supports with double-acting legs, the return line should not present problems and it may be of the same size of hose as the supply line, the allowable pressure loss being shared equally between the two. But with supports having single-acting legs, lowering under the influence of gravity alone, there is often trouble in getting the canopy clear of the roof and it is not difficult to see why. The weight of the canopy divided by the area of the legs supporting it provides, in most cases, only 150 - 200 kN/m^2 (20 - 30 lb/in^2) and seal friction will reduce even this. Considerable care is then needed to obtain satisfactory operation. It is essential for the reservoir to be located at the lower end of the face if there is a slope, so that the gravity head assists rather than opposes the flow. The largest convenient size of hose should also be used. Even so there may be difficulty on faces where a rapid rate of chock movement is required and it is then desirable to use separate return lines for the flows from the legs and from the rams.

18. No discussion of hose would be complete without mention of the vexed question of the form of end joint to be used. For a number of years one or two support manufacturers used flat-faced joints sealing with copper washers, whereas the remainder of mining hydraulic equipment had conventional British 60° cones. So far as sealing is concerned, there was little difference between these (Ref. 5), although a development of the flat joint in which an O-ring is used for sealing proved markedly superior except for a very occasional tendency for the O-ring to be lost down the hose. Unfortunately there is no room for a fully-retained seal in either type of joint unless the bore diameter is reduced. Eventually the N.C.B. decided to standardise on cone joints for all interchangeable parts. There is now a renewed threat of a dual standard, however, since the staple-lock hose end has been widely adopted abroad and the British mining industry is being pressed to employ it too. It clearly has some advantages, particularly for the multibore hose recently introduced for control lines, but for general use there appear to be some disadvantages too.

OTHER COMPONENTS

19. It is a great merit of any mains-type installation that the equipment provided at the points of use may be kept simple whilst a full range of accessories can be provided at a single control station. But it is a particularly far cry to present-day power packs from the early water-hydraulic tanks, which were hardly designed at all but merely bought from the local builders' merchant! Reservoirs as now being specified are provided with all of the following items:-

Integral soluble oil compartment, thermally insulated from the main tank to prevent overheating of low flash-point oil.

Level indicators, low-level alarms, and sealed covers on both compartments.

Automatic topping-up when minimum working level is reached, with oil proportioning device.

Settling chamber and magnetic filter for return fluid.

Relief valve in case of unloader valve failure or filter blockage.

Thermostatic cut-out.

20. The question of filtration in powered support systems is still somewhat controversial. Strainers in the pump suctions and pressure-line paper-element filters are now provided on almost all power packs. Elements need changing a number of times to clean up a newly-installed system, but thereafter a rate of entry of about 1 gm of filterable dirt per working hour has been noted, elements thus lasting two to three weeks. The fluid also contains an extremely large amount of material, as much as 0.2 gm/litre, below filter size, although at present it is not clear whether this does harm. It is in fact hard to get a correlation at all between the type or location of the filters used and the rate of valve failure. Dirt may enter the system at many

different points - on piston rods, through the tank breather, when hoses are replaced - and the chief comments it is possible to make are the fairly obvious ones, that:

(a) The finest filter in a system should be at the power pack, where it is easiest to replace elements, and

(b) Particularly critical components, e.g. yield valves, should be protected by filters immmediately adjacent to the fluid entry.

INSTRUMENTATION AND TESTING

21. The great advantages of reasonable instrumentation are now starting to be better appreciated in general industrial hydraulics, even though the user has probably obtained the whole system in a developed and tested state as a package deal and diagnosis is merely a matter of locating a faulty component for replacement. Although conditions underground are very unfavourable for instruments, the need for them is even greater. A system may, in effect, have been designed locally and it is extremely desirable to check that both the design and the installation are satisfactory before it goes into service. Later, the opportunities for deterioration are great and the system may even be extended indiscriminately, so that repetition of the checks from time to time is equally necessary. Moreover, the people concerned must be capable of interpreting the results of the tests.

22. The one instrument regularly provided is a pressure gauge on the power pack. Very often, though, it is visibly hors de combat. Press-to-read valves are now specified so as to protect gauges somewhat, but there is still room for types better able to withstand mining conditions and the pulsations of a three-cylinder pump.

23. But measurement of pressure tells only part of the story and flow meters are also needed for some important tests. It is surprising that the latter instruments are not used more widely in hydraulics generally: they are quite as essential as the electrical equivalent, the ammeter. The only pitworthy type available several years ago was the totalising water meter. This can in fact be very useful when fitted in the make-up water feed to a power pack, since it indicates the amount of external leakage from the system and permits a check that the amount of soluble oil used is consistent with the amount of water added. For other tests, however, direct reading of flow rate is necessary and for this a robust and cheap instrument had to be specially developed, in conjunction with a manufacturer. It is a variable-area meter, spring-loaded in such a way that small flows such as leakage can be indicated with the same accuracy as larger ones.

24. In practice, the operation of an unloader valve can be used to give a rough estimate of flow rate. For example, during the idling period recorded in Figure 1 the valve cut out for about 4/5 of the time and cut in for the remaining one-fifth. The mean flow into the system must therefore have been one-fifth of the output of the pump. This flow would have been the total of the external leakage and the internal leakage through defective valves to the return line. Internal leakage during idling periods may be measured directly by putting a flowmeter in the return line, but an instrument of the type described above should not be left in this

position since the pressure loss through it is about 150 kN/m² (20 lb/in²) and this pressure would be imposed on the whole of the return system, preventing the lowering of single-acting supports.

25. An important test is that of the volumetric efficiency of the power pack when on load and for this a flowmeter is essential, used in conjunction with a by-pass connection taking the whole output back to the tank through a throttling valve. Ideally the whole characteristic curve such as Figure 4 should be obtained, but for simplicity it is being suggested that a check should just be made that the output at ¾ of the maximum pressure should not be less than ¾ of the rated output, i.e. the characteristic must enclose the '¾ x ¾ point'.

26. Recordings of pressure are generally needed only for special investigations, for which they are an invaluable way of finding out what is happening. The recordings of Figure 1 were actually taken on instruments of the recently-introduced intrinsically-safe electrical type, which are certainly very convenient to use. Earlier work used simple mechanical recorders, however, such as have been available for many years and require no more adaptation than a stronger case to make them suitable for mining use.

FUTURE POSSIBILITIES

27. Hydraulic powered supports are now an essential feature of longwall mining and there is no doubt that in the years to come greater rates of movement will be required of them, together with improved reliability. Greater attention to all the subjects mentioned in this paper, and probably others, will be required.

28. Already the hydraulic system of the supports is also called upon to power ancillary equipment such as chain tensioners, winches, and anchor stations. Further such items will certainly make their appearance, but these must be introduced with some understanding of the effect they will have on the supply system, because it will be unacceptable to limit their use to periods when no supports are being moved. Hydraulic motors for the continuous high-power rotary drives of conveyors and power-loaders have of course already been tried (Ref. 6), though on separate mineral-oil systems rather than those of the supports, and while these were technically successful the advantages were not generally considered sufficient to be worth pursuing. Recently some types of high-torque motor have given remarkably good results when tested on dilute emulsions and it would at least be theoretically possible to have water-hydraulic mains as the sole power supply to an entire district. However, the advantages of such a proposal might be more apparent than real. Hydraulic power, though vital for many mining purposes, is never an end in itself.

29. There is one unresolved factor in chock hydraulics which might usefully be mentioned; the value of the maximum pumped pressure. British water systems initially used a level of about 7 MN/m² (1000 lb/in²), and this has gradually increased to 10 - 14 MN/m² (1500 - 2000 lb/in²) with some isolated instances of the use of 20 MN/m² (3000 lb/in²). The pressure in the support legs at yield, on the other hand, was with some types

as high as 70 MN/m² (10 000 lb/in²) but is now generally 40 - 50 MN/m² (6 - 7000 lb/in²). There has been much discussion about what should be the ratio between the yield and the setting loads (Ref 7). The British, relatively low, setting load gives satisfactory results on a very large scale with little indication that an increase would be desirable. In Germany, however, a very close ratio is insisted upon, and this is provided, in both continental designs and those exported from this country, by means of increasing the pumping pressure to 28 to 35 MN/m² (4 - 5000 lb/in²), the yield pressure still being about the same. Both approaches seem about right for the respective yield/set ratios involved. For the British requirement, the use of a higher pumping pressure would not in itself bring any advantage (Ref. 8); indeed, it would involve rather slender rams and a change from double-wire braided hose to the multi-spiral reinforced type.

ACKNOWLEDGEMENTS

30. Thanks are due to the author's colleagues amongst the N.C.B. staff, with manufacturing firms, and at B.H.R.A., who have contributed to the work referred to. The Director of the Mining Research and Development Establishment has kindly given permission for this paper to be published. It does not claim, however, to be an official expression of the views of the N.C.B.

REFERENCES

1.   KIBBLE J.D.   "Trends in Hydraulic Mining Equipment". Hydraulic Pneumatic Power Sept. 1965.

2.   STEINMÜLLER A.G.   "Development and Manufacture of Ultra-High-Pressure Hoses". Ölhydraulik u. Pneumatik 10 (1966) No. 77.

3.   CROOK A. and THOMASSON P.G.   "The Behaviour of Unloading Valves in Long Pipeline Systems". BHRA Report No. SP992, 1st Fluid Power Symposium, January 1969.

4.   KRAHE J.   "The Control & Dimensioning of the Hydraulic Supply of Coal Faces with Powered Supports".   Glückauf Vol. 107 No. 9, 29th April 1971, p. 332.

5.   KIBBLE J.D. and MAKOWER C.S.   "Connections for Wire-braided Hose", Hydraulic Pneumatic Power & Control, Oct. 1963.

6.   LANSDOWNE R.F. and MONKS H.   "A contribution of the Central Engineering Establishment, N.C.B. to Hydrostatic Transmission at the Coal Face". The Mining Engineer, 56, May 1965, p. 475.

7.   ASHWIN D.P. et al.   "Some Fundamental Aspects of Face Powered Support Design".   The Mining Engineer, 119, Aug. 1970 p. 659.

8.   KIBBLE J.D.   "Basic Factors in the Design of Hydraulic Circuits", Prac. I.Mech.E. 1969-70, Vol. 184, Pt. 1, No. 1, pp. 25-35.

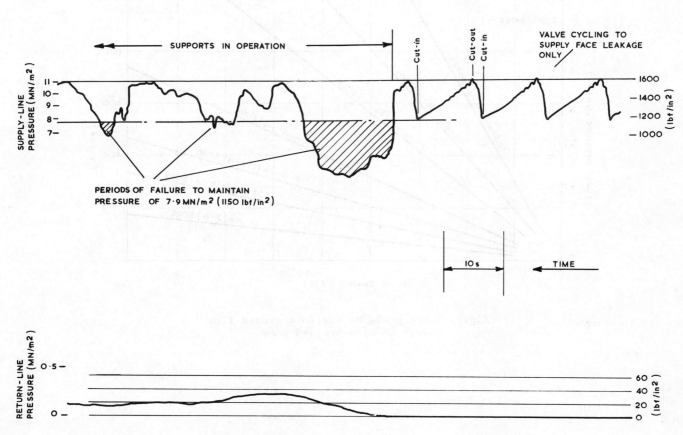

Fig.1. Recording of pressure in face main hoses

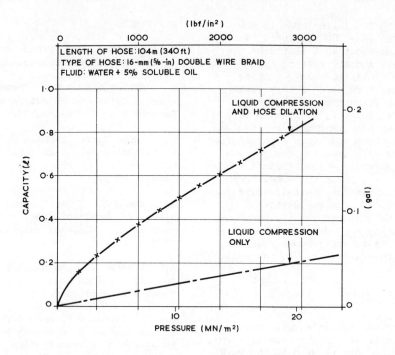

Fig.2. The hose accumulator effect

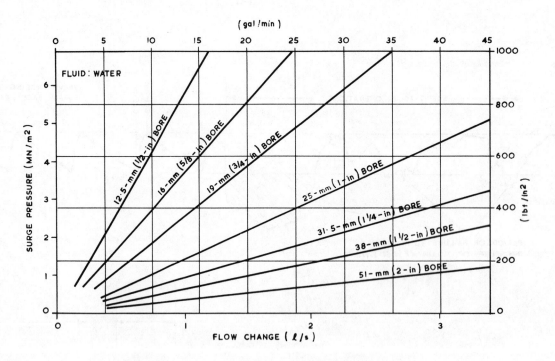

Fig.3. Surge pressure due to a sudden flow
change in wire-braided hose

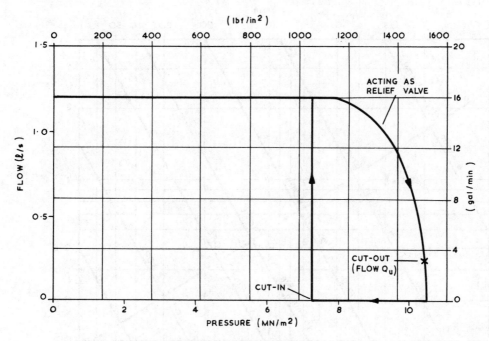

Fig.4. Pressure/flow characteristic
for unloader valve

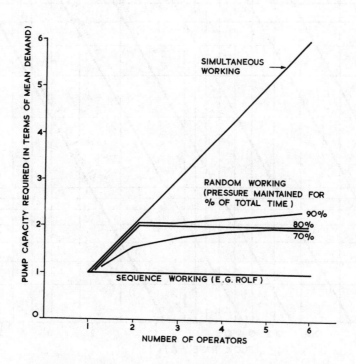

Fig.5. Pump capacity required for various
working conditions

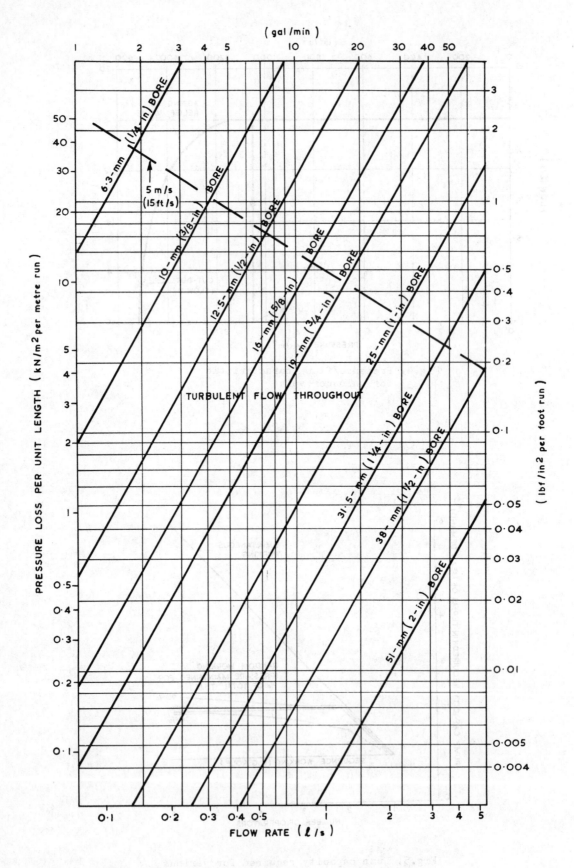

Fig.6. Pressure loss due to the flow of water
in smooth-bore pipe or hose

C31/74

SERVICE, MAINTENANCE AND OVERHAUL OF POWERED SUPPORTS

S. C. WALKER, CEng, MIMechE, MWInst, MAMEME

Area Chief Engineer, National Coal Board, South Midlands Area,
Coleorton, Leicestershire

The Ms. of this paper was received at the Institution on 9th August 1973 and accepted for publication on 23rd October 1973. 33

INTRODUCTION

1.   The capital invested in Powered Supports is
among the most significant of any single class of
items.   Considering an Area as a Business Unit
and taking the South Midland Area as a typical
example, our current holding of powered supports
totals 14,447 of which 9,669 are in use and 2,133
are either being installed, recovered or overhauled.
The average cost of each support is in the order
of £900, the total asset being approximately
£13,000,000 at current replacement prices.

2.   Regulation 10 of the Coal and Other Mines
(Mechanics and Electricians) Regulations 1965 requires "the manager of every mine to ensure that
there shall be at all times in force a scheme in
respect of all mechanical apparatus at the mine
other than simple mechanical supports".   The
modern powered support is far from simple and thus
must be included in the Managers Scheme for the
Mine.

3.   To maximise the utilisation of powered supports
they are designated as plant pool items and the
movement of these items is under the direct control
of the Area Plant Pool Controller who plans
supports allocations up to ahead of requirement.
Even with such advanced planning our utilisation
factor is regrettably low - mainly due to the
difficulty of matching supports to varying seam
thicknesses.   In the face of such difficulties
the importance of "engineering" availability cannot
be overstressed.

4.   Much stress is often made of our 'legal' maintenance requirement.   Sound maintenance should not
be simply because the law requires it but rather
that it is sound economic sense.   The importance
of the maintenance function has grown in parallel
with the increasing complexity of supports.

5.   As a service to production, management of the
support maintenance function should have special
regard to:
    i.   the maintenance of supports (and associ-
    ated equipment) in good condition to minimise
    breakdown and other production delays.

    ii.   ensuring maximum support availability.

    iii.   securing a safe working system.

The maintenance of supports is a multi-level
function embracing three distinct but co-related
areas of activity which will be separately considered, i.e.

    i.   on face servicing

    ii.   Interface transfer maintenance

    iii.   Workshops overhaul

6.   Well established Maintenance Management procedures are vital and for maximum economy must be
rigidly observed, particularly with reference to
the movement of supports.   As an example, prior
to the introduction of rigid controls a complete
face installation of 257 supports was transferred
and the cost of discrepancies alone totalled
£9,805.   In the first twelve months of rigid controls 1,321 supports were moved with a total dis-
crepancy charge of £3,234.   Discrepancies now
average about 50 pence per support!

7.   Generally speaking Management must initiate
two main types of control;   budgetary or overall
control for higher management and the more detailed
control necessary for servicing, maintenance or
overhaul.

8.   To ensure effective maintenance in British
Mines there must be sufficient competent persons
to supervise and effect the proper installation,
examination, testing and maintenance (The Coal and
Other Mines (Mechanics and Electricians) Regulations
1965 Reg. 5(1)).   Purpose trained staff may be
appointed under Reg. 11 of the above Regulations
to assist in such matters providing they are
properly supervised and competent to perform their
task.   The emphasis is of course on 'training'
and to satisfy these requirements, the National
Coal Board arrange that:-

    i.   All entrant trainees spend a familiarisa-
    tion period at one of the training faces.

    ii.   Craft apprentices receive instruction on
    powered supports (among other items) at the
    Engineering Training Centre.

    iii.   Ad hoc courses are organised for fitters,
    support maintenance men, support operators,
    etc., of about one week duration.

    iv.   Regular courses are organised with Manu-
    facturers for a variety of personnel from
    Shift Charge Engineers down to those authoris-
    ed under Regulation 11.

    v.   With any type of support, "new" to the
    Area special ad hoc courses are organised
    locally.

ON FACE SERVICING

9. Maintenance has been defined as the work necessary to ensure that the equipment is in "an acceptable condition": in the case of a powered support such an acceptable condition is clearly something closely approaching the "as new" condition. Powered Roof Supports maintenance staff should be provided with suitable pocket size check lists to ensure a methodical approach and to act as an aide memoir.

10. Appendix I illustrates check lists currently used for examination of powered supports and associated power packs. Similar check lists are available for other types and makes of supports, power packs, etc.

11. Examinations 'A' are normally scheduled to be carried out at daily intervals; Examinations 'B' at weekly intervals and Examination 'C' at monthly intervals.

12. Further servicing will clearly be necessary when operational difficulties are experienced in maintaining adequate setting and ramming pressure. Excessive convergence could be an indication that the chocks are yielding at pressures less than the pre-set values, thus indicating that a formal procedure of yield load testing should be adopted. Well used supports will often yield at a pressure somewhat lower than that pre-set by manufacturers or by Central Workshops due to erosion of valve seats. Conversely an extremely high yield pressure may be experienced on coal faces where the roof convergence/advance rate is not sufficient to initiate operation of the yield valve and results in the yield valve sticking. Fortunately the latter phenomenon is an infrequent occurrence.

13. Full details of the technique of in-situ yield testing is covered in M.R.E. Bulletin No.17 "Testing powered supports on the face", such techniques being regularly practiced at many mines. Yield testing is time consuming and an adequate period must be allowed for this work to be carried out and thus ensure that seals, valves and hoses are able to withstand this pressure.

14. All modern powered supports are fitted with suitable provisions for yield testing, consisting of permanently fitted nipples which contain a miniature non-return valve and a small O-ring seal to which can be connected the coupling body. The latter contains a probe bored for the passage of fluid. When the two portions are coupled together the probe enters the nipple, forces the non-return valve from its seat and allows fluid from the high pressure circuit to enter the coupling body and give a reading on the pressure gauge attached to it.

15. Several commercial types of boosters, or more correctly, hydraulic intensifiers are available; experience indicating that it is particularly important to select a type which is convenient to use and light enough to be carried about easily. Conversely, very small boosters have limited fluid delivery and extend the time taken for the operation. As with most things the good old British compromise succeeds.

16. A simple hydraulic circuit of a booster is illustrated in Fig. 1.

17. Using a suitable booster, support maintenance fitters would be instructed to:-

a. Connect the booster input hose to the main supply line, preferably by connecting it to one outlet of a support control valve in place of one of the ram hoses and then moving the valve handle to pressurise that outlet. The booster exhaust is best connected to the main return line or alternatively allowed to discharge to the goaf.

b. Check that mains pressure is available by opening the booster throttle valve. Using the jet of fluid wash the coupling nipples on the support.

c. Connect a T-piece coupling with pressure gauge to a check nipple on the first nipple to be tested. If the gauge indicates the full yield pressure, this prop circuit is satisfactory. If not, this may be because the circuit is faulty or because insufficient convergence has occurred to build up the pressure. To determine which:-

d. Connect the booster to the rear nipple of the T-piece adaptor. Open the booster throttle valve: this will bring the leg circuit up to supply line pressure if it is below this value. Using the booster control valve increase the pressure to the yield valve. As this is approached, reduce the rate of flow with the throttle valve to avoid pumping too rapidly through the yield valve. The latter must be tested at a slow rate of flow to simulate working conditions. If a correct yield pressure cannot be reached, or if, once reached, it dies away rapidly, the prop circuit is faulty, and maintenance is necessary.

e. If the correct pressure has been reached it is still necessary to ensure that the support can hold this pressure for at least several minutes. By disconnecting the booster and proceeding to likewise test the next, second and third leg circuits a suitable pressure holding period can be allowed.

f. Return to the first circuit tested to ensure that it continues to hold test pressure and thus prove the circuit satisfactory. If not, then maintenance of the hydraulics is necessary.

g. Proceed along the face as above to the agreed testing pattern.

18. Probably the most desirable frequency and method of testing the yield valve on powered supports having regard to manpower costs (and availability) and the beneficial results obtained therefrom is that of "sample testing" - say 10% at about three monthly intervals. When the results of testing prove the deterioration of a number of supports on the face it indicates a trend of fault common to the whole system such as fluid lubricity/cleanliness/pressure loss, etc. which demands further, in depth, investigation.

19. Medium pressure circuit testing is a regularly used method of fault diagnosis, the actual methods being very adequately covered in M.R.D.E. Bulletin No. 21 "Hydraulic Flow-meters".

20. The system leakage rate should be established when there are no chocks or rams in operation and the unloading valve set to the theorectical correct pressure for the setting of the supports. It is essential that the "leakage rate" is maintained within the limits suitable for the unloading valve being used, failure to conform to this condition will result in the unloading valve rapidly hunting between the "on" and "off" condition, in which event the valve will quickly be destroyed. If difficulty is experienced in controlling the leakage rate a suitable accumulator will reduce the frequency of valve operation and thereby improve the valve life.

Hydraulic Fluid Considerations

21. In the hostile environment of the coal face the maintenance of a suitable working fluid is of supreme importance, the specification of which must have regard to the necessary qualities of non-flamability, lubricity, viscosity and low overall cost. The most suitable compromise, satisfying these rather conflicting requirements, that is currently available is the 5% concentration of dilute emulsion.

22. It is essential when preparing a soluble oil emulsion that the soluble oil should be added to the water and not the water added to the soluble oil (going back to our 'chemistry' days: the "O" is before the "W"). The mixture must then be thoroughly agitated to form a homogeneous emulsion. If an incorrect or reversed procedure is used, an unstable emulsion may result, differing in nature from that required and in extreme cases, it may be found impossible to form an emulsion even though the correct proportions may have been mixed together.

23. A range of different soluble oils is required to meet the widely differing types of water and conditions encountered in British mines (and no doubt in others). It should be noted that most soluble oils produce different types and colours of emulsion, some being opaque and some clear. Colour charts should be made available by the oil suppliers and should be regularly consulted by the maintenance staff. Regular laboratory checks to ensure correct emulsion strength should be effected to 'back up' the more frequent use of the refractometer. Fig. 2. Visual inspection alone can be most misleading and where such practices are used, they should be discontinued forthwith.

24. Prior to deciding which grade of soluble oil is required for making an emulsion, a sample of the water to be used should be dispatched either to the suppliers or to the consumers laboratory for testing and recommendations.

25. Emulsion stability is dependent on the maintenance of the emulsion at the recommended 5% which should be strictly enforced for all normal conditions of use.

26. Contamination should be eliminated by the use of sealed tanks fitted with the necessary equipment to give clean, correctly diluted emulsions. Coal dust, stone dust and high temperature operation will reduce stability and may result in the breakdown of the soluble oil emulsions. If a soluble oil is observed to be contaminated, it should be drained from the system and replaced with a new, clean supply.

27. Filtration is all important and the practice of using individual filtration with one filter per support or collective filtration with the filter mounted on the tank is a debatable issue. Under well controlled conditions collective filtration should be adequate but evidence accumulated in the South Midlands Area appears to economically justify individual filtration. Whichever system is adopted however, it must be properly maintained and this item of maintenance is in the writer's opinion one of major importance.

INTERFACE TRANSFER MAINTENANCE

28. In an ideal situation any replacement face should be fully kitted up sometime prior to the completion date of the proceeding face. Coal face life however, varies widely from a few short months up to in excess of two years.

29. Broadly speaking, all coal face equipment should be so designed to be capable of a two year on face life or to be capable of handling one million tons of coal without major overhaul. Such ideals are now in certain circumstances being achieved.

30. It is an increasingly common practice where coal faces have a short working life (often unpredictably so) in one of the less hostile environments of where suitable powered supports are not readily available to effect a face to face transfer of equipment.

31. Once the decision to effect such a face to face transfer has been made and whilst the working face is still in production, a critical assessment of equipment condition should be made two to three months prior to termination of production. The examination is made by the Area Powered Supports Engineer or his assistant in the company of the Mine Supports Engineer. From this examination and from an examination of reports of regular maintenance a schedule of Spare Parts Requirements is prepared preferably up to two months before the transfer.

32. An example of such an examination report is included in Appendix II.

33. At this stage the relative locations of the working and replacement faces must be carefully considered.

34. If the face acquiring the powered supports is reasonably close to the production face, the supports may be transferred as complete units in which it may be both very desirable and economic to carry out mining work to increase the roadway dimensions in the vicinity of the adjacent face ends. Such work will provide an acceptable minimum working area for the lifting of the supports on to the transport media, i.e. sledges, transporters, etc. In this regard a simple but excellent system has been used at Coventry Mine which consists of fixing wheels at each end of the supports by means of fabricated brackets and thus allow the complete assembly to travel the standard underground rail tracks, Fig.3.

35. In order to readily facilitate the fixing/removal of the above mentioned wheels, hydraulically operated jacking platforms were provided which consisted of a simple platform fitted with eleva-

ting jacks coupled via appropriate valves to the support hydraulic system. Time expended in the preparation of such simple yet effective systems tailored to suit the individual requirements of the mine is not only a sound economic investment but adds materially to the safety of the handling system. Fig. 4. Adequate means of lifting are an obvious necessity. Fig. 5.

36. Reverting back to the aforementioned 'special' powered supports examination, the required service exchange or new items are ordered from the local Central Stores and delivered to the mine generally within two weeks after the appropriate ordering action. Additional staff are drafted to the working face and the suspect components are changed after which yet further tests are made which include:-

a.   Pressure testing of support legs and seals.

b.   Backflushing of each individual filter on each powered support (where fitted) and on the power pack.

c.   Systematic testing of control valves.

37. In all this work, designed to remove if possible any discrepancies prior to the actual transfer the importance of consulting previous P.P.M. reports and updating them cannot be over emphasised.

38. At this stage the lubricity of the working fluids will be improved by increasing the concentration of the dilute emulsion from 5% to 10% (maximum) to help fight against corrosion. Anti-corrosive grease and/or oils will be applied to the exposed cylinder rods and approved penetrating oils will be applied to hydraulic nipples, bolts and nuts, etc. The above mentioned maximum of 10% should not be exceeded otherwise difficulties could arise from the instability of the resultant emulsion. Although the increase in concentration from 5% to 10% does increase the viscosity of the emulsion, at such levels the change is tolerable, but above these figures viscosity problems will increase and give an increase in pressure drop across the filters, pipelines, etc., and finally tend to convey impurities around the circuit, all of course combined with a reduced fire resistance if carried to extremes.

39. If, due to geological or other factors, it is impracticable to transfer the supports as an entity the aforementioned procedures should still in general be adopted with certain modifications. For example, as the planned date of transfer approaches major suspect but still operational items would probably not be replaced in situ on the production face but carefully marked and replaced by new or reconditioned assemblies during the rebuilding stage at the new face.

40. During interface transfer, or indeed at any time that hydraulic components of any type are out of use all valves, hose ends, nipples, etc. must be made dust tight by the use of the correct size and type of plastic caps. Also during this period all major load bearing parts such as welded bases and canopies should be well cleaned and examined for evidence of weld cracking, fatigue or distortion of any kind.

41. Powered supports are designed to work between a minimum and extended maximum working height. These dimensions determine the suitability of supports for a particular seam. The base and canopy areas of support are very relevant for working in particular varieties of strata condition.

42. When the coal seam has friable roof strata, large area canopies and specially designed friable roof bars may become essential. Similarly for soft floor conditions large area bases become desirable.

43. Although strictly speaking, the above points are not really maintenance problems, consideration to them must be given when formulating a face to face transfer maintenance policy and the required modifications made during the "rebuild" period. These matters may be of such influential importance as to enforce a strip down rather than transfer the support as an entity.

44. Underground testing of powered supports, other than those previously mentioned is obviously difficult. After overhaul at a Workshops, supports are tested in a suitable test rig and in order to provide a similar type of test the engineers at Coventry Mine devised a test rig that can readily be erected in situ or dismantled for transport, Fig. 6. The overall length of the rig is identical with the standard track section in use at the mine and can thus be readily positioned.

45. In operation the chocks, still mounted on their travelling wheels are positioned centrally in the rig, the central section of the track is then collapsed by means of hydraulic cylinders, thus allowing the floor beams to take the weight of the support, Fig. 7. The support is then coupled to the test hydraulic system, which could, if the test area is adjacent to the new face, be the permanent power pack. Routine tests are then carried out including full boost tests in the manner previously described.

WORKSHOPS OVERHAUL

46. The workshops overhaul is the real opportunity to restore, as near as practical to the original condition. In fact when advantage is taken during this period of overhaul to incorporate improvements and the full range of current modifications the operational performance after overhaul may be an improvement on the original "as new" condition.

47. Almost without exception all workshops overhauls are now carried out in Board owned and operated Central Workshops which are strategically positioned throughout the coalfields. The workshops concerned are:-

1.	Cowdenbeath	(Scotland)
2.	Ashington	(Northumberland)
3.	Elsecar	(South Yorkshire)
4.	Duckmanton	(North Derbyshire)
5.	Walkden	(North West)
6.	Bestwood	(South Nottinghamshire)
7.	Ansley	(South Midlands)
8.	Tredegar	(Wales)

48. Rationalisation exercises have been carried out over the whole spectrum of workshops overhaul activities and in consequence supports are not of necessity overhauled at the "nearest" workshops but rather at that establishment specialising in the

particular make and type of support. Such specialisation results in increased throughput and in consequence a quicker return, a small concentration of spare parts and of course lower overhaul repair costs.

49. The workshops overhaul should be preceeded by a critical examination of the supports under operational conditions and a report on the examination prepared in a like manner to that outlined for face to face transfer maintenance. Close liaison must be maintained between the Area Powered Supports Engineer and the appropriate Central Workshops management in order that they may have prior knowledge as to the condition of the supports they, in due course, are to receive and to simplify spare provisioning.

50. After removal from the mine supports may be stored on the surface for a period which may coincide with freezing or other adverse weather conditions and programmes must be arranged to prepare the supports to withstand these hostile conditions. In practice it has been found beneficial sometime prior to the removal of the support system to:

a. Clean out reservoir, change filters and thoroughly filter the system.

b. Increase concentration of dilute emulsion from 5% to 10% maximum.

c. Treat all external working surfaces with a suitable water repellant corrosion preventative, non-flam paste. A suitable type designed for brush application and maximum adhesion supplied in the thixotropic form and much used in the S. Midlands Area is Centigard 994 AB by Century Oils.

d. Progressively change the hydraulic fluid to a preprepared balanced emulsion with anti-freeze and improved rust inhibiting characteristics. Such fluids should ideally have a different colour from that of the regularly used fluid.

e. Finally when dismantling the roof supports the maximum quantity of the latter fluid should be retained in the system and all hose ends, connections, etc. sealed with plastic protection caps.

f. Central Workshops Procedures are well documented, the final requirements being detailed in the "Central Workshops Final Inspection and Testing Procedures" issued by the N.C.B. Test procedure sheets are included in the above mentioned documents for all types of powered supports in use within the Board and compliance with such procedure ensures that the overhauled product is comparable in performance with the "as new" equipment.

51. The work flow in a Central Workshops engaged on overhaul of powered supports must obviously differ in many degrees from that employed by manufacturers. A typical work flow diagram is indicated on Fig. 8.

52. Supports as received by the Workshops from the Mines are in an extremely dirty condition, Fig. 9, and the first operation is to externally clean the support by means of the HYDRO-BLAST which is a cleaning unit using a high pressure (2,000

p.s.i.) water jet to which a scouring grit is introduced, Fig. 10. The complete support or batch of smaller components is mounted on a ball and socket joint adjustable in all planes and thus every part of the support is accessible.

53. The cleaning process is in three parts comprising:-

i. "Wash" with high pressure water to remove coal dust, coal, clay and other extraneous matter.

ii. "Blast" with high pressure water plus grit to remove scale and corrosion.

iii. "Rinse" with high pressure water to remove residual grit.

54. The usual means of screening and centrifuging to clarify the water and recover the grit is used.

55. The supports are now stripped for inspection and compared with N.C.B. Specifications following which the required forms of repair are carried out which include:-

i. Straightening on a 200 ton press to remove distortions from bases, beams and canopies. Small jacks are also used to remove indentations from channel and boxed sections.

ii. The replacing of fittings, brackets and lugs or the straightening of the same which is carried out in the smithy.

iii. The re-welding of any cracked components after pre-weld preparation has been carried out.

iv. Removal of the studs which have sheared in operation and the re-tapping of such holes as required.

v. Honing of support leg cylinders on a self-centring honing machine.

vi. Lapping of valve seats which is carried out on a lapping polishing machine after which the reclaimed surfaces are tested for flatness to a polarising arrangement which will differentiate irregularities in the order of 0.00001".

56. At the completion of each of the above parts further inspection is carried out, finally leading to a re-assembly of the complete support. Testing to N.C.B. specified standards and painting.

Sub-Assemblies

57. A service exchange arrangement is organised to supply mines with legs, rams, valves, etc. which are overhauled to a specified standard and supplied to the mines as complete sub-assemblies and are used as required during "on face" servicing or more practical during inter-face transfer maintenance.

INFLUENCE OF MAINTENANCE ON DESIGN

58. Maintenance difficulties are experienced at numerous points and could be simplified to the advantage of all concerned. Among the major items worthy of further consideration are:-

Corrosion Prevention

59. The deterioration of engineering materials due to the effects of corrosion has been assessed by numerous authorities to cost the Nation in the order of £250M per annum. Usually such estimates are under-estimates since they are usually based on the annual value of steel production, its life and the cost of protecting it.

60. In the case of powered supports the protection against internal corrosion and against the corrosion of working parts is best effected by the maintenance of proper working fluids, and in special circumstances by those measures outlined in earlier chapters, but further work should be economically carried out by improvements in design and by better protection of the external surfaces.

61. Good design and geometrical arrangements are important in reducing corrosion attack, and every effort should be made in the design of powered support structures to avoid any hollow cavities, etc. which could collect moisture and dirt. Convex round sections are ideal in many cases. Crevices should be completely avoided in all structures where corrosion is due to atmospheric conditions and to direct contact with liquids.

62. Crevices give rise to a particular form of corrosion known as crevis corrosion and liquids applied in such crevices tend to change in composition thus leading to a change of electrical potential. Invariably the crevis is anodic and increased corrosion is caused.

63. A particular important point to watch in this regard is the practice of recessing cap screws. Painting is probably the most common anti-corrosive treatment applied to mine structures in general. Paint to a good specification is capable of ensuring reasonable metal protection combined with that of good appearance. The current practice of painting underground equipment white has probably something to commend it from the safety point of view but far more attention is needed to ensure even reasonable standards of corrosion prevention.

64. In certain cases, particularly those sections in close proximity to the floor of the face, could benefit from the use of stainless steel bolts.

Bolting

65. The current practice by many powered support manufacturers is to use the cap screw almost exclusively as a bolting medium. The use of such cap screws is perhaps ideal for initial assembly but if designers were to spend even a brief period with mine engineering staff drilling out such set screws and re-tapping after they have sheared, I am sure they would re-design these connections. Most engineers would show preference to the use of a stainless steel nut and bolt.

Flushing Shields

66. Maintenance access is much reduced by the flushing of the waste, to obviate which a variety of flushing shields are used - generally made up at the mine. The provision of an acceptable range of adjustable flushing shields using a standardised pattern of fixture should be an integral part of all support systems.

67. The arrangement of hydraulic hoses combined with the positioning of valve blocks, etc. particularly when "adjacent control" techniques are used often impedes maintenance. The use of multi-bore hose assemblies would reduce this problem and the extended use of such hoses should be vigorously persued.

68. The N.C.B. currently standardise on the use of the cone joint as a hose end fitting and many benefits have been derived from such standardisation. Many engineers are now looking however, with increasing favour towards the use of staple lock hose end fittings. The use of these fittings could possibly reduce maintenance. Dual standards should not be tolerated for any length of time and if the staple lock fitting is proved to confer real benefits revised specifications should be made.

Lighting

69. It goes without saying that maintenance must always be improved when carried out under well illuminated conditions. Coal face lighting fittings are fixed to the supports in a variety of ways all rather "make-shift". All new supports should be provided with a standardised means of fixing these lighting fittings and if at all possible made an integral part of the supports system.

APPENDIX I

Powered Roof Supports

Oils and Greases.   Examination 'A' - Check and leave in safe working order.

a.   Check controls for correct operation, security, leaks and audible evidence of the fluid by-passing.   Rectify as found necessary.

b.   All hoses and connections for leaks and ensure that the main feed and return lines are not trapped or stretched tight.

c.   Canopy and cantilevers for damage and that all associated pins and bolts are present and in good condition.

d.   Flushing shields for damage and correct position.

e.   Legs for external damage and leaks from the leg seals.

f.   Leg aligning rams (where fitted) for leaks and correct operation.

g.   Leg mountings, clamps and/or security chains (where fitted) for damage and security.

h.   Rams for leaks and external damage to the piston rod that would damage the seals.

i.   Relay bar and bolts, clevis and clevis pins and that the spill plate is securely attached to the A.F.C.

j.   Base or bases and any connecting bridges or straps together with pins or bolts for damage.

Examination 'B' - Check and leave in safe working order.   As Examination 'A' plus

a.   Boost test a proportion of the chocks and record the results.

b.   Carry out a dial gauge check on all chocks.

c.   Check filters - replace as necessary.

Check List MA59

Power Packs for use with Powered Roof Supports - Gullick and Bonser Type

Oils and Greases.   Examination 'A' - Check and leave in safe working order.

a.   The level of the soluble oil solution in the tank and where a soluble oil injector or volume proportionating type tank is in use, check the supply of soluble oil.

b.   The percentage content of soluble oil in the fluid from the return hose to the tank using a refractometer - should be between 5% and 10%

c.   That all tank covers are securely and correctly fitted.

d.   Suction and delivery filters - where fitted, clean or change as found necessary.

e.   Pressure gauges are in working order and un-damaged.   Check pump operating pressure and record.   Adjust as required.

f.   Performance of pump when running for any abnormal noise or vibration and excessive over-heating.

g.   The oil level in the pump crankcase and top up as required.

h.   Pump glands for excessive leakage and top up as required.

i.   Ensure the ram chamber is free from debris.

j.   Hoses and connections are free from leaks and that they are not trapped and there is sufficient slack hose to allow for face advance.

k.   Ensure that all guards are secure.

Examination 'B' - Check and leave in safe working order as Examination 'A' plus.

a.   Bearings for wear.

b.   Connecting rod bolts and nuts for security.

c.   Lubricating pipes for correct position, security and freedom from fracture.

d.   Inspect the lubricating oil and change if found necessary - clean the strainer.

Examination 'C' - Check and leave in safe working order as Examinations 'A' and 'B' plus.

a.   The motor/pump coupling for condition and alignment.

b.   Security of all assembly and holding down bolts.

c.   Drain the fluid tank, clean out and change any filters.   Refill with the correct proportion of soluble oil/water solution.

Typical cost for overhaul and replacement of parts after 5 months use.

Service Exchange Items Ansley Stores

Vocab.	Part No.	Item	Qty.	Cost £.	Total Cost £.
80/13/892/0001 No.	K 5795/T 4	100 tcn leg 24"	3	82.000	246.00
80/13/8802	K 5794/T 3	50 ton leg 20"	3	57.000	171.00
	K 3392/T 2	Mk 9 D/A Ram	25	34.000	850.00
80/13/4052	K 3659/T 1	Heavy Duty Aux.	6	12.000	72.00
	K.978	Leg Valve	24	15.000	360.00
80/13/0929	K 929 (Mod)	Ram Valve Ansley T. Type	15	12.000	180.00
	K 5330	Sandwich Valve	12	30.000	360.00

New Items - Ansley Stores

Vocab.	Part No.	Item	Qty.	Cost £.	Total Cost £.
80/13/1943	K 1843	100 tcn Rockers	6	17.438	105.00
80/13/1942	K 1842	50 ton "	6	10.075	60.00
80/13/3810	K 3408/T 7	Mk. 9 Relay Bar	6	19.302	116.00
80/13/3811	K 3409/T 7	Guide Connector Mk. 9	12	2.680	32.00
	E 2365	Spacer Assy. Mk. 5	10	0.933	9.00
	K 1882	Pivot Pin (brackets base)	12	0.517	6.00
80/13/3812	K 5334	Clevis Mk. 9 $1\frac{1}{8}$" JAW	30	2.338	70.00
80/13/8939	K 5331	Push Bar Guard	6	3.900	23.00
80/13/2866	K 2366	Ram Guard	6	4.705	28.00
80/13/7718	K 4226/T 9	Fixed Guard 30"	6	11.162	67.00
	K 2331/T 2	Pivot Pin (rear)	6	3.354	20.00
	K 3363	Pivot Pin (front)	6	4.750	28.00
80/13/4058	K 3662	Pivot Pin (Cantilever)	12	2.092	25.00
13/14/0217		$\frac{5}{8}$" 8 link chains	192	0.750	144.00
		1" x $\frac{3}{4}$" BSF Skt. HD Cap Screws	50		1.500
		1" x $\frac{1}{4}$" BSW Skt. HD Cap Screws	50		1.250
		$1\frac{1}{2}$" x $\frac{1}{4}$" HEX HD HT Screws	50		0.950
		$1\frac{1}{4}$" x $\frac{3}{4}$" BSW Skt. HD Cap Screws	50		4.200
		1" x $\frac{1}{2}$" Skt. CSK HD Cap Screws	50		3.300
13/38/3424		$\frac{1}{2}$" x $\frac{1}{2}$" Male CF Nipples	100		10.000
13/38/3423		$\frac{3}{8}$" x $\frac{3}{8}$" Male CF Nipples	200		20.000
13/37/0133		$\frac{1}{2}$" x $\frac{3}{4}$" Male CF Reducing Nipple	150		18.000
13/37/0131		$\frac{3}{8}$" x $\frac{1}{4}$" " "	100		10.000
80/13/1414	K 1414	$\frac{3}{8}$" x $\frac{3}{8}$" x $\frac{3}{8}$" Male CF TEE	100		100.000
	K 4371	$\frac{1}{2}$" x $\frac{1}{2}$" x $\frac{3}{8}$" Male CF Swivel Tees	100		100.000
		$3\frac{1}{2}$" x 5/16" Split Pin	200		3.800
		3" x 5/16" Split Pin	200		2.800
		$2\frac{1}{2}$" x 5/16" " "	100		1.400
		$\frac{1}{2}$" Bonded Seal	500		15.000
		$\frac{3}{8}$" " "	500		15.000
		$\frac{1}{4}$" " "	200		6.000

Dust Caps

	Qty		Total Cost
1" Male	400	)	
1" Female	400	)	
$\frac{1}{2}$" Male	300	)	12.000
$\frac{1}{2}$" Female	300	)	
$\frac{3}{8}$" Male	300	)	
$\frac{3}{4}$" Female	300	)	

Hoses

Size	Length	Type	Ends	Qty	Cost £	Total Cost £
½"	4' 3"	12	CF 90° x 135°	30	1.684	51.00
½"	2' 0"	12	CF 90° x 135°	30	1.261	38.00
¼"	5' 0"	3	CF S x 90°	50	1.800	90.00
¼"	4' 6"	3	CF S x 90°	50	1.756	88.00
¼"	1' 6"	5	CF 90° x 90°	30	1.096	33.00
⅜"	1' 3"	1	CF S x S	20	0.954	19.00
⅜"	2' 0"	1	CF S x S	30	1.100	33.00
⅜"	10"	3	CF S x 90°	50	0.750	37.00
⅜"	9' 9"	2	CF S x 135°	50	2.452	122.00
⅜"	1' 6"	3	CF S x Banjo	50	0.954	48.00

Labour   430

TOTAL COST   £ 4,289.00

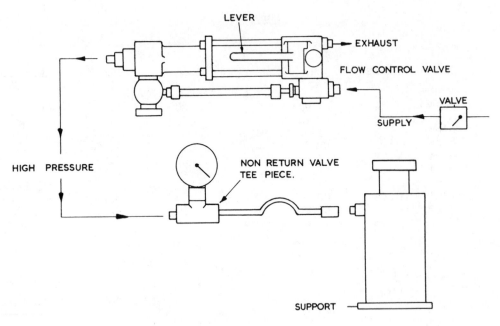

1.   Booster Hydraulic Circuit

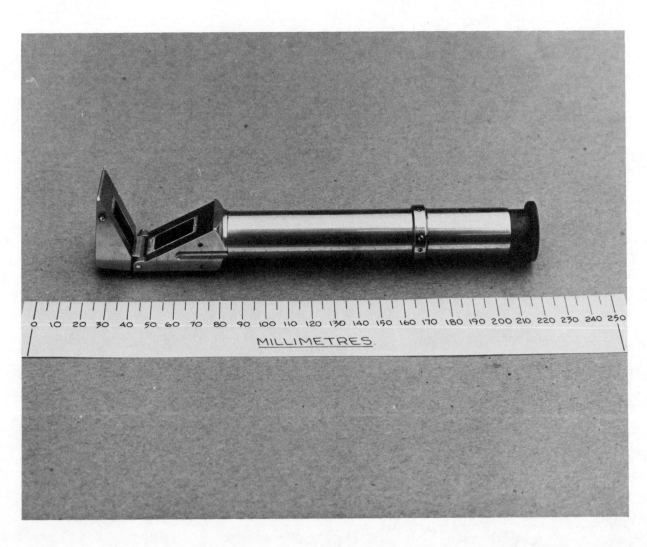

2.   Refractometer

3.   Support fitted with temporary wheels

4.   Support Jacking Platform

5.   U.G. Lifting Arrangement

6.   U.G. Transportable Test Rig with Support

7.   U.G. Transportable Test Rig

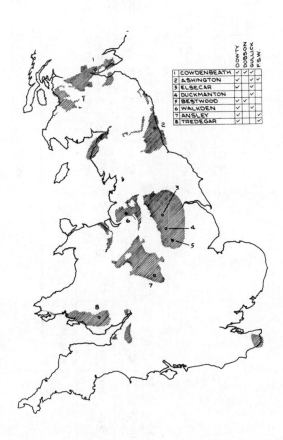

8.   Situation of Central Workshops engaged on support overhaul
       in relationship to coalfields.

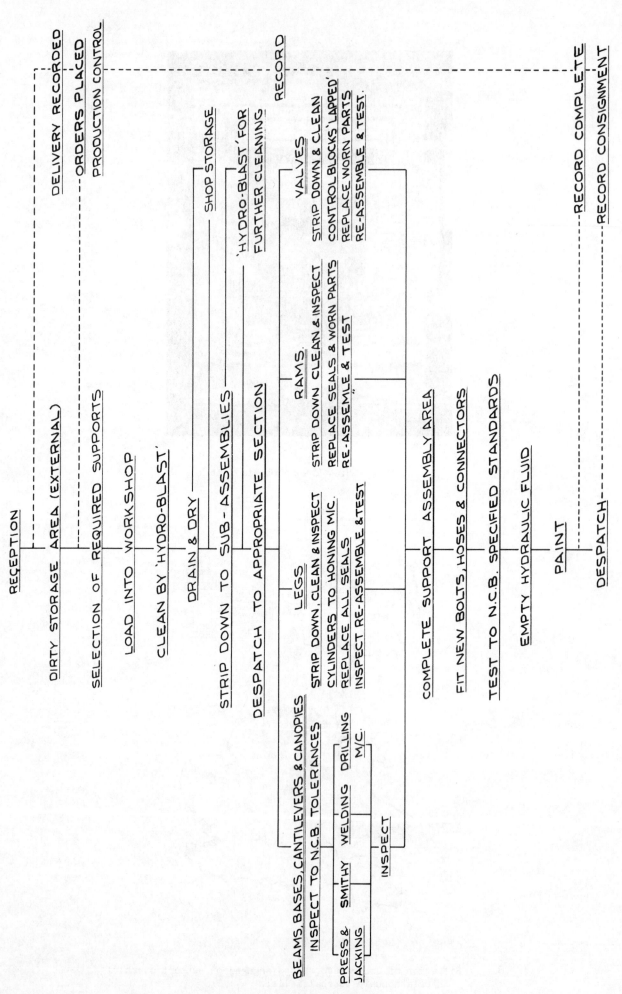

RECEPTION

DIRTY STORAGE AREA (EXTERNAL)

DELIVERY RECORDED
ORDERS PLACED
PRODUCTION CONTROL

SELECTION OF REQUIRED SUPPORTS

LOAD INTO WORKSHOP

CLEAN BY 'HYDRO-BLAST'

DRAIN & DRY

SHOP STORAGE

'HYDRO-BLAST' FOR FURTHER CLEANING

STRIP DOWN TO SUB-ASSEMBLIES

DESPATCH TO APPROPRIATE SECTION

RECORD

VALVES
STRIP DOWN & CLEAN
CONTROL BLOCKS 'LAPPED'
REPLACE WORN PARTS
RE-ASSEMBLE & TEST.

RAMS.
STRIP DOWN, CLEAN & INSPECT
REPLACE SEALS & WORN PARTS
RE-ASSEMBLE & TEST

LEGS
STRIP DOWN, CLEAN & INSPECT
CYLINDERS TO HONING M/C.
REPLACE ALL SEALS
INSPECT RE-ASSEMBLE & TEST

BEAMS, BASES, CANTILEVERS & CANOPIES
INSPECT TO N.C.B. TOLERANCES

PRESS & JACKING   SMITHY   WELDING   DRILLING M/C.

INSPECT

COMPLETE SUPPORT ASSEMBLY AREA

FIT NEW BOLTS, HOSES & CONNECTORS

TEST TO N.C.B. SPECIFIED STANDARDS

EMPTY HYDRAULIC FLUID

PAINT

DESPATCH

RECORD COMPLETE
RECORD CONSIGNMENT

9.   Workflow Diagram

10.   Support as received

11.   Support after cleaning

C32/74

BRITISH EXPERIENCE WITH FIRE RESISTANT FLUIDS IN THE MINING INDUSTRY

J. B. HALL, TEng(CEI), MAMEME
Deputy Chief Mechanical Engineer, National Coal Board,
Mining Department Headquarters, South Parade, Doncaster, Yorkshire

G. C. KNIGHT, MSc(Mech Eng)
Head of Rotary, Hydraulic and Electrical Group, National Coal Board,
Mining Research and Development Establishment, Stanhope Bretby,
Burton-on-Trent, Staffordshire

P. KENNY, BSc, FInstP
Head of Applied Materials Science Group, National Coal Board,
Mining Research and Development Establishment, Stanhope Bretby,
Burton-on-Trent, Staffordshire

The Ms. of this paper was received at the Institution on 12th September 1973 and accepted for publication on 23rd October 1973. 22

SYNOPSIS   In 1964 the National Coal Board adopted a policy to introduce fire-resistant fluids in selected hydraulic systems.   Implementation of this policy has depended on the setting of acceptable standards of fire-resistance and overcoming the technical problems associated with the use of fluids which meet those standards.   Economic factors and toxicological problems have also had to be taken into account since fluids which may be technically suitable may also be excessively expensive or inadmissable in the mining environment.

The application of fire-resistant fluids is often limited by the lubricating characteristics of the fluids and progress has been made in assessing these properties. Performance testing of machines has established the useful range of applications in many practical situations and has allowed operational problems to be anticipated and overcome.   Recommendations made from the results of laboratory testing have allowed steady progress in increasing the utilisation of fire-resistant fluids underground.

The success in the implementation of the Board's policy may be judged by the fact that all 726* powered roof support installations in the industry are operating on dilute emulsion; 12166 of 12476 fluid couplings are working on either non-toxic phosphate ester or water and 3237 of 3459 hydrostatic transmissions underground are working on invert emulsion.

INTRODUCTION

1.   The interest of the mining industry of Western Europe, including Great Britain, in the development and use of fire resistant fluids, followed a serious incident at Marcinelle,Belgium, in 1956. As a result, the ECSC countries set up a group of experts who, over the years, have produced four reports covering specifications and testing conditions relating to fire resistant fluids used for power transmission, and Great Britain set up a Joint NCB/MOP**Working Party on the use of Flammable Oils Underground. This working party produced draft requirements for Fire-Resistant Hydraulic Fluids which were based on the use of both a spray and a wick test. Fluids which complied with the requirements of these tests were developed and examined and in 1964 the NCB adopted a policy to introduce fire-resistant hydraulic fluids to selected systems mainly in the underground situation.

2.   In the period between setting up the Joint Working Party and the introduction of the first applications of fire-resistant fluids in the collieries, a great deal of work was undertaken in various establishments belonging to the NCB, the Ministry and certain oil companies who were keen to be able to supply fluids for hydraulic purposes to the draft requirements. Also during this period fires arising from the use of flammable oil were reported these being, fortunately, few in number and without loss of life. The most serious of these occurred in 1964 in hydraulic equipment

on the surface of a mine adjacent to the top of the down-cast shaft.

3.   The equipment used in mining which utilises hydraulic fluid may be divided into three main categories and Britain has produced a somewhat different solution to the fluid problems associated with each.

4.   These three categories are as follows:-

i) Powered support systems. Many of these originally used mineral oil in large quantities which was contained in a mass of pipes and props spread over a large area on the coal face.

ii) Hydrostatic transmissions associated with both mobile and stationary equipment. Many of these contain large volumes of fluid, mainly confined in a tank, and are often in hazardous situations in the intake air current.

iii) Hydrokinetic transmissions. These are mainly traction type fluid couplings but with a significant number of scoop control couplings, some of high power.

5.   The process of application of fire-resistant fluids to the above mentioned types of equipment has been controlled and co-ordinated over the years by regular discussions at the NCB Mechanical Engineering Conferences and by the establishment of working groups with specific remits. Specifications were established for particular fluid types to meet the necessary standards of fire resistance and, at the same time satisfy the toxicological, operational and economic requirements. NCB Specification 463/1965 (revised 1970) covers Emulsifying Oils for Dilute Emulsions in Powered Supports and NCB Specification 570/1970 deals with Fire Resistant Fluids for use in Machinery

---

* Numbers quoted are as at September 1972.

**The functions of the Ministry of Power, to which HM Inspectorate of Mines and the Safety in Mines Research Establishment were responsible, were transferred to the Ministry of Technology and later to the Department of Trade and Industry.

and Hydraulic Equipment. Purchase of fluids to these Specifications is strictly controlled and only those which are NCB Approved may be used.

TESTS FOR FIRE RESISTANT PROPERTIES

6. The principal hazard arising from the use of flammable hydraulic fluids in mines is the products of combustion from the possible ignition of fluid sprayed from a pressurised source or the possible ignition of fluid soaked materials. The two test methods that have been adopted based on these situations evolved from extensive work over many years by the MOP Safety in Mines Research Establishment and more recently by the NCB. Operational experience with fluids selected in this way has justified these requirements.

Spray test (Ref. 1)

7. Water-based fluids at 65°C, and other fluids at 85°C, are sprayed at 6.9 MPa (1000 lbf/in^2) through an atomising nozzle to form a hollow cone spray. When the spray is established an igniting flame from an oxy-acetylene torch is repeatedly applied to and withdrawn from different positions along the length of the spray and the maximum duration of burning after withdrawal of the igniting flame is noted. The flame from the fluid shall not persist for longer than 30 seconds after the removal of the igniting flame.

Wick test (Ref. 1)

8. A length of woven asbestos tape is soaked in the fluid under test and then placed in a reservoir of fluid with one edge exposed, forming a wick. A small igniting flame is applied to the exposed edge of the wick and the persistence of flame on the wick after removal of the igniting flame is measured. Six repeat measurements are carried out for each of five different periods of application of the igniting flame. The average of each set of six results is determined and the largest of these averages is taken as the Mean Persistence of Flame; this value must be less than 60 seconds.

TOXICOLOGICAL ASPECTS

9. The use of fire resistant hydraulic fluids is solely aimed at increasing safety by reducing the hazards associated with combustion and it is axiomatic that the introduction of other hazards must be avoided. The most important of other possible hazards are those associated with the toxicity of the fluid, its vapour, or its products of combustion if involved in a major fire not necessarily initially concerned with hydraulic equipment.

10. Hydraulic fluids depend for their fire resistant properties on either their water content or the presence of some chemical element in one or more of their constituents which inhibits the combustion of the fluid as a whole. Fluids of this latter type when deliberately burnt generally produce large volumes of thick smoke which may contain substances which are offensive, irritant or toxic. Water-containing fluids on the other hand usually produce only those products normally associated with the more complete combustion of mineral oil and are therefore more acceptable in the underground

situation. This is one of the main reasons for the usage of water containing fire resistant fluids in Great Britain wherever practicable. It is interesting to note that of the sixteen fluids which now have NCB Approval only one is a non-aqueous fluid.

11. The chemical composition of the non-aqueous fluids available from world sources varies considerably and thus when the toxicological aspects are considered it is necessary to know the detailed chemical composition. As a consequence all such fluids which have been or are currently being investigated by the NCB are examined in detail for composition and possible application before tests for toxicity are specified and undertaken.

ECONOMIC CONSIDERATIONS

12. Fire-resistant fluids vary in price by a factor of 70000 from the least expensive dilute emulsion to the most expensive synthetic fluid. Cost must therefore be carefully considered before selection is made. As an indication of the cost of the more commonly used fluids the mean prices in the United Kingdom are given below as a ratio of the mean price for mineral hydraulic oils:

	Relative Mean Price	
Mineral hydraulic oil	1	(reference value)
Dilute emulsion (at a 5% concentration in water)	0.05	
Invert emulsion	1.19	
Water glycol	2.65	
Non-toxic phosphate ester	6.06	

(Ratios are based on an arithmetic mean of the prices for all NCB Approved grades within each category.)

FLUID PROPERTIES AFFECTING THE SELECTION OF HYDROSTATIC MACHINES

13. Investigations of the properties of dilute emulsions for use in powered supports were started in 1956 and four years later the work was extended to the study of fire-resistant fluids for use in power transmissions. Facilities for the testing of fluids in full-scale hydraulic systems were set up in 1965. These continuing investigations have helped in assessing the feasibility of using fire-resistant fluids for different applications, have fostered improvements in properties and consistency of properties of the fluids and have resulted in modifications to hydraulic equipment where necessary.

14. Fluid properties such as viscosity and stability are relatively easy to define and control and NCB Specifications incorporate appropriate requirements (Ref. 1,2). When it is not a property of the fluid itself but a satisfactory interaction between the fluid and a machine component that is required, the situation is more difficult to deal with. Recognisable interactions are the physical and chemical compatibility of the fluids with the materials of construction of machinery, and the tribological effects of the fluid on moving parts. Other interactions may arise in a complex manner so that they are revealed only by full-scale testing of equipment.

Compatibility with materials

15. The compatibility of a fluid with various materials can generally be assessed by fairly simple laboratory tests, deleterious effects usually showing up quickly enough to allow short test times. A wide range of test methods for metals, seal and hose materials and paint coatings have been and continue to be used for assessment and approval purposes, but most of these methods are unsuitable for specification purposes. The policy has been to state in NCB Specifications the basic requirements only.

16. All the water-containing fluids are required to be non-corrosive to immersed steel but satisfactory vapour-phase inhibition is more difficult to achieve and protective coatings are often necessary. Dilute emulsions are required to be compatible with the usual seal materials in powered supports, while compatibility of the power transmission fluids is achieved by appropriate restrictions on the metals and non-metallic materials used.

Lubricating properties

17. Lubrication tests, though not ideally suited for specification purposes, have an important part to play in fluid assessment, since it is frequently the lubricating properties of fire-resistant fluids which limit their use. The lubricating properties that appear critical are assessed in terms of the wear of sliding parts, fatigue of rolling element bearings or erosion of surfaces.

18. Sliding wear

Studies of sliding wear have shown that the water-containing fluids are poorer lubricants than non-toxic phosphate esters and mineral oils (Ref. 3). Invert emulsions are generally better than aqueous glycols which, in turn, are generally better than dilute emulsions. Though it can be readily demonstrated that dilute emulsions are superior to water as lubricants, the design of powered support systems does not make demands on their lubricating properties.

19. Rolling fatigue

Studies of rolling fatigue have demonstrated two main problems in assessing fluids for their effects on the fatigue life of rolling element bearings (Ref. 4,5). First, fatigue life of a bearing cannot be determined other than by running the bearing until failure occurs. Secondly, fatigue lives are very scattered, so several replications are required and the results must be expressed in terms of statistical probability of failure (see Figure 1). In order to achieve a reasonably short testing time the fatigue process must be accelerated in some way. Tests greatly accelerated by overloading the bearings are open to criticism and the outcome has been lack of agreement between results from different workers and confusion as to the validity of laboratory results in general.

20. Recent work has shown how the problem might be overcome (Ref. 6). For mineral oil lubrication there is a cubic relation between bearing load and bearing life, and the results from accelerated tests are normally extrapolated by means of this relationship. By recognising that the power in the relationship may not be 3 for other fluids,

improved agreement is obtained between results obtained under different conditions. Figure 2 illustrates the concept. The ratio (C/P), where C is the dynamic capacity of the bearing and P is the bearing load, is used as the measure of degree of acceleration and is plotted on logarithmic scales against the 10% life of the bearing. Results obtained from different bearings and different rigs, at various degrees of acceleration, can thus be brought together. It can be seen that, because of the different slopes of the lines for different fluids, the relative performances of the fluids can change as the degree of acceleration of the test is varied. For example, invert emulsion can be seen to be similar to aqueous glycol at low (C/P), i.e. high acceleration, but superior at high (C/P) representative of service conditions.

21. From the different performances of fluids illustrated in Figures 1 and 2 it can be recognised that some fluids may give particularly poor results when used in machines containing several bearings. For example, aqueous glycol exhibits a large degree of scatter (low slope in Figure 1) and a low sensitivity to load reduction (low slope in Figure 2). There is therefore a relatively high probability of failing even the more lightly loaded bearings in the machine. The incidence of bearing failures in a multibearing system lubricated with a fluid such as aqueous glycol is consequently relatively high.

22. Erosion

The third mode of failure resulting from tribological effects is erosion of surfaces. The erosion of valves operating on fire-resistant emulsions has been documented (Ref. 7), but there has been little basic study of the problem. Erosion may be due to cavitation, high velocity fluid impingement or suspended particle impingement. Cavitation erosion is more readily produced in water-containing fluids than in mineral oil but examinations of eroded valves do not suggest a mechanism predominantly of cavitation.

Selection of pumps and motors

23. The selection of the type of pump and motor to be used in a system will be based on many design factors and the intended operational fluid will impose some further restrictions (Ref. 8).

24. Some 380 pumps and motors comprising about 50 types and produced by 40 different manufacturers have been tested in the laboratory. From this work it has been found that tribological problems are very dependent on fluid contamination levels and the following considerations are based on the assumption that adequate standards of filtration are applied.

25. Synthetic fluids such as phosphate esters will generally give good performance and equipment lives comparable with those attainable on mineral oils. It is nevertheless essential at the design stage to give attention to the selection of compatible seal materials and to ensure that the relatively high density and low viscosity-index do not have an adverse effect on the operation of the system.

26. Fluids which contain substantial quantities of water have a more marked effect on equipment lives as is suggested by the previously described laboratory tests.

27. The sliding wear situations existing in hydrostatic machines do not now present serious problems if sufficient consideration is given to their design and material selection. Early tests showed the need to eliminate certain materials from machines to be used with particular fluids, for example aluminium bronzes and silver from machines using invert emulsions. There are however still exceptions: most vane pumps suffer excessive wear to the stator rings when operating on water-containing fluids and cam pumps suffer wear to their brushes.

28. The effect of the fluid type on the lives of rolling bearings presents more fundamental problems which need to be recognised. In gear pumps where the equipment life is ultimately dependent on the life of the bearings supporting the gears, the load must be regulated to ensure that a satisfactory degree of reliability is obtained. This is achieved by combination of two basic means; either by limiting the maximum pressure at which the system is to work, or by restricting the width of each gear section, even at the complexity of having to use a multiple section pump to achieve the required capacity.

29. The gear pump is at present unsuitable for use with dilute emulsions because of the high internal leakage resulting from the low viscosity but work to overcome this disadvantage is currently being undertaken by some leading manufacturers.

30. Axial, radial and in-line piston pumps and motors combine a complex interdependence on different lubrication aspects, many incorporate hydrodynamic, hydrostatic, squeeze film and rolling element situations; erosion may cause further problems. By careful selection many machines have been shown capable of reliable operation and long-life on most fluids with the possible exception of dilute emulsions. Here the combination of lubrication, low viscosity and erosion problems present serious difficulties but several machine under development have given encouraging results.

31. Ram pumps incorporating elastomeric 'stuffing box' type seals perform satisfactorily with all fluids and are widely used with dilute emulsions. Seal life is however inversely proportional to operating pressure and may eventually prove a limitation as operational requirements become more demanding.

REVIEW OF PROGRESS TO THE PRESENT POSITION

Powered support systems

32. Although historically hand set hydraulic props had worked on mineral oil, it is interesting to note that the early power operated roof supports used dilute emulsions and that for a number of years parallel development took place on both mineral oil and emulsion systems.

33. In the early 1960's an awareness of the risks associated with systems containing large volumes of oil (Ref. 9,10) led to all further designs being based on the use of dilute emulsions. Several problems had to be tackled, the corrosion of materials, particularly ferrous; the stability of emulsions made up with available waters and the maintenance of the required oil content; the erosion of valve materials; the reliability of

reciprocating non-metallic seals and the high leakage rates resulting from the low emulsion viscosity. In spite of some remaining difficulties all of the 726 installations are working satisfactorily on this fluid.

34. Modern mining techniques involving high rates of advance on coal faces are leading to the need for pumps capable of higher output capacity than at present, operating against higher system pressures, and work on these is proceeding.

Hydrostatic transmissions

35. The facility for providing easily controllable variable speed drives occupying small volumes made hydrostatic transmissions attractive to the mining industry and such systems increased rapidly in number during the 1950's. Hence when the decision was taken in 1964 to introduce fire-resistant fluids, all of the available systems had been designed for use with mineral oils. Consideration of the information on the various fluids then available led to an agreement to endeavour to operate hydrostatic transmissions on invert emulsions.

36. Trials were therefore made with installations selected with regard to the number of men at risk from fire and its effects, and with regard to the envisaged technical problems. Early efforts were thus concentrated on the hydraulic drives associated with conveyor bunkers as these were usually situated in the intake airways. A further classification of equipment with a high degree of risk was that associated with the down-cast shaft (Ref. 11) and trials soon extended to such systems.

37. As a direct result of some operational problems emerging from these otherwise encouraging early trials it became necessary to redeploy some of the laboratory testing facilities to finding effective answers. This close involvement with service problems has continued up to the present time and has provided valuable correlation between the results of laboratory tests and operational experience. It has been proved that a period of service operation can be successfully simulated by a laboratory test under continuously applied full load in about one-fifth of the time.

38. The laboratory work has thus allowed detailed examination of pump and motor performance and life and of the influences of circuit design on system reliability. Tests on a large proportion of the hydrostatic machines available in Britain, including many from elsewhere in Western Europe and America, have established the following principles for the successful use of invert emulsions:

i) Of the range of inexpensive fixed capacity machines available, the gear pump has proved the most robust and reliable. Units that have been well designed and carefully manufactured have been found to operate successfully at speeds of 157 rad/s (1500 rev/min) against pressures up to 13.8 MPa (2000 lbf/in^2) and give good volumetric efficiencies. Regard must nevertheless be paid to limiting the loads on the rolling bearings supporting the gears by restricting the width of the gear sections in accordance with the system duty.

ii) Vane pumps and cam pumps have, up to the present, been unsuccessful. The lower film strengths and boundary lubrication properties of invert emulsions, compared to those of mineral oils, have led to excessive wear of the stator rings or brushes. Such pumps are not expected to operate reliably other than at speeds below 100 rad/s (960 rev/min) and pressures below 6.9 MPa (1000 lbf/in^2) and their use is generally discouraged.

iii) Variable delivery pumps, mainly of the axial piston and bent axis types, are now relatively successful. High standards of reliability have been achieved by manufacturers giving careful attention to the selection of materials, the design of valve plate/rotor interfaces and slipper pad thrust bearings, and the provision of rolling bearings of generous capacity. A number of pumps having capacities up to 8.3 dm^3/s (110 gal/min) have been found to work satisfactorily against continuous pressures of 13.8 MPa (2000 lbf/in^2) and some up to intermittent pressures of 17.2 MPa (2500 lbf/in^2).

iv) Motors of the gear and axial piston type have proved successful in the same operating conditions as their pump counterparts. Furthermore several types of radial piston motor have been developed to give high standards of reliability, again, by careful selection of materials, attention to the design of hydrostatic bearings and the provision of generous rolling bearing capacity. Radial piston motors utilising multi-lobe cams in conjunction with ball or roller piston followers have presented special difficulties because of the influence of the fluid on the fatigue life of the cam surface under the high hertzian stress conditions; only one motor of this type has given adequate reliability.

v) Valves which have been designed for use with mineral oil have been found to operate equally well with invert emulsion. Special care is however necessary in the selection of pressure relief valves that are required to discharge for long periods as the erosion life of seat and poppet components may be adversely affected.

vi) The provision and maintenance of high standards of filtration have been found vital for reliable operation. Wherever possible the use of elements having a 15 μm (nominal) rating is advised.

vii) Standards of good hydraulic system design relating to pump inlet pressures, pipe sizing, the design of reservoirs and the provision of means of heat dissipation must be closely observed.

39. By the adoption of the above principles to a wide range of mining machinery and systems considerable progress has now been made with the application of invert emulsions in the NCB as is shown by Figure 3.

40. It is interesting to note that many hydrostatic transmissions have been found to operate on invert emulsion with higher standards of reliability than hitherto on mineral oils largely because of the care taken to reappraise the design of the hydraulic system, the selection of the components used, and the standards of filtration.

Hydrokinetic transmissions

41. Traction type couplings having aluminium casings and operating on mineral oil were introduced to the coal face situation when belt conveyors were first replaced by the flexible chain conveyors in the early 1950's. The advantages of this type of drive using a squirrel-cage motor with direct-on-line starting were soon appreciated and the principle quickly spread to roadway conveyor drives where the electrical equipment associated with slip-ring motors was complicated, large and expensive. A further advantage of this type of drive for conveyors is that it permits multi-motor systems and this arrangement is widely used.

42. The introduction of high power trunk conveyors in the mid 1950's led to the application of the more complex scoop control coupling in the larger systems.

43. The traction couplings used are fitted with thermal discharge devices comprising a fusible plug made from a eutectic alloy with a melting point of 140°C. This temperature is about 36°C lower than that used in other industries. In spite of this precaution a number of fires occurred at couplings and extensive investigations showed that these originated from the auto-ignition of discharged fluid. These incidents led to two parallel courses of exploration to improve the safety of the coupling: one to reduce the temperature of the discharged aerosol spray, and the other to use fire-resistant fluids.

44. The temperature of the aerosol spray was reduced by 55°C to about 150°C by repositioning the fusible plug from the periphery of the coupling to a position nearer to the centre.

45. Attempts in the early 1960's to use invert emulsion in a traction coupling were unsuccessful largely because of the belief that the pressure within the coupling would need to be kept close to atmospheric. Pressure release devices caused the loss of water from the emulsion reducing its fire resistance. It therefore became necessary to examine the use of non-water containing fluids. One of the principal difficulties was to find a material of sufficiently low toxicological risk and the only fluid approved, even up to the present time, is a non-toxic phosphate ester which was already developed as a plasticiser. This fluid was found suitable for both traction and scoop-control couplings; it was first used in a significant number of installations during 1964 and has continued in widespread use up to the present time.

46. The advantages of water as a working fluid in traction couplings were obvious in terms of safety, convenience and economics. Development by the coupling manufacturers resulted in them advising the NCB in May 1965 that they were confident that water could be used in a suitably designed new fluid coupling or in existing couplings suitably modified. This was achieved by accepting the principle of containing the vapour pressure of the water at its operating temperature within the coupling. This pressurisation was facilitated by the fact that the NCB had earlier appreciated the risks of incendive sparking associated with the use of aluminium at the coal face and had introduced steel cased couplings.

47. Early trials proved the concept feasible and during 1968 arrangements were made to purchase new couplings in the 37-49 kW (50-65 hp) range suitable for running on water, and a conversion programme covering the oil-filled couplings of this size was instituted. This was followed by a similar decision and conversion programme

covering the 68-90 kW (90-120 hp) couplings. Figure 4 shows the progress made up to the present time. Consideration is currently being given to the use of water filled couplings of even higher power.

48. About 10 per cent of the total number of couplings in use are of the scoop control type. The complexity of these couplings has, up to the present, precluded the use of water as a working fluid and operation is entirely on non-toxic phosphate ester. Even with this fluid it has been thought prudent to fit thermostatic switches to scoop-control couplings that run unattended, thus limiting the fluid temperature to 150°C. This removes the possibility of severe overheating and the production of dense fumes.

CONCLUSION

49. For the past ten years the National Coal Board has followed a policy of replacing mineral hydraulic oil in underground equipment with fire resistant fluids. Continuous progress has been made up to the present time when comparatively few installations are still operating on mineral oil.

50. Success is attributed to:

    i)   the adoption of a feasible policy resulting from several years of preliminary investigation which included the determination of a standard of fire resistance subsequently proved to be satisfactory,

    ii)   constant attention to toxicological factors,

    iii)   a realistic assessment of economic factors,

    iv)   continuing extensive laboratory investigations of tribological and other operational effects, carried out in close association with service experience,

    v)   close liaison with manufacturers of fluids and hydraulic equipment,

    vi)   close liaison with H.M. Inspectorate of Mines and Safety in Mines Research Establishment.

51. Some problems remain under active investigation but these are specific and operational. No problems have arisen that would suggest that the basic decisions taken have been in error from a point of view of safety or feasibility.

ACKNOWLEDGEMENTS

    The authors wish to express their thanks to Mr. W. J. Currie, Director of Engineering and to Mr. D. J. Skidmore, Director of Research (Mining) for their permission to publish this paper.

    The views expressed are those of the authors and not necessarily those of the National Coal Board.

REFERENCES

1.   NCB Specification No. 570/1970 'Fire Resistant Fluids for Use in Machinery and Hydraulic Equipment' National Coal Board: London.

2.   NCB Specification No. 463/1970 'Emulsifying Oils for Dilute Emulsions in Powered Supports' National Coal Board: London.

3.   TURSKI, A.B.   Studies of Engineering Properties of Fire Resistant Hydraulic Fluids for Underground Use. Mining and Minerals Engineering, vol. 4, Nov. 1968, pp. 50 - 61, vol. 4, Dec. 1968, pp. 48 - 58, vol. 5, Feb. 1969, pp. 50 - 57.

4.   BIETKOWSKI, R.   Ball Bearing Lubricants. Use of Fire Resistant Hydraulic Fluids. Colliery Guardian, vol. 219, May 1971, pp. 235 - 239.

5.   KENNY, P. and YARDLEY, E.D.   The Use of Unisteel Rolling Fatigue Machines to Compare the Lubricating Properties of Fire-Resistant Fluids. Wear, vol.20, May 1972, pp. 105 - 121.

6.   YARDLEY, E.D. and KENNY, P.   To be published.

7.   KELLY, E.S.   Erosive Wear of Hydraulic Valves Operating with Fire-Resistant Emulsions, Proc. 2nd Fluid Power Symposium Jan. 1971, B.H.R.A.

8.   KNIGHT, G.C., JONES, S.F., KENNY, P. 'Hydraulic Fluid Fires and Fire Resistant Hydraulic Fluids'. Draft Paper for the Tribology Group of Institution of Mechanical Engineers to be published 1973/74.

9.   Report of H.M. Chief Inspector of Mines and Quarries for 1958. Her Majesty's Stationery Office, London, pp. 22 - 23.

10. Report of H.M. Chief Inspector of Mines and Quarries for 1959. Her Majesty's Stationery Office, London, page 19,

11. Report of H.M. Chief Inspector of Mines and Quarries for 1964. Her Majesty's Stationery Office, London, pp. 17 - 18, paras. 51 - 54.

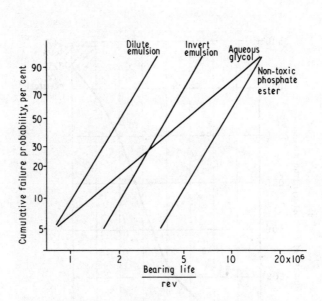

Fig.1

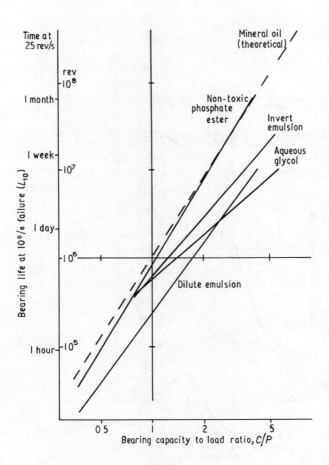

Fig.2

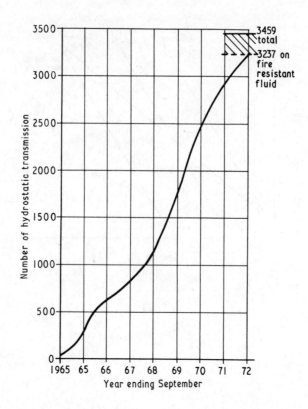

Fig.3

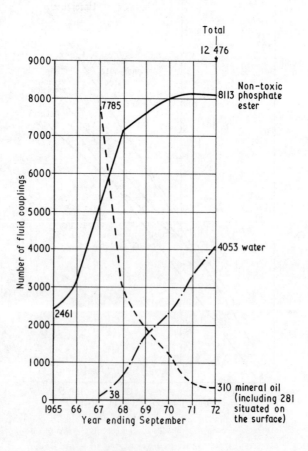

Fig.4

FIRE-RESISTANT HYDRAULIC FLUIDS IN THE FRENCH MINES

G. M. G. BLANPAIN, Ing Art & Métiers

Ingénieur de Recherches, Laboratoire de Cerchar à Verneuil-en-Halatte,
Boîte Postale 27 à CREIL 60 103

The Ms. of this paper was received at the Institution on 10th August 1973 and accepted for publication on 23rd October 1973. 3

SYNOPSIS

The development of hydraulic transmissions has resulted in an increased consumption of hydraulic fluids. In the French mines, mineral oil, which is still the best hydraulic fluid available, continues in wide use because there are no strict regulations forbidding it. As against this the users are in the process of gradually replacing this oil by fire-resistant fluids in all applications where the risk of ignition genuinely exists and is of major importance: e.g. the very design of hydrokinetic couplings constitutes a very real danger when they are used underground with oil. The fluids employed are not taken underground unless they have been approved on the basis of recommendations issued by the Mines Safety Commission. The selection applied differs from that current in the United Kingdom primarily in respect of the test for ignition in an atomized spray and in the toxicity test.

The majority of powered support installations operate with soluble-oil emulsions; some of them with polyglycol solutions. Machines subjected to light mechanical loadings have been operating satisfactorily for several years with polyglycols or viscous emulsions. In equipment subjected to heavy loadings, e.g. haulage winches, satisfactory results have been obtained using doped polyglycols. These fluids make it possible to achieve acceptable lengths of service life with bearings, and even with vane pumps. The anhydrous polychlorinated-diphenyl-based products also give satisfactory results in heavily-loaded equipment. They are however expensive and impose a certain number of restrictions. By reason of their simple design, hydraulic couplings have been converted for use with anhydrous fluids, thus eliminating the dangers associated with this type of device when operating with oil.

1. Over the last ten years, hydraulic transmission systems have come into considerably wider use in industry as a whole, and also in the coal mines. This development has brought with it a continuous rise in the consumption of hydraulic fluids. The fact that the range of application of hydraulic transmissions has widened has imposed improvement of the characteristics of the oils used both in respect of tribological properties and physico-chemical properties. The fire-resistant fluids were developed in parallel to these advances, and their application spread greatly as a result of a number of major accidents which arose in installations using oil.

2. In the French coal mines, there has been a gradual substitution of fire-resistant fluids for oil in all applications where the fire risk is considerable. One might in fact say that any hydraulic installation still operating on oil is, in general, subject to only a slight fire risk or none at all.

3. In what follows we shall examine the problems involved in the use of hydraulic transmissions underground, then the criteria for selecting and certifying fire-resistant fluids and finally we shall look at the fluids in use in our mines.

SAFETY PROBLEMS RESULTING FROM THE USE OF HYDRAULIC FLUIDS UNDERGROUND

4. The search for non-flammable or fire-resistant fluids is not of yesterday. It began with the first accidents consequent on the use of oil under pressure in the vicinity of flames or major heat sources.

5. One of the devices which attracted most attention in underground use is the hydraulic coupling. In fact, the very principle of the device results in it producing in the fluid a degree of heating which is higher and occurs at a more rapid rate, the greater the torque transmitted. Moreover, to avoid the motor being overloaded to a damaging extent, a safety device in the form of a fusible plug has been incorporated. When this plug melts, at around 140°C, the hot fluid, which may locally exhibit a temperature considerably higher than 140°C, is expelled with considerable velocity. The possibility of the oil becoming charged electrostatically as it passes through the fusible-plug orifice gives rise to a risk of auto-ignition. A coupling is quickly emptied, but the ignited oil can cause a fire, and the fire will be considerably more serious if the coupling is adjacent to a mass of coaldust, a hydraulic hose, or an electric cable. If firedamp is present, the risks are even greater.

6. The flexible hoses and connections so frequently used in hydraulic systems are very vulnerable. They are required where complex movements have to be incorporated in machines: articulated arms, turrets, etc. It would be technically feasible to make the links between two points which move with respect to another by using

rotary or telescopic joints, but these would be bulky, would involve "parasitic" friction and would be more complicated in design.

7. These flexible hoses are subject to variable flexing or twisting movements; even the strongest hoses are no longer fit for service after a few hundred thousand cycles of pressure and release; they deteriorate even more quickly if the hose has been punctured by a fall of rock, caught as it ran over an a.f.c. spillplate or pinched when a hydraulic cylinder came under pressure. Rupture of the hose causes the oil to be expelled in an atomized jet, which can be ignited if it comes into contact with a flame or a hot surface.

8. Flexible hoses are not the only elements which give rise to atomized jets; a split in a pipe, the breakage of an 0-ring or a leak at a joint can each be a source of danger if not isolated by a strong housing.

9. This makes it possible to classify machines in increasing order of risk.

10. First we have the machines with their hydraulic components entirely isolated by strong hermetically-tight housings, with no external hoses: here the risk of ignition and of a resultant fire is virtually nil.

11. Similarly, reduction gearboxes in which the oil is enclosed in a stout, tight receptacle cause no risk, and can be operated on oil. The only factor governing the choice of fluid in this instance is its capacity to provide proper lubrication of the bearings and gears.

12. Next come the units which comprise hoses or connectors situated outside the housing: here the use of fire resistant fluids is highly advisable and is becoming general practice.

13. Finally, hydrokinetic couplings, which are virtually all used with fire resistant fluids.

14. The substitution of fire resistant fluids for oil poses one major problem which, while different in nature, is linked to the ignition problem: namely, the toxicity of the fluid. Handling hydraulic fluids - including the different kinds of oil - must be possible without any danger, particularly in the event of contact with the skin or the eyes. Moreover, at high temperatures (200°C for couplings, 700°C for atomized jets of fluid expelled by red-hot brakes), the resultant aerosols must not exhibit acute toxicity. The fact that mine workings are confined further imposes the requirement that aerosols of hydraulic fluids should not present any chronic toxicity.

CRITERIA FOR SELECTING FIRE RESISTANT FLUIDS

15. In many countries, and for a number of years, the national authorities have made the replacement of oil by fire resistant fluids compulsory. The difficulties encountered in the process have prevented the deadlines imposed from being met; exemptions have been granted to make it possible to continue coal-winning while making a local and temporary use of oil as the hydraulic fluid.

16. Nevertheless, the technical departments of the French coal industry use fire-resistant fluids in every case where the technical advances already achieved allow of it.

17. The fire resistant fluids in use in France are subjected to certification tests on several points:

- ignition
- toxicity
- technical factors.

18. The documents laying down the certification rules are Standards NF-M 82654 and M 82655. The rules embodied in the Fourth Report of the Mines Safety Commission at Luxembourg are observed as closely as possible. The French regulations sometimes differ in detail from these rules.

Ignition tests

Test on an atomized jet

19. The most highly selective test is the ignition test on an atomized jet (ECSC type). This test was laid down after the mine catastrophe at Marcinelle in Belgium on 8th August 1956. The test seeks to reproduce the conditions which occurred in that accident.

20. The fluid is atomized at 65°C under a pressure of 70 bars by being expelled from a jet nozzle with an 0.4 mm orifice. The jet of atomized fluid forms a cone with a small apex angle - approximately 7°. The length-to-diameter ratio of the jet nozzle is 4:1. In this way the conditions of the test represent those occurring when a hose has been punctured. The fineness of the droplets varies with the fluid used; the freer-flowing the fluid, the smaller the droplets. The contact surface with the air also varies with the viscosity; the lower the viscosity, the larger the contact area. In addition, it is most exceptional that an atomized jet caused by a puncture in a hose has an unimpeded path of more than 3 to 5 metres before meeting some obstacle; such obstacles generally lie only 0.5 to 2 metres away. In the ECSC test, a screen is placed 1.75 m from the jet nozzle to represent the obstacle. This screen, on which the droplets impinge with a velocity in excess of 70 m/sec, acts as a reflector; the impact of the reflected droplets on the incident droplets reduces their diameter. The finest droplets are observed at about 1.20 m from the jet nozzle.

21. The flame of an oxy-acetylene torch - set to a flow of 13 litres/minute of oxygen and 15 litres/minute of acetylene - is applied at right angles to the axis of the jet near the nozzle, and is displaced at a velocity of 4 cm/second. The torch is then maintained for five seconds at a distance of 1.20 metres from the nozzle. Under these conditions, the jet must not ignite after its passage through the flame, and no flame must reach the screen.

22. This test is met satisfactorily by products of Type A (oil-in-water emulsions), Type C (solutions of polyglycols) and Type D (anhydrous chlorinated substances). As against this, the invert emulsions (water-in-oil emulsions), anhydrous products Type D of the esterphosphate group and, of course, mixtures of these latter with oil fail to pass this test.

23.   The essential differences between this test and that applied in the United Kingdom lie in the design of the jet nozzle and in the criteria used in selecting the fluid. In addition, the British test does not use a screen. The jet nozzle described in the NCB Specification is an atomizing jet used for fuel oil; the apex angle is large, about 30°, and the size analysis of the aerosols formed is virtually independent of the viscosity. The criteria used for selecting "fire-resistant" fluids allow the jet to be ignited by the torch flame but require that the flame be extinguished within 30 seconds of withdrawal of the torch. It is not my business to give criticism of two such widely-differing conceptions of the ignition test. Each has its defenders; both were laid down with the same desire to achieve safety. Moreover, work is to be begun under the aegis of the EEC, together with our British colleagues, in order to harmonize our methods.

24.   It is noticeable that for several years past there has been no instance of a fire in which fire-resistant fluids have been involved, either in the United Kingdom or in the French mines. As against this, a number of fires have occurred in French industrial installations, involving fluids selected by the less stringent tests on atomized jets (in particular, esterphosphate fluids).

Flame propagation test

25.   Our ignition tests also include the test of propagation of the flame in a mixture of coal and fluid. This test checks that the mixture of coal and fluid does not support propagation of a fire already burning elsewhere. This coal/oil mixture reproduces what happens in the vicinity of poorly-sealed reservoirs of fluid; the leaks result in the formation of a pasty mixture which, if it contains oil, can propagate combustion.

Toxicity tests

26.   The products which have satisfactorily passed the ignition tests described above are then subjected to the toxicity test.

27.   The fluid is first given an "identity check", by means of infra-red spectrophotometry. The spectra so obtained are not analysed but serve as an identity reference for the relevant product.

28.   In respect of oral toxicity, the test used determines the dose which causes the death of 50% of a sample of male white mice. The fluid is administered by buccal injection; the observation period is 14 days. A first approximation of the lethal dose is obtained on the basis of a restricted number of animals. The test is then recommenced on several groups of mice, which are given 0.4; 0.6; 0.8; 1.2 times the approximate dose so established. For each dose, the percentage fatality rate is plotted on a logarithmic probability scale as a function of the dose expressed in grams of fluid per kilogram of animal weight. The dose producing the death of 50% of the animal sample is read off from the graph.

29.   Several different tests are used to determine the toxic capacity of the fluids. Aqueous products are subjected to a total toxicity test: goldfish are placed in a receptacle filled with water containing between 10^{-1} and 10^{-5} parts of

hydraulic fluid to one part of water. This test has a total duration of 120 hours.

30.   The irritant index is determined for all these types of products, in respect both of the eyes and the skin, albino rabbits being used as test animals. A drop of fluid is placed in the conjunctival sac of the rabbit's right eye, and the state of the eye is observed in comparison with that of the left eye. The observation period is five days. The skin irritant effect is determined by observing the cutaneous irritation on the shaved sides of the same animals. A sticking-plaster soaked in the fluid is kept in contact with the skin for twenty four hours; the observation period is fourteen days.

31.   Hot or cold tests on aerosols are carried out on Wistar rats; ambient temperature for oil-in-water emulsions, 70°C for polyglycols, 50°C and 150°C for the anhydrous fluids. The aerosols are produced cold or hot according to the type of fluid, and then cooled down before being introduced into the cages, where the rats are exposed for three hours. The animals are observed for a period of fourteen days.

32.   The thermal decomposition test is also carried out using Wistar rats. The thermal decomposition of the test fluid is effected at 200°C and at 700°C in a closed metal receptacle. The vapour formed is mixed with air and then, after cooling, introduced into the cages, where the rats are exposed for one hour. The observation period is fourteen days.

33.   The results obtained for a particular fluid are indexed from 1 to 10 on the basis of an indexing grid. Each product is assigned an index of from 1 to 170, by addition of the indices from each of the separate tests described, these indices being factorized by various coefficients, according to the test in question. Any product which has an index of 10 before the weighting in any single test, or reaching an overall index of 50 after weighting, is rejected.

Technical criteria other than tribological

34.   Only when it satisfies both the ignition test and the toxicity test is a product subjected to the numerous technical tests. We shall not describe here the entire series of tests, which are mostly conventional. However, we shall examine certain tests in some detail.

Density and viscosity

35.   Several physico-chemical characteristics make it possible to identify and compare different samples. This is true of the density, the viscosity, and the ash content. The density and viscosity values at 0°C, 20°C, 50°C and 100°C are important factors involved in the conditions governing suction in pumps. The requirement is that at low temperature the pumps should be able to suck in the fluid from the tanks; this is the case of a pump situated near the downcast shaft in winter conditions. At normal running temperature the viscosity must be sufficient to maintain a volumetric efficiency appropriate to the equipment. One problem arose with the anhydrous fluids: in view of their very low viscosity-index - often negative - their use is restricted to workings with a relatively high and constant

temperature, situated some distance away from the downcast shaft.

36.   The flow temperature or thaw point is used to calculate the minimum temperature of use.

Water content

37.   The water content of the fluid is determined in the laboratory:

by the Karl Fischer method for anhydrous fluids,
by the solvent entrainment technique for aqueous fluids.

Benzene is used as the entrainment solvent for the polyglycol solutions.   When the water content of the polyglycol-based fluids in use diminishes, the fluid may become inflammable at the same time as its viscosity increases.   It is therefore necessary to check the water content periodically, so as to adjust it, if necessary, by adding water.

Corrosion

38.   The acid index or the pH value makes it possible to obtain information rapidly as to the corrosive action of the fluids on metallic surfaces. In addition, a corrosion test is performed - 28 days at 35°C - on different metals: steel, aluminium, copper, brass, zinc, cadmium, copper/ zinc, aluminium/zinc, so as to check that these metals are not attacked or that the fluids do not form deposits which could interfere with the proper operation of the equipment.   These tests are supplemented by tests of corrosion in the vapour phase;   we check that, once the equipment has been emptied, the fluid gives adequate protec- tion of the metals against corrosion by the moist vapours (see Figure 1).

Ageing

39.   The ageing tests check that no acid is formed in the presence of oxygen and metallic catalysts.

Shear

40.   The products must not deteriorate when passing through slots or nozzles in the distributors and valves: nor must the additives be destroyed or the constituents become polymerized.   The test with the KURT ORBAHN type of injector simulates this process of deterioration, which is character- istic of the fluids for hydraulic transmissions. An injection pump forces the liquid through a Diesel injector;   normally, we used to work on 50 through-passes at a pressure of 100 bars, but currently the figures are 250 through-passes at 175 bars.   After being subjected to this shear test, the fluid may not exhibit a variation in viscosity in excess of 10-20% according to temperature, nor any major variation in the acid index or pH value, nor any reduction in water content exceeding 8% for fluids of type A or 15% for oil-in-water emulsions.

Foaming

41.   The foaming test serves to check that the accidental introduction of air does not lead to abundant foam formation, and in any case not more than 200 ml in the test conditions.   The tests are performed at 20°C/95°C/20°C for the anhydrous fluids, 20°C/50°C/20°C for the aqueous fluids.

A complementary characteristic of the preceding one is the requirement that a fluid which has become aerated should de-aerate rapidly, otherwise:

- the compressibility of the hydraulic fluid increases, and this can cause increased yield of hydraulic props, as well as making the response time of hydraulic controls much longer;

- The air may reappear during the pump suction stroke, thus encouraging cavitation in the pump or the destruction of the lubricating layers between the surfaces in frictional contact.   The de-aerating time - defined as being the time at the end of which the previously-aerated fluid contains no more than 0.2% by volume of air - is determined by means of an apparatus described on the relevant DIN standard and in the Fourth Report of the Mines Safety Commission. This apparatus provides a means of obtaining a point-localised knowledge of the apparent density of the fluid during de-aeration.   We have supplemented this device with an auto- matic balance which plots the curve of apparent density as a function of time; from this curve it is easy to calculate the de-aeration period (see Figure 2).   In general, the de-aeration times of fire- resistant fluids are from three to four times as long as those of the conventional oils.

Storage life

42.   For oil-in-water emulsions, the storage behaviour must be checked;   no break-up of the emulsion may occur at rest at 25°C and 50°C after 600 hours in store.

Effect on seal strength

43.   Finally, it is necessary to check that the elastomers used in the seals in the hydraulic equipment do not undergo excessive variations in volume (+ 4% or - 2%) or in Shore hardness ($\pm$ 4) at 150°C for the anhydrous fluids, or at 60°C for the aqueous fluids.   The period of immersion is 21 days.   It would be possible to establish the behaviour of all the elastomers in existence, but in practice we restrict ourselves to three given grades of elastomers, which are the most widely used in hydraulic systems.

Tribological properties of fire-resistant fluids

44.   Fire-resistant fluids have been subjected to a large number of tests because:

- the hydraulic fluid has a very important part to play as the lubricant in the equipment

- the aqueous products are very widely used.

45.   Hydraulic equipment consists of a complex assemblage of bearings, gears, slide rods, ball- and-socket joints, moving at relative speeds which can sometimes be very high and which impose considerable loadings.   In practice, we encounter the entire range of lubrication conditions from the state of hydrodynamic lubrication to the various limit states - "boundary" lubrication or extreme pressure lubrication.   In the case of the

aqueous fire resistant fluids, the problem is different and is further complicated by the very fact that water is present.

46. The tribological properties cannot be assessed by means of a single test device; in principle, the only satisfactory test is that made on the actual equipment in conditions approximating to those of actual service.

47. However, it is possible to make a partial determination in advance of the behaviour of an aqueous fire resistant fluid by subjecting it to several tests in different lubrication test devices.

Stick-slip test; affinity for metal surfaces

48. One of the first prerequisites for a lubricant is that it should exhibit a satisfactory affinity for metal surfaces. The interface tension between liquid and metal is a good index of this affinity: it can be determined by measuring the angle of contact, which is frequently a somewhat delicate operation. One indirect means of assessing this affinity is the "stick-slip test" (see Figure 3). This is a device for selecting oils for slide-rods. Two blocks of metal moving at comparatively low relative speeds are applied to each other under a known load; the lubricant is applied between the two surfaces in frictional contact. The lower block is displaced, and the friction caused by rubbing against the upper block causes the latter to undergo movement counter to a calibrated spring. The kinetic friction value is measured during the movement, and the static friction value with the machine at rest. The ratio between the coefficients of static and dynamic friction is about 1 or less than 1 for greasy fluids, which thus have a high affinity for metal surfaces: the sliding movement is smooth, without jerks. The ratio between the two coefficients is very much greater than 1 for those fluids which exhibit no affinity for metal surfaces; here the movement is jerky.

49. Polyglycol-based fluids originally had a very poor affinity for steels. Many failures quickly occurred, resulting in this type of fluid being abandoned more or less completely. These products have been improved in this respect by means of additives and in France these fluids, when "doped", have a good affinity, with beneficial results on the length of life of equipment.

Wear tests; four-ball machine

50. A wear test is carried out using the conventional four-ball machine. This is a long-duration test, namely, 1 hour at a low loading - 40 daN. The indentation diameters for hydraulic transmission oils are small - 0.4 to 0.8 mm, as is also the case for the anhydrous fire-resistant fluids - 0.6 to 1 mm. The polyglycol solutions give indentation diameters up to 1.6 mm. As against this, doped fluids give indentations less than 1 mm in diameter.

51. The very-high-pressure characteristics of the fluids are assessed by means of the same four-ball machine. Two features are taken into account: the "seizure" loading and the corrected average loading. No comparison can be made between the results obtained with fire resistant fluids and with oil; the thermal characteristics and the

nature of the fluids differ too much. On the other hand, comparison of several fluids of the same type yields an accurate classification.

Tests with bearings

52. Special comment must be made in respect of the functioning of ball bearings where Hertzian contact occurs under load. Here the phenomenon which occurs is not true wear, but a sort of spalling. This happens as a result of progressive fissuring under the repeated and cumulative action of high Hertzian stresses which arise at depths of the order of one-tenth of a millimetre; any intergranular inclusions or impurities present in the metal constitute so many points of reduced strength, from which a sub-surface crack may become initiated (see Figure 4). After a number of repeated runs, the cracks emerge at the surface (see Figure 5), and spalling occurs, with rapid and destructive effect.

53. Bearing tests have been carried out. We first tested a needle-roller bearing, the inner annulus of which had been irradiated. The measured contamination of the oil circulating through the bearing enabled us to plot the curve of metal removal as a function of time. This made it possible to check that the amount of steel removed is almost nil, until the first signs of spalling appear; from this moment onwards, the rate of metal removal increases rapidly and we immediately observe serious damage to the bearing. A modification to the four-ball machine (making the three lower balls mobile) gave us a simple bearing test device, which yielded some interesting information. In particular, the doped polyglycol-based fluids give an increase in the service life of bearings approaching that obtainable with oil. Actual tests on a pump with needle bearings confirmed these encouraging results.

Wear test; Vickers pump

54. Another wear test specific to hydraulic fluids is the Vickers pump test. The wear on the vanes and rotor, components of this pump particularly prone to wear, makes it possible to classify and compare fire-resistant fluids. Unfortunately, difficulties in obtaining replacement cartridges for these pumps have led to the test being relatively little used in France, so that the results available are fragmentary.

Bench tests

55. We should here recall that these tests do not suffice by themselves as a basis for selecting a fire resistant fluid for underground use. Bench tests of the equipment must also be made in conditions as close as possible to those of actual service. On such test benches, the pressure or torque values in the pumps or motors can be varied with time to a predetermined programme. For example, we can simulate the normal running pressures or peak pressures arising when armoured conveyors or ploughs are started up. During these tests, we observe the increase in play, the surface states and the weight of the components subject to wear, as well as the degradation of the test fluid.

Tests after certification of fire resistant fluids

56. Products which have satisfied all these specified requirements are "approved for trial". From now on, they can be used underground. Naturally, the choice is governed by factors of price and delivery time. Those fluids "approved for trial" which do not attract any criticism from the users over a period of service of more than six months are then "approved". This approval can be withdrawn if the fluid behaves abnormally.

57. When fire resistant fluids are delivered for use, it is advisable to submit them to reception tests, which comprise checks on certain important properties: ignition, viscosity, corrosion. It has happened that products have been refused after these reception tests as a consequence of a change in the composition on the proportion of the basic components. The approval is withdrawn in such cases. The composition of the fluid has to be re-examined by the manufacturer, who then has to submit a "corrected" fluid for approval procedure.

FIRE RESISTANT FLUIDS IN USE IN FRANCE

58. The fluids approved in the French mines are:

- the oil-in-water emulsions (THI-A).

  Also grouped here are the viscous fluids which can exhibit values up to 30 cSt at 50°C, these being mixed emulsion/solution products.

- the polyglycol solutions in water (THI-C).

- the anhydrous chlorinated hydrocarbon type of fluid (THI-D).

59. The invert emulsions (THI-B) and the anhydrous esterphosphate fluids are eliminated by the jet spray ignition test. Only one fluid of type B approximately satisfies this test.

60. The substances approved up to the time of writing fall into the following groups:

> 8 Type A fluids
>
> 16 Type C fluids
>
> 18 Type D fluids

In all there are 42 approved fire resistant fluids.

61. The consumption of hydraulic fluids in the French coal-mines as a whole, underground or at the surface, is as follows:

> 25% pure products for THI 1A* type emulsion (28 000 metric tons of emulsified products).
>
> 10% ready-to-use product of THI 2A and THI 4A types
>
> 45% THI C type
>
> 4% THI D type
>
> 15% of hydraulic transmission oil

These consumption figures represent about one-quarter of the total consumption of lubricants of all kinds, including greases.

---

* THI x A = THI A of Engler viscosity equal to x.

THI 1A type oil-in-water emulsion

62. These fluids are used in individual hydraulic props or powered supports (see Figure 6). The rams which advance the face conveyor or the drivehead also operate on these fluids. The low viscosity of the emulsions gave rise to considerable leakage in slide-valves. This design had therefore to be replaced by gland-type units less liable to leaks.

63. In support installations, pumps of the type with in-line pistons (Ferromatik, PMH Westfalia) have given no trouble; they operate at 200 bars pressure. As a general rule, vane pumps, gear pumps and axial or radial piston pumps should not be used with fluids of THI 1A type. However, satisfactory results have been obtained after modifying some pumps.

64. The products are taken underground in the form of emulsifiable oil, mixing being generally carried out underground using automatic feed-controllers. Such devices do not always yield good-quality or correctly-proportioned emulsions. Design modifications have been studied, and have solved the problems encountered.

65. A large number of tub-pusher installations are operating satisfactorily on emulsions in the Nord and Pas-de-Calais Coalfield. These units are virtually all made by a single French manufacturer. The equipment has been in satisfactory service for a number of years, so that now only 4 tub-pusher installations out of a total of 416 still operate on oil.

66. The Nord and Pas-de-Calais also use more than 30 drill jumbos which are functioning satisfactorily on emulsions of Type A.

67. The use of THI 1A fluids presents few problems provided that the emulsions are properly prepared using water of suitable hardness. Some problems associated with the presence of bacteria were encountered: a break-up of the emulsion and corrosion of the storage tanks. Cleaning and total disinfecting had to be carried out to eliminate this troublesome pollution.

THI 2A and 4A type emulsions

68. These emulsions have been tried out predominantly in the Provence Coalfield. Being viscous substances, they have adequate lubricating power for all normal applications.

69. These substances are used in support units still fitted with slide valves.

70. Unfortunately, it will probably be necessary to abandon the use of these fluids as a result of a considerable rise in price. The price was, a little while ago, below that of the polyglycol solutions (0.84 FFr per litre), but has now risen markedly (1.95 FFr per litre).

THI C polyglycol solutions

71. These types of product are relatively widely used in the countries which adhere to the recommendations of the Mines Safety Commission. In France, competition has brought the price to a comparatively low level, ranging from 1.20 FFr to 3 FFr per litre (price of oil - 1.40 FFR per litre).

72. These fluids are used in the same applications as the fluids of THI 1A type. They are generally preferred for support installations with slide-valves. Tub-pusher units also operate on these fluids, especially in the Nord and Pas-de-Calais and the Cévennes Coalfields. In this instance, gear pumps with plain bearings have been in use for a number of months, without any problems arising.

73. A number of trials have been made on hydro-static power installations, use being made in this instance of doped fluids. At the present moment, efforts are being made to replace oil by one such fluid in a suspended loco unit comprising eight slow-speed hydraulic motors and one axial-piston pump. Bench tests are planned before the actual underground application begins.

74. Precautions are necessary when using THI C fluids. Any oil which has been previously used for testing the equipment must be carefully removed. During starting-up, the load must be increased very gradually, with rest periods to allow the fluid to de-aerate. Air vents are not always provided by the equipment manufacturers or else they are located in inaccessible places, or do not allow the air to discharge to atmosphere. The user must watch this important point carefully, to ensure proper utilisation of the hydraulic fluid.

75. The THI C fluids offer the advantage of having a good viscosity index, which makes them preferred by some users. Moreover, the materials of which the seals are made, the hoses and the paints used with oil can all be re-used.

76. The storage tanks and filters must all be much larger than those for oil. Generally, the designers multiply the filtration area by a factor ranging from 2 to 3.

THI D anhydrous fluids

77. These anhydrous fluids replace oil in hydraulic couplings because of their low vapour pressure. It has been found necessary to replace the conventional seal material by fluorinated elastomers. In addition, owing to the high density of these fluids, the filling is less compared with that necessary with oil. Currently, of 4000 couplings in service, only 8 are still working with oil, but these are couplings mounted on obsolescent installations or on loco-motive units.

78. These fluids are being used successfully in monorail installations in the Lorraine and Cévennes Coalfields. In the Cévennes, slow-speed motors (see Figure 7) used to drive a.f.c.'s and ploughs are filled with THI D fluid. These installations range up to an installed rating of 132 kW. The pumps used are of the axial piston type and have a throughput of 412 litres/minute, at a pressure of 185 bars.

79. The THI D fluids require a check to be made of the suction head of the pump, and generally the power pack units have to be designed in terms of these fluids.

80. The D category fluids are not compatible with the conventional seals used with mineral oils; use should be made of Viton synthetic rubbers for the joints or for the sections of hose with which

the fluids come into contact. The compatibility of these fluids with the internal paint cover in the storage tanks must be studied beforehand. Since these fluids generally give good anti-corrosion protection to metal surfaces either out of the fluid or immersed, internal painting of the tanks can be dispensed with.

INSTANCES WHERE FIRE-RESISTANT FLUIDS ARE NOT YET EMPLOYED

81. A certain number of installations are still functioning on oil. Excluding powered support installations, conveyor rams and drivehead-shifting cylinders, less than 10% of the equipment still operates on oil.

82. Among the hydraulic equipment still not converted to fire resistant fluids, we have:

   monorail winches - 20% using THI

   monorail locomotives - 50%

   cutter-haulage winches

   tunnelling machines and continuous miners

   loaders

   shuttle-cars

   tyre-mounted roof-bolters

   scout-cars

   drilling jumbos - 82% already using THI

   torque converters

   arch-straighteners

   ripping machines

These machines generally have robust housings which contain the pumps, motors and valves.

83. A few machines which have vulnerable hoses outside the housings and still operate on oil continue in service. This is the case with suspended locomotives and certain winning machines. Trials are under way with a view to replacing oil by a fire-resistant fluid in these two categories of equipment shortly.

----

84. The replacement of oil by fire-resistant fluids is progressing gradually and somewhat slowly in the French coal-mines. There has been a certain degree of hesitation in the face of premature trials in which oil was replaced by fire resistant fluids without precautions - sometimes even the elementary ones - being taken. In such cases, the equipment deteriorated rapidly. This entire operation of eliminating oil from underground working must be carried out methodic-ally. The installation requiring conversion must be carefully examined; the requisite modifications need to be determined, so that the equipment can function normally on fire resistant fluids. Special attention must be given to the pump suction conditions, the filter performance, the replacement of seals and paints, the operating conditions for the bearings and the Hertzian contacts, and the nature of the materials used. In addition, the various section of the circuits must be very carefully cleaned. When the installation is being started up, loads must be applied gradually and precautions must be taken in respect of air

vents and the de-aeration of the fluid.

85. The ultimate aim is that all mining equipment
which presents a danger if operated on oil should
be specially designed to be able to use a
specific fire resistant fluid. This would make
it possible to allow for all the requirements
and constraints which are consequent upon the use
of these products. Another way would be to make
the equipment safe, even if used with oil, by
placing all the hydraulic circuits inside robust
housings.

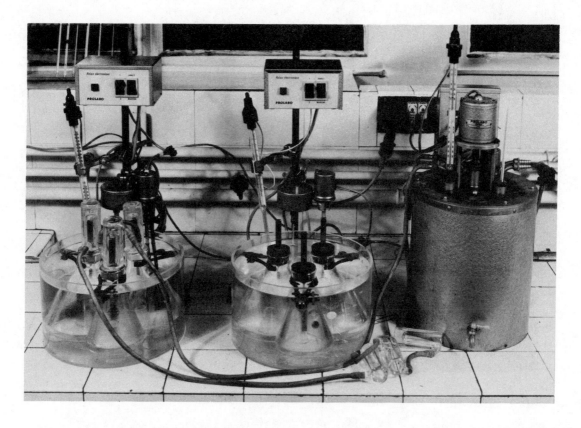

Figure 1 – Appareillage d'essai de corrosion en phase vapeur   Photo Cerehar

Figure 2 – Appareillage de détermination du temps de désaération   Photo Cerchar

Figure 3 - Machine "Stick Slip Test"

Photo Cerchar

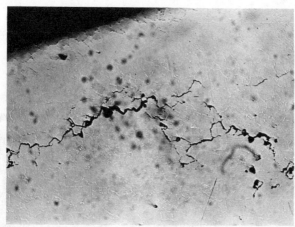

Figure 4 - Propagation d'une fissuration en sous couche sur un axe de roulement à aiguilles

Photo Cerchar

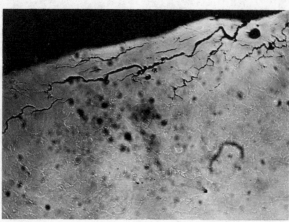

Figure 5 - Fissuration débouchant à la surface d'un axe de roulement à aiguilles

Photo Cerchar

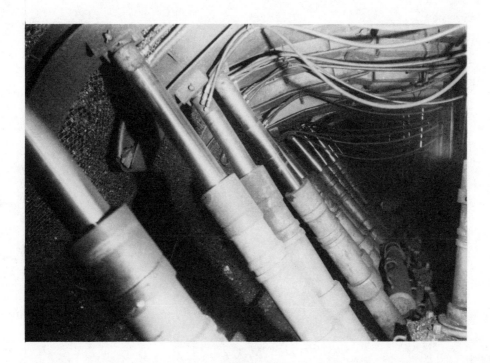

Figure 6 - Soutènement marchant utilisé avec une émulsion huile dans l'eau
dans une taille à soutirage

Figure 7 - Tête motrice de convoyeur blindé utilisant du fluide THI D

C34/74

THE ADAPTATION AND DEVELOPMENT OF HYDRAULIC POWER EQUIPMENT TO OPERATE WITH 5/95 TYPE NON-FLAMMABLE FLUIDS

R. J. IFIELD, FRAeS, FIEAust

Director of Engineering, Ifield Laboratories Pty. Limited,
45 Carters Road, Dural, New South Wales, Australia

The Ms. of this paper was received at the Institution on 25th July 1973 and accepted for publication on 23rd October 1973. 23

SYNOPSIS   Water has many theoretical advantages as a high pressure hydraulic power transmission fluid and 3% to 5% synthetic fluid additives are available to provide satisfactory lubrication properties. The advantages of this 5/95 fluid have been realised in special pump and motor designs, and existing equipment can in most cases be modified to provide a satisfactory performance on this fluid.

INTRODUCTION

1. The author has been concerned for over thirty years with the design and development of high pressure hydraulic systems operating on very low viscosity fluids.   There are important technical advantages in employing low viscosity fluids as the hydraulic medium; over the past ten years the Company with whom the writer is associated has concentrated considerable independent effort on the design and development of quiet high efficiency pumps and motors operating at high pressures on these fluids.   In more recent years these independent developments have been concentrated on the use of water as the hydraulic medium, because of the additional technical advantages of this fluid, which are discussed in the paper.

2. Some of the problems which have been dealt with during the course of these successful independent developments, such as establishing the design requirements for quiet very high efficiency operation of pumps and motors, are beyond the scope of this paper, but the developments relating to operation on water as the hydraulic medium are relevant and some of these will be discussed in the paper.

3. It has long been recognised that the use of mineral oils in hydraulic power equipment represents a fire hazard and that oil fires are particularly hazardous in the coal mines.   In 1967 the N.S.W. Ministry of Mines engaged the services of the Company with whom the author is associated, to examine and report on the feasibility of converting the hydraulic equipment used in the N.S.W. coal mines for operation on non-flammable fluids. This led to a series of annual development contracts to prove the practicability of converting different items of hydraulic power equipment to operate on 5/95 non-flammable fluids.

4. The paper opens with a discussion on the advantages and the problems associated with the use of water as the hydraulic medium; it then deals with the development guidelines and the problems encountered and solved under the development contracts.   It discusses the problems expected to arise in converting other equipment employed in the mines and the expected solution to these problems based on experience gained in independent development work.

TECHNICAL CONSIDERATIONS

5. If water is used as the hydraulic fluid, it is necessary to include an additive to inhibit corrosion and provide lubrication, and the additive must not cause foaming or render the fluid toxic. Synthetic fluids are available to meet these requirements as 3% to 5% additives to water.   These 5/95 fluids are completely stable, they comfortably meet the non-flammability requirements for use in the mines, their cost is low, they reduce pollution from spillage, and important technical advantages have been proved in the independent developments.

6. A large part of the efficiency losses in hydrostatic transmission systems is due to the fluid viscosity, which affects the pressure losses in pipes and portings and the viscous shear losses at bearing surfaces.   These losses limit the permissible speed rating and hence the power rating for acceptable efficiencies at pumps and motors. Because of this there can be considerable advantages in developing hydraulic equipment to operate on low viscosity fluids such as water.

7. A significant part of the total efficiency losses at high pressure pumps and motors is due to the compressibility of the fluid.   For example, the combined compressibility losses of a typical axial in-line variable pump and fixed displacement motor, operating on mineral oil at a pressure of 300 bars, are about 12.8%, 19.3% and 32.5%, with the pump operating at maximum, half and quarter maximum displacements respectively.   These losses can be greatly reduced by reducing the unswept volume in the pumping cylinders, but a change to water as the pumping fluid reduces these losses by about 25%, because of the reduced compressibility of water.

8. Other things being equal, the reduced viscous shear losses and the reduced compressibility losses reduce the heat input to the fluid.   This, in combination with the higher specific heat value and the higher thermal conductivity of water, results in lower and more uniform temperatures throughout the system and in reduced thermal deformation at important sealing faces.   This compensates for the reduced viscosity in minimising leakages.

9. The use of water as the pumping medium introduces problems to be overcome.   In the independent development of pumps and motors to operate on 95% water fluids, these problems were known

and were dealt with in the designs. The main problems are as follows:-

(a) Greater attention is required to seal against leakages, but, given effective seals, the overall efficiencies benefit from the reduced compressibility losses and reduced viscous shear losses.

(b) The viscosity of mineral oils increases very rapidly with increasing pressure and it appears that heavily loaded ball and roller bearings depend on this characteristic for a satisfactory service life. Certainly the life of these bearings is not satisfactory with water based fluids, and heavily loaded ball and roller bearings must be isolated from the water and separately lubricated.

(c) In many cases it is not practical to isolate ball and roller bearings from the water and it is necessary to replace them with hydro-statically balanced plain bearings, but tests have shown that a well-designed hydro-statically balanced plain bearing is more efficient than a ball or roller bearing operating under similar conditions.

(d) The liability to erosion at sealing faces appears to increase as the fluid viscosity is reduced, so that greater care in design and in the choice of materials is required to resist erosion with water as the hydraulic fluid.

(e) Elastomers appear to be satisfactory as static seals in the 95% water fluids, but the elastomer materials wear rapidly in these fluids under sliding conditions, particularly where they are used as shaft seals. It is therefore necessary to avoid sliding contact with elastomer seals. This is not a major problem; the normal 'O' ring seals employed may have PTFE tyres sliding in the cylinders; shaft seals may be in the form of face type seals with an atmospheric drain between the water in the pump or motor housing and the oil in the driving gear box.

10. Means for hydro-statically balancing thrust loadings are well known and are applied, for example, at the port faces and piston slippers of piston pumps. A successfully developed technique for hydro-statically balancing journal loadings will be discussed later in the paper.

11. There is a problem of wear at annular concentric face seals which operate under boundary lubrication conditions. This problem exists when using mineral oils, for example, at the annular concentric sealing lands at the port faces of piston pumps and at the end sealing faces of gear pumps, inside the root diameters of the gear teeth. The liability to failure due to wear at these sealing faces is increased with low viscosity fluids. Whatever fluid is used, this wear can be greatly reduced by re-wetting and cooling the surfaces at frequent intervals.

12. Fig. 1 shows part of the ported end face of a nine cylinder axial piston pump rotor, in which the normally concentric annular sealing lands are replaced by radially wavy lands (Ref. 1) so designed that all areas of the flat counterface at the stationary port face are re-wetted and cooled at frequent intervals during rotation. This not only reduces the wear rate, but it approximately halves the friction co-efficient, thereby increasing the efficiency and reducing the heat input to the surfaces.

13. Fig. 2 shows part of the end face of a gear for a gear pump, in which the normal annular concentric sealing land inside the root diameter of the gear teeth is interrupted by shallow recesses formed in the ends of the gear teeth, so that all areas of the flat counterface are re-wetted and cooled at frequent intervals. It is beneficial to apply this technique to all highly loaded surfaces operating under boundary lubrication conditions.

GUIDLINES FOR CONVERTING MINING EQUIPMENT

14. It was known that the British National Coal Board had been successful in employing inverted fire resistant fluids for hydraulic equipment used in the British coal mines. Although these fluids display similar viscosity characteristics to conventional mineral oils, they have inferior lubrication proporties; thus generally the volumetric efficiencies of standard pumps and motors have proved to be satisfactory, but it was necessary to impose limits to the operating duties for a satisfactory service life. The limits imposed in most cases do not affect the performance of the mining equipment.

15. The mining equipment used in the N.S.W. coal mines differs from that used in the British mines, and generally the equipment is required to operate closer to the design limits; a different development approach was required to permit the equipment to function at maximum duties on a fire resistant fluid.

16. The N.S.W. coal mines are operated by a number of different companies, each employing a variety of different machines, and it was decided that the most practical approach was to employ a standardised type of fluid for all mining equipment and to modify the equipment where necessary to operate successfully on this fluid. Any item of equipment which could not be conveniently modified for this fluid was to be replaced by more suitable equipment.

17. Whatever standardised type of fluid was employed, it would be necessary to modify the hydraulic equipment to suit the fluid. Because of the previously discussed technical advantages of the 95/5 water/synthetic fluid and the fact that this fluid most comfortably met the non-flammability requirements, it was decided to standardise on this type of fluid. The programme included co-operation with fluid suppliers to determine the requirements, mainly to provide the most satisfactory lubrication properties from a non-foaming, non-toxic, corrosion-inhibiting additive to water. At the date of writing this paper, three different fluids from three different suppliers have proved satisfactory as 3% to 5% additives to water.

18. The records showed that mineral oil fires were most prevalent on mining shuttle cars, so it was decided to deal firstly with the conversion of these vehicles. There are three major different makes of shuttle car used in the N.S.W. coal mines and the hydraulic equipment for these vehicles differs in each case. At the time of preparing this paper, one of each of two makes of shuttle cars had been successfully converted to operate on 95% water fluids and they are in operation in two different mines under normal duty conditions. It is expected to convert one of the third make of shuttle cars to operate on this type of fluid during the next period contract. It is anticipated that the programme will then be extended to convert the hydraulic power equipment on other mining machinery to operate on this fluid.

CONVERSION OF TWO MAKES OF MINING SHUTTLE CAR

19. The equipment for these vehicles operates at a maximum pressure of 83 bars; it includes single and tandem gear pumps, single gear type motors, a steering control valve and various rams.

20. Although the design and material requirements for maximum performance on the 95% water fluid were known, the modifying of existing equipment presents a different problem from designing units to meet the needs and it was necessary to find alternative solutions to several of the problems. The development contracts called for the conversion of these vehicles as a matter of urgency, so the work was carried out in rather an 'ad hoc' manner, with the least amount of work to convert the units. However, the results have proved quite satisfactory.

21. The conversion of rams and valves was a simple matter, mainly in fitting PTFE tyres at sliding seals. Generally the standard fits at spool valves were satisfactory and there have been no erosion problems at this moderate working pressure.

22. The major work was in modifying and proof testing the gear pumps, which are of the externally toothed gear type, having axially slideable end plates hydro-statically balanced to provide a loading against the end faces of the gears, and the gears were journalled in needle roller bearings.

23. The needle roller bearings for the pumps were replaced by plain bearings of an asbestos-filled phenolic resin (abbreviated herein to APR). It is possible that some other materials would be equally effective. These bearing materials require a relatively large diametral clearance, and they were bored eccentric to the outside diameter so that the gears operated in their correct position under working conditions.

24. It was found that the end plates of the gear pumps wore rapidly at the concentric sealing zones inside the root diameters of the gear teeth, so these zones were machined back and fitted with APR washers machined level with the surfaces of the end plates. This was effective in providing a satisfactory life, but it now appears that more recent improvements in the fluid may render this change unnecessary for this relatively low duty.

25. One of the major problems was to provide effective sealing in the limited available space at the pump drive shaft to avoid contamination of the gear box oil by the 95% water fluid. The first seal is subject to the high pressure and the rotating shaft does not necessarily run true. Eventually it was necessary to employ three seals: a connection to the pump inlet port is provided between high pressure and low pressure face seals and an atmospheric drain is provided between the low pressure face seal and a low pressure grease or oil retaining seal.

26. A satisfactory efficiency, equal to that of standard units operating on conventional mineral oils, was achieved by the fitment of seals to static areas which had previously relied only on the diametral fit of components. After conversion the pump volumetric efficiencies were superior to the average standard units operating on mineral oil, and the first shuttle car to be converted has already given a service life equal to the average life achieved on mineral oils.

CONVERSION OF THE THIRD MAKE OF SHUTTLE CAR

27. The third make of shuttle car differs from the two makes already modified, mainly in the use of high pressure variable displacement pumps and motors as hydro-static variable speed transmissions to drive the vehicle. The remainder of the hydraulic equipment can be modified in a manner similar to that applied to the units in the other vehicles.

28. The high pressure pumps and motors are of the axial in-line piston type having a maximum displacement of .07375 litres. They operate to a maximum speed of 2700 rpm and to a peak pressure difference of 345 bars. The design of the standard unit includes a large ball journal at the input end of the drive shaft and a small roller bearing at the tail end of the drive shaft beyond the port face.

29. In the preliminary work on these units the small roller bearing was replaced by an APR plain bearing running in the pumping fluid. The large ball bearing was isolated from the pumping fluid by seals and was separately lubricated.

30. In its standard form, the leakages on the 95% water fluid were excessive, but these were reduced to negligible values by fitting PTFE seals to the pistons, and after this modification the overall volumetric efficiency was considerably superior to the standard unit operating on mineral oil. The gain was mainly a result of the reduced compressibility losses in these units, which have relatively large unswept volumes.

31. The standard units have hardened steel cylinder barrels bearing against stationary bronze port faces. Tests on the 95% water fluid resulted in erosion of the bronze port face. This erosion problem was remedied by hard chrome plating the stationary port face and cadmium plating the cylinder rotor face.

32. At the time of preparing this paper, a pump modified as described has given a satisfactory performance on rig test over a period of about forty hours up to the maximum duties; it has yet to be proof tested under motoring conditions and is to be tested up to 1000 hours before being fitted to a shuttle car for mining operations.

33. It is expected to convert one of these shuttle cars for operation on the 95% water fluid during the 1973/74 period development contract.

EXPECTED PROBLEMS IN CONVERTING OTHER EQUIPMENT

34. Converted gear pumps have been tested with the 95% water fluid in the largest displacements and at pressures up to 138 bars, which is the highest pressure used for gear pumps in the mines, so no major problems are expected in converting all the existing gear pumps to operate on this fluid.

35. Tests on vane pumps operating on the 95% water fluid resulted in a high rate of wear at the vane tips. Only a small number of these units are employed in the N.S.W. coal mines and it is not proposed to expend development efforts on them, because they can readily be replaced by converted gear pumps.

36. Most of the continuous mining machines employ piston pumps operating at pressures up to 276 bars. The control valves and rams used on these machines are representative of this class of equipment already modified for operation at pressures up to 83 bars, but there may be erosion problems at the valves when operating at the higher pressures, and development action may be required to determine more suitable materials or surface treatments. If necessary, the spool valves may be replaced by seated pilot-operated check valves or by face type valves.

37. Two different makes of high pressure piston pumps and motors are employed for the mining machines. One make and type of unit is similar to that employed on the third make of shuttle car and will respond to the same modification action. The other make of pump and motor is expected to require similar treatment in the fitting of piston seals, but it differs in that the journal loading is carried on a large roller bearing which cannot be conveniently isolated from the 95% water fluid. In order to convert this second make of piston pump and motor for operation on 95% water fluids, it will be necessary to replace the large roller journals with hydro-statically balanced journal slippers at the large diameter bearing surface.

38. Fortunately this problem is similar to the journal bearing problem encountered in the pumps and motors which have been the subject of the independent development, and the highly successful journal slipper which has been developed may be applied to these units.

39. During the development of the journal slipper various designs were tested, but the major problem was to ensure uniform loading at the sealing face and uniform deformation under loading, and the only scheme which proved satisfactory was that illustrated at Fig. 3, where the slipper sealing face is of part-spherical form, bearing on a part-spherical rotating journal (Ref. 2). The slipper is then symmetrical about its vertical centreline, so that deformation under loading is symmetrical and does not result in leakage at the sealing face. Also the slipper is quite free to align itself in any direction of movement.

40. The journal may be located by two or three fixed bearing pads and the hydro-statically balanced slipper is placed to suit the direction of journal loading. This journal loading varies from zero at zero piston stroke to its maximum value, depending on the pump displacement and the combined pressure at both ports. In some motor applications both ports may be at high pressure. The effective slipper area must be sufficient to provide hydro-static balance when supplied by the highest pressure, with the pump at maximum displacement and with high pressure in both ports.

41. In order to deal with the requirements, the slipper is free to slide radially in a cylinder having an area equal to the effective area of the slipper sealing face; it is spring loaded against the sealing face with sufficient force to overcome seal friction, and it includes a ball valve closing a small orifice which is fed from the highest port pressure. The valve closing element is tied to the slipper, so that an inward movement of the slipper closes the valve. Thus if the hydro-static balance pressure is excessive for the journal loadings, the valve closes and further movement causes the slipper face to leave the journal to result in leakage and a reduction of pressure. In practice, a total journal movement of about .05 mm radially is sufficient to raise the hydro-static balance pressure from zero to the highest available pressure.

42. This automatic regulation of the hydro-static balance pressure at the journal slipper can be provided in a variety of ways, but the scheme illustrated and described has been successfully developed and it achieves the desired results with practically zero leakage of high pressure fluid. It has been thoroughly proved in tests on the 95% water fluid.

CONCLUSIONS

43. Apart from comfortably meeting the non-flammability requirements for hydraulic fluids used in the coal mines, the 95/5 water/synthetic fluid is low in cost, it reduces polution from spillage and it permits increased efficiencies to be obtained from equipment specially designed for this type of fluid. Experience to date indicates that most existing hydraulic equipment can be modified to operate successfully on this fluid.

ACKNOWLEDGEMENTS

44. The author wishes to thank the N.S.W. Department of Mines for permission to publish information relating to the conversion work which has been carried out on their behalf under development contracts and particularly to acknowledge the co-operation of Mr. Mairet, Senior Inspector of Mechanical Engineering, Department of Mines, on this work.

45. The author wishes to thank the British Coal Board, and particularly Mr. G. C. Knight, for co-operation in providing information on the work in Britain on converting mining machinery for operation on fire resistant fluids.

46. The author wishes to thank the Directors of Ifield Laboratories Pty. Limited and of Advanced Products Pty. Limited for permission to publish information relating to their independent development work, and he acknowledges the help given by his colleagues more directly concerned with the development work.

REFERENCES

1. Patents applied for by Advanced Products Pty. Limited.

2. Patents applied for by Ifield Laboratories Pty. Limited.

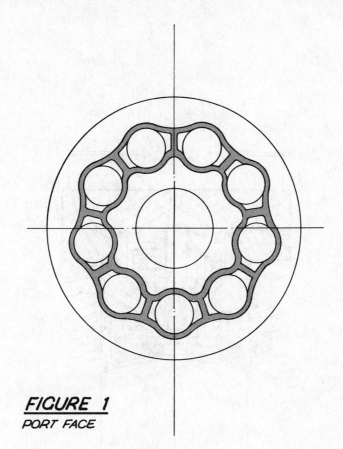

FIGURE 1
PORT FACE

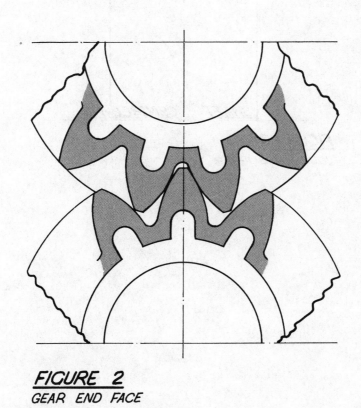

FIGURE 2
GEAR END FACE

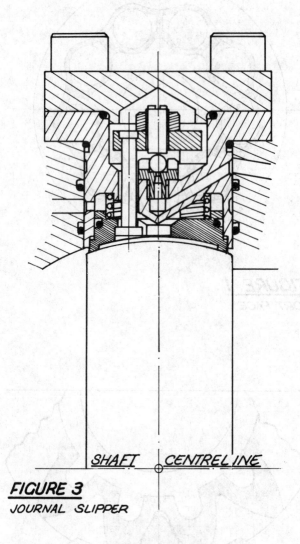

SHAFT CENTRELINE

FIGURE 3
JOURNAL SLIPPER

C35/74

HYDRAULICS ON MOBILE UNDERGROUND MACHINES

B. C. R. FOSTER, HNC(Mech Eng)

Chief Designer, Dosco Overseas Engineering Limited,
Ollerton Road, Tuxford, near Newark, Nottinghamshire

The Ms. of this paper was received at the Institution on 28th July 1973 and accepted for publication on 23rd October 1973. 34

SYNOPSIS   The paper deals with the design and application of Hydraulics as used on mobile roadheading machines of the type manufactured mainly for the National Coal Board. The particular requirements of this type of machine are broken down into sections dealing with:-

(A) Description of hydraulic requirements.
(B) Circuit design.
(C) Filtration.
(D) Hydraulic Fluids.
(E) Choice of components.
(F) Cooling.
(G) Future Trends.

The particular requirements of each topic are expanded to illustrate the problems, considerations and working requirements, not forgetting regulations which combine to necessitate the final resultant design.

Some examples of past problems are given. Comments are also made on the effects of variations in working climate and other conditions that have to be catered for.

INTRODUCTION

(i) Description of Machines

The modern Dosco roadheading machines have been developed as a result of vast experience in the field of underground roadheading, employing in the majority of machine designs available, the characteristics of the extremely successful 'cutting boom' principle, by which a rotating cutting head, having replaceable cutting picks, can be manoeuvred by the operator to any position within the cutting range, thus achieving selectivity in the cutting pattern.

All machines manufactured are electro-hydraulically operated and are of weights from upwards of 15 tons (15.240 tonnes). Electric motors are used for the prime mover for the hydraulics, the pump being connected via a coupling to the electric motor, which is either water or air cooled, dependent upon requirements. Electrical power is also used directly via a reduction gearbox for the cutting head on the majority of machines.

The machines are self-contained except for the trailing cable which carries the incoming electrical power supply, and also hoses carrying cooling water for the machine's cooling circuit.

The machine as illustrated (Fig. 1) is the Mark IIA Roadheader which is a much stronger and more powerful version of its predecessor, the D.R.C.L. (Dosco Roadway Cutter Loader), of which in excess of 250 machines have been produced. The Dosco/Bretby Dintheader (Fig. 2) serves a dual purpose of roadheading and 'floor dinting' (the re-cutting of correct profile necessitated by excessive floor heave). This machine utilises a cutting mat chain

instead of a cutting head and boom, but otherwise the basic hydraulic design is similar to that of the Mark IIA.

(ii) Mode of Operation

On the Mark IIA Roadheader material is cut by the cutting head mounted on the trunk which can be positioned by hydraulic cylinders to any position within the cutting profile. In the case of the Dintheader material is cut via cutting chains mounted on a jib frame, raised and lowered hydraulically. The cut down material is then loaded by a scraper conveyor which is powered on both machines by a slow speed, high torque motor and reduction gearbox. From the scraper conveyor the material is transferred to a belt conveyor, also powered by a slow speed, high torque motor. This conveyor is pivoted from the rear of the machine and can manoeuvre through quite a large angle, thus facilitating the negotiating of sharp changes of direction. From the belt conveyor the material is usually either loaded on to the fixed conveyor system underground or mine cars.

It can be seen, therefore, that the machines perform the complete task of cutting down the strata and gathering up the pile of cut down material which is then loaded on to the mine conveyor system.

(A) DESCRIPTION OF HYDRAULIC REQUIREMENTS

The foregoing is a brief description of two machines which form part of a range of different types manufactured. The basic hydraulic circuits, however, for all the machines are similar, and use hydraulic cylinders, motors or rotary actuators to achieve the desired conversion from hydraulic power into mech-

anical forces. All powered machine movements are
achieved hydraulically, except for rotation of the
cutting head. Hydraulic cylinders are utilised for
the majority of movements, as these are generally
the most reliable and easily installed at the
design stage. Hydraulic motors are used for the
transmission of drive to loading conveyors and
track drives. Motors are either used directly or
fitted to reduction gearboxes to increase their
torque output. Rotary actuators are used where
complications would make designs awkward if powered
by cylinders.

Provision is made for power take offs on machines
to give additional flexibility for powering roof
drills, sludge pumps, packing or stowing equipment,
etc. Winches of various sizes can also be fitted
if requested.

Electrical power is used for the rotating cutting
head, the reasons for this are twofold, (a) the
horsepower requirements are relatively high, and to
power hydraulically would require a large increase
to the hydraulic equipment, as system flows in most
cases would be at least doubled. Cooling and compactness of the machine would then present problems.
(b) On boom type machines the hoses feeding the
hydraulic motor would have to be flexible, as large
angles are manoeuvred by the trunk, and hoses to
withstand 2000 p.s.i. (140 bar) continuous pressure
are at the moment too rigid for continuous reliable
service.

(B) CIRCUIT DESIGN

(i) General

The design of the circuit for all machines is
deliberately kept simple in order that any problems
are more easily identified. Some previous attempts
of machine circuits have proved to be over-
sophisticated, and when problems arose, the causes
proved extremely difficult to trace, as misleading
and unpredictable results are obtained which tend
to obscure the real cause of the trouble.

The average maintenance fitter, the man who is
responsible for the correct operation of the
machine, is not an expert in hydraulics, and therefore it is essential to ensure that he can understand quickly the reason for malfunction.

(ii) Description of Circuit

The illustrations (Figs. 3, 3a and 3b) show a
typical hydraulic circuit for a roadheading machine.

(a) Suctions and Pumps
Oil is drawn through, in this case, four suction
strainers of .005" (0.127 mm) mesh. These are of
the type that can be cleaned by rotating a handle
external to the tank wall, the filter body being
fitted, immersed in the oil tank. Suction hoses
convey the oil to the pump which is driven by the
electric 'power pack' motor. Pumps are of the
multi-bank gear type, experience so far indicating
that these give the best service for our requirements. Gear widths are kept to a minimum to
achieve maximum bearing sizes within the pump,
giving maximum working lives. Where large flows
are required, gears are used in parallel.

(b) Flow Divider to Filters
Pressurised oil from the pump passes into a flow
divider, which splits up the oil into the flows

finally required. A relief valve is fitted between
pump and flow divider to safeguard the pump should
the flow divider jam or seize up.

From the flow divider the various flows now are
piped through pressure filters and then to their
respective directional control valves. These are
usually of the multi-bankable type and are operated
manually, by linkages or handles directly on to the
valves. Pump pressure is limited by the main inlet
relief or mid-inlet relief valves situated in the
directional control valve. To achieve compactness,
the use of mid-inlet sections serves to allow one
drain section, for two or more feeds.

(c) Pressure Indication
Pressure indication is achieved by a rotary
selector and single heavy duty gauge. This gauge
is not connected to any service unless pressure
readings are required. To achieve pressure
indication a small bore hose is taken from the
respective inlet section on the control valve to
the rotary selector, which has six pressure ports.
Each valve is given a number corresponding to that
on the selector. This number is then selected and
the knob on the selector pushed in, this then
'pipes in' that respective pressure line to the
gauge which indicates the pressure in that line.
When the knob is released, it springs back, disengaging the gauge to the pressure line and allowing the gauge to drain. Thus long life is assured
as a heavy duty gauge can be fitted, and is subjected to the pressure line only as and when
required.

(d) Control Valves
Designed into the control valves (Fig. 4 shows a
typical valve) are various 'in bank' overload
protection devices for certain services which must
be protected when the spool is in the neutral
position blocking off the working ports. These are
either (i) 'overload port reliefs' which are small
relief valves connected from the working ports to
tank internally within the valve, and are set to
relieve according to the service requirements in
question. These are used for the protection of
hoses and cylinders, where external forces could
produce very high pressures in the feed lines. An
example of this is on the 'boom arcing' service
which receives considerable shock loading from side
to side during simultaneous cutting and raising of
the trunk. Overload port reliefs here hold the
trunk steady up to the pre-determined pressure,
and above this the trunk will 'give' to relieve
built up pressure in excess of the designed maximum, or (ii) 'cross over' reliefs, which are used
for hydraulic motors. In this type, when the
relief valve setting is reached, the oil is
directed to the opposite working port. Thus the
oil re-circulates and the motor is protected from
cavitation.

Outlet sections are normally of the 'tank drain'
type, but in certain applications the 'pressure
beyond' type are used where a 'downstream' valve
bank utilises the same oil as the 'upstream' valve,
but has second priority over the oil supply.
'Regenerative' outlets are used also where it is
necessary to provide a small 'back pressure' in
the drain line to safeguard equipment against
cavitation. Some hydraulically operated Impact
Hammers require this feature.

Where multi-bank valves are used, the parallel
passage type are used whereby the service requiring
the least pressure will receive the oil. The

series type are not generally used as the operation of two handles simultaneously on the same oil supply results in a sharing of pressure, which would be undesirable in operation.

(e) Services

From the directional control valves the oil is directed to the respective services via flexible hoses.

Certain items of equipment such as maintenance lifting jacks are not fitted with overload protection devices, as it is considered dangerous to rely on these valves to support machine weights. Instead the cylinder design is such that safety margins are higher to accept pressures greater than those intended.

Equipment mounted on the machine whose weight is supported against gravity by oil are fitted with pilot operated check valves or over-centre valves to safeguard against accidental lowering in the event of hose failure. The over-centre valve is used for double acting cylinders where the load is controlled and prevented from 'running away' by the design of the valve. An example of the use of an overcentre is to support a machine mounted conveyor which is pivoted such that the delivery end can be raised or lowered. The valves would be situated directly into the cylinder cap supporting the conveyor's weight, thereby removing any extra potential leaking spots such as rigid pipe joints, etc., had the valve been mounted remotely from the cylinder.

On some machines the use is made of dual overcentre valves for the prevention of overspeeding of tracking on steep gradients. The regenerative outlet is also used here to provide a 'make-up' to safeguard the motor against cavitation, and some manufacturers of hydraulic equipment offer a complete block valve called the 'Motion Lock Valve' features plus the addition of a 'shuttle valve' for the automatic operation of a fail safe bank brake or other such positive mechanical lock. The brake is operated on by spring pressure, and released by hydraulic pressure.

The oil from the control valve drains is collected into a manifold which passes the oil in turn through a heat exchanger unit, usually water cooled. The cooled oil is then fed back into the tank.

The tank design is such that return oil is at the opposite end to the suction side, thus ensuring that all the available capacity is kept flowing and there are no stagnant areas. A magnetic weir inside the tank is also fitted to attract metallic particles. Oil level is sensed by an electrical switch, and return oil temperature by an electric probe, either of which will switch off the power pack motor if oil is low or temperature too high.

(C) FILTRATION

Previous brief mention of filtration of the hydraulic oil has been made, but this topic is elaborated in this section.

(i) Suction Filtration

This is achieved by utilising the easily cleanable type of unit, but this is for convenience fitted into the oil tank, but with the external handles placed in a suitable position. The required practice is for the machine's operator to occasionally give these handles a couple of turns. This rotates the mesh vanes against finger plates which remove the accumulated contaminant which then falls to the tank base. The filters are rated at .005" (0.127 mm) mesh. Provision is made in the tank for the periodical removal of the accumulated pile of contaminant.

Suction filtration is considered essential as there is always the possibility of contaminant entering the oil tank, through loose or badly fitted cover plates, which would not be removed by the pressure filters until it had passed through the pump.

(ii) Pressure Filtration

Pressure filtration is incorporated to protect valve gear, motors and cylinders from damage resulting from contaminant from pump or flow divider failure and is at present 15 μm (590 uin) and the units used are the replaceable element type. The filters are available in various sizes to suit the service flow. The filters are placed between pump, or flow divider and directional control valves. A by-pass circuit with visual indicator is fitted in order to show that elements require changing, and to protect against starvation, should filters become fully blocked.

A more compact type of pressure filter having higher capacities than previous units are now available. These are now preferred as they are much more attractive to position on the machine with regard to improving access for maintenance. These are also now rated at 10 um (394 μin), giving additional protection to the circuit.

(iii) Other Filtration

As mentioned previously, the tank design is such that all return oil must pass over a weir plate. This weir plate orifice area is provided with magnets which remove metallic particles as the oil passes around them. The use of magnets for filtration would appear dubious, in addition to suction and pressure filtration, but experience has shown that these are effective, especially on initial machine 'bedding in.'

The tank itself is open to atmosphere via air breathers fitted to the tank lids.

Coal Mining regulations now require that oil tanks can only be replenished by sealed couplings having a 15 um (590 μin) filter, and suitable hand pumps are being fitted to machines to transfer the oil from barrel direct to tank. This has now obviated the need for the wire mesh guard fitted to tanks, as the previous practice was to ignore the self-sealing filler and remove the cover plate, which resulted in considerable contaminant entering the tank.

(D) HYDRAULIC FLUIDS

Until some 4-5 years ago, mineral oil was allowed underground within the National Coal Board, but since that time the use of 'Fire Resistant Fluid' (F.R.F.) has been mandatory. For the mobile roadheading type of machine the use of 60/40 water in oil emulsion is allowed, i.e. 60% oil and 40% water. At the time of introduction many problems were encountered and eventually solved. It became necessary, for instance, to change to gear type pumps from the vane type in use at that time as the gear pump had a far better life at 2000 p.s.i. (140 bar).

All equipment in fact had de-rated lives, pumps, motors, valves, seals. Leather back-up washers were discontinued due to swelling problems, the internal painting of oil tanks had to be stopped.

Machines today are suitable for either mineral oil or 60/40 water in oil emulsion. All machines are despatched from the Works with mineral oil in case the machines are left standing unprotected in the winter, and if filled with F.R.F., freezing problems could arise.

To change from one type of oil to another, the system must be thoroughly flushed out.

With F.R.F. it is also necessary to periodically check the mixture strength and restore to the correct proportions.

Viscosity of oil plays a large part in the design of the equipment. Machines are designed using a viscosity of 360 Redwood No. 1 (Aquacent Light @ 70°F.), but at start up temperatures, viscosities can be up to 1000 Redwood No. 1, so this is considered when sizing such things as suction hose bores and pressure filters.

Machines working underground can be in quite high ambients, and therefore it is advantageous to quote those ambients for which machines can accept the use of heavier grades of oil to avoid viscosities falling far less than 360 Redwood No. 1, which is undesirable for such things as hydraulic motors which would suffer from excessive slippage.

(E) CHOICE OF COMPONENTS

Many specific types of hydraulic equipment have been referred to, the object of this section is to attempt to explain the reasons behind these particular choices.

(i) Hydraulic Cylinders

There are many companies manufacturing standard cylinder designs, termed 'off the shelf' units, which are necessarily somewhat of a compromise on design as they are intended to suit several different markets, and low price is important. The length of pistons and open end bushes tend to be the same, irrespective of stroke. Experience has shown that these cylinders have certain weaknesses which are bourne out in operation on mining machines of the Dosco type, and hence it is necessary to design cylinders directly suited to the application. There are two basic classes of cylinder construction. (i) 'Heavy Duty' which are sturdily constructed, having the very best materials used for piston rods and bushes, with very large wall thicknesses for the cylinder body.
(ii) 'Medium Duty' which are of lighter construction but still, however, of sturdier design than the 'off the shelf' designs.

Heavy duty cylinders are used for powering machine movements such as 'arcing' or 'lifting' of the cutting boom, and suffer the greatest amount of shock loading and abuse, Medium duty cylinders being used for the remainder of movements such as stabilisers or conveyor slewing, which do not have such arduous duties.

(ii) Hydraulic Motors

These are usually of the radial piston type, slow speed, high torque, and sizes used have ranged from torque outputs of 60 lbf.ft. (80 N m) at 2000 p.s.i. (140 bar) to 8,000 lbf.ft. (11 000 N m) at 2000 p.s.i. (140 bar). These motors are chosen for their high starting torque characteristics, and in most cases are physically attractive for mounting.

An interesting development by one leading manufacturer of this type of motor is the two speed motor which, by means of simple pilot operation, the stroke of the eccentric can be altered to provide full torque at normal speed, or half full torque at twice the normal speed.

These motors can be used to advantage on such things as hydraulic track drive, whereby a fast tracking speed can be provided at low torque requirements for fast manoeuvring of the machine. Another application is for a two speed winch, the rope speed of which could be either manually or automatically boosted at low pull requirements.

Gear motors are used where the application is for motors using speeds in excess of 600 r.p.m., but these usually necessitate the design of a reduction gearbox.

(iii) Directional Control Valves

These are of the spool type with parallel passage, as previously mentioned, having, where required, overload protection in the working banks. Simplification is achieved here with regard to hosing, as the necessary porting is achieved within the valve. These 'in bank' reliefs have their limitations, however, and where necessary, the use of special purpose valves, such as the very fast acting 'differential area poppet' relief valve, are used instead in the service line.

(iv) Filtration

Choice of components here has been the result of good reliable service from the suction strainers and pressure filters which both have desirable features from the maintenance point of view.

(v) Hosing

Due to the articulation to which the majority of services have to the main body of the machine, flexible hosing is essential in most places, the use of rigid piping being for areas not readily accessible or prone to damage. The mandatory specification within the N.C.B. (P174) covers the type of flexible hosing to be used, which is that of the two wire braided type. This hose gives good service, however, if pressures in excess of 2000 p.s.i. (140 bar) are used in bores in excess of 1" (25.4 mm), it is preferable to utilise 4-ply spirally wound hose. This is a very rigid hose although still flexible, and is not easily articulated. J.I.C. hoses and fittings are available as an alternative fitting to BSP parallel, should the customer so wish.

(F) COOLING

For N.C.B. machines adequate water supply is available for cooling the hydraulic fluid. This is achieved by directing the hot return fluid from the directional control valve drains into a manifold, also housing the temperature probe, from where it is directed into a heat exchanger, where the fluid passes over pipes having cooling water flowing through them. The cooled fluid is directed back into the tank, whilst the water, having received heat from the fluid, is directed via the rest of the machine's water circuit, which also cools the electric motor, and on to dust suppression sprays, mounted on the trunk. In this way a suitable return fluid temperature is maintained. Problems can arise in high ambient conditions where the temperature of the return fluid becomes high, and facility is provided in tank design for the addition of extra heat exchange units if required.

Machines not working within the N.C.B., however, sometimes have restrictions on availability of cooling water, and here, the arrangements for cooling the hydraulic fluid are generally of the 'closed circuit' design. This is where the same fluid cooling unit is used, but the cooling water is pumped round a closed circuit, and the hot water is cooled by a fan which blows air through a radiator. The radiator can be housed beneath the machine's belt conveyor and towed by a conveyor trolley. It is also possible in certain applications to dispense with the water and cool the fluid direct by passing this through the radiator unit and pumping back to tank.

(G) FUTURE TRENDS

These are varied and are generally aimed at easing maintenance and improving efficiency, as well as taking advantage of advances in the design, performance and quality of hydraulic equipment.

(i) Hoses

Rationalisation of hoses to achieve utilisation of a fixed, limited range of available hose lengths with straight female connectors will undoubtedly be of benefit. The revision to the N.C.B. Specification P174(1973) will achieve this.

(ii) Quick Release Couplings

The time taken to replace a faulty hose of the standard BSP swivel ends is excessive when a breakdown occurs. The use of one of the various forms of quick release hose ends, although initially more expensive, would prove beneficial in the long run on those hoses particularly exposed to damage. Negotiations are now taking place with the N.C.B. with a view to introducing this type of fitting.

(iii) Valves

The use of modular mounting of valves saves hosing and also removes the necessity for dismantling of hoses to change valve gear, the valve being mounted direct on to manifold blocks via 'O' rings.

Pilot operation of directional control valves, although complicating circuits somewhat, allows the remote fixing of valves, which can be large and difficult to accommodate, with the added advantage that the operator control panel now can be much more compact, housing only the smaller valves which 'pilot' the main control valves.

(iv) Circuit Pressures

These are at the moment limited to 2000 p.s.i. (140 bar) with F.R.F. within the N.C.B. It is questionable that increased pressures are more efficient, especially as the cost of the equipment designed to work at higher pressures is excessive.

(v) Pumps

The use of larger flow requirements, as machines tend to get larger and heavier, with greater working forces, has meant that the existing available range of pumps are now too small. Negotiations have taken place with the manufacturers of pumps to instigate the design of larger ranges of pumps which will offer better performance for longer periods.

CONCLUSION

The object of this paper has been to illustrate the manner in which hydraulics is employed to provide power for, and to control those machines presently being manufactured, also to indicate thoughts for future development to improve the product. The main aim is one of simplicity and "ruggedness" leading to ease of maintenance, as this is considered to be of prime importance to the success of this type of machine when in its working environment.

The views expressed are those of the author and not necessarily those of his Company.

Fig.1. Mark IIA Roadheader

Fig.2. The Dosco/Bretby Dintheader

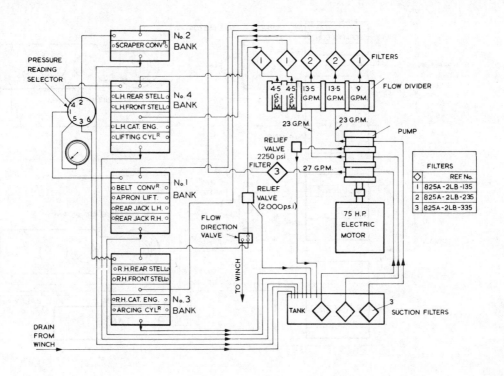

Fig.3. Hydraulic power supply to valve banks

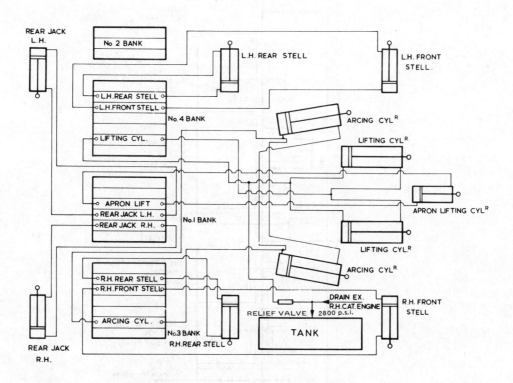

Fig.3a. Hydraulic cylinder circuits

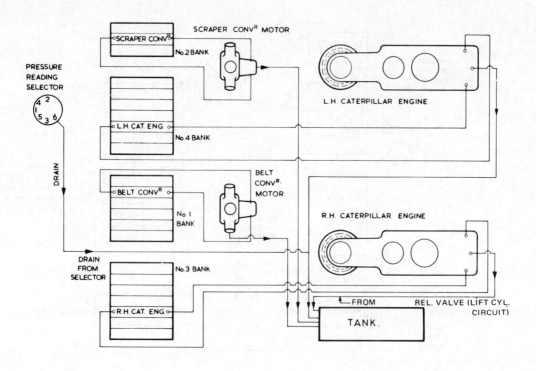

Fig.3b. Hydraulic motor circuits

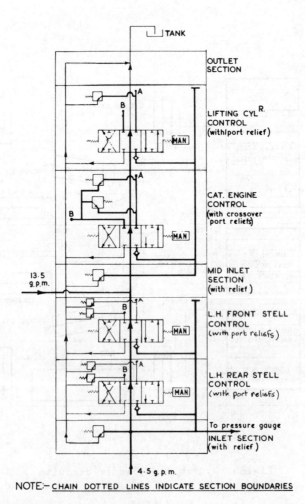

NOTE:— CHAIN DOTTED LINES INDICATE SECTION BOUNDARIES

Fig.4. Symbolic layout of No.4 Valve bank

170

C36/74

THE HYDRAULIC SYSTEM OF A UNIVERSAL CUTTING MACHINE FOR ROOM AND PILLAR MINING

D. CLARK, B Sc(Hons)

Mining Engineer, Distington Engineering Company, Special Steels Division,
British Steel Corporation, P.O. Box 8, Workington, Cumberland

The Ms. of this paper was received at the Institution on 25th July 1973 and accepted for publication on 23rd October 1973. 3

SYNOPSIS   This American machine is the latest in a long line of coal cutting machines made by the Goodman Company of Chicago since the latter part of the 19th century.   It is high powered and robust, designed to cut rock such as coal, salt, potash etc. as a prelude to blasting by explosives.

In order to be able to cut at any angle and at any height within its range, the cutter head, fitted with a cutting chain, is positioned by hydraulic cylinders at the desired angle and height; the head is then swung hydraulically in an arc to cut the rock in the position required.

The machine is equipped with a hydraulically powered infinitely variable speed drive, forward or reverse and its cuttings are systematically piled to one side of the machine by hydraulically driven Archimedian screws, known as "bug dusters".   It is also fitted with a hydraulically controlled cable reel, hydraulic power brakes and hydraulic stabilizers.

The paper begins with a general description of the machine and its function, followed by a detailed description of all the hydraulic circuits with notes on performance underground.

UNITS AND NOTATION

All units are American. Thus tons are 2,000 pound units, gallons are American gallons equal to .83 Imperial gallon or 3.8 litres, temperatures are degrees, Fahrenheit, pressures are pounds per square inch, viscosity is measured in Saybolt Second Units at 100 degrees Fahrenheit, the relation to Redwood being   Redwood = .85 Saybolt.

INTRODUCTION

1.   Minerals such as coal, salt, potash are frequently mined by driving rectangular openings into the seam, such openings being known as rooms or headings.   The opening is maintained at a constant width and height, generally in the range of from 18 feet wide by 5 feet high to 100 feet wide by 30 feet high, with extraction of mineral taking place at the far end of the opening. Extraction methods vary but one which is common and well established is to cut a gap known as a "kerf", some 6 inches wide into the base of the heading for its full width and extending forward into the solid strata for a distance varying from 6 feet to 20 feet.   The face is then drilled to a pattern and blown down by explosives, subsequently being loaded out and transported away by machines. The basic purpose of the kerf is to reduce the amount of explosives needed by creating a plane of weakness: it therefore helps to contain and limit the violence of the explosion and in addition it provides a relatively smooth floor for later working by the machines.

2.   The kerf is made by a cutting machine and as flexibility is required in the positioning of the kerf preference is given to machines which have the ability to cut in any plane and at various heights above and below the floor.   Such machines are known as Universal Cutting Machines and have reached their present state of highly advanced

development largely in the U.S.A. where mining of the type described is more popular and extensive than anywhere else in the world.

3.   A machine of this type is the Goodman Model 2500 Universal Cutting Machine, of which five are now working in United Kingdom salt mines.   Its motions and movements, except for the cutting chain itself, are all hydraulic powered, using hydraulic oil with a paraffin base (200 - 300 s.s.u. Vis. Max at 100°F).   Special machines are also available powered by non-flam ester fluids for use in U.S. coal mines but this paper will deal with the conventional mineral oil machines now working in this country.

4.   Figure 1 shows one of these machines at work in a salt mine - particularly interesting is the scale of the opening, and of the machine, compared to the man.   Such machines weigh over 20 tons and have a total length of about 35 feet, a width of 10 feet and a height to 6 feet.   The dirt, shown at the right foreground, is the pile of cuttings from the kerf thrown out by two Archimedian screws or bug dusters.   Figure 2 is a studio photo of the machine, specially taken to show the bug dusters, cutting chain and its great size.

HYDRAULIC SYSTEM

Circuit description

5.   The 2500 hydraulic system consists of three basic circuits, powered by three individual pumps driven from a 60 HP motor through a two output shaft gearbox.

The circuits are:-

1.   Tram circuit - 0 to 35 GPM variable volume pump

171

2. Cylinder and cable reel circuit -
    15 GPM section of vane type double pump

NOTE: This circuit is divided into two
        sections by means of a proportionator
        (gear type)

    (a) Cable reel and steer circuit -
        Constant 9 GPM

    (b) Other cylinder functions - variable
        6 GPM to 34 GPM by switching oil
        from bug duster circuit.

3. Bugduster Circuit - 44 GPM section of
    vane type double pump.

Extensive use of flow dividing and recombining is
necessary on the double vane pump circuits in
order to meet the widely differing flow requirements of the multiplicity of functions needed in
the operation of a complex machine of this type
with a minimum of pump outputs. Such action is
possible because not all functions are needed
concurrently, e.g. when the stabilizer is
operated the cable reel is static. The most
important of these is the cylinder boost circuit
which increases the flow rate to the cylinders
from 6 GPM to 34 GPM at a time when the bug
dusters are not running in order to obtain quick
positioning of the cutter bar when the bar is out
of the kerf; this minimises dead time during
repositioning and is very important under
intensive conditions of working.

Tram circuit

6. The tram circuit shown at Figure 3 is based
on the "Dynapower" hydrostatic transmission
system comprising one variable volume reversible
output pump having an output of 0 to 35 GPM, and
a right and left side variable volume motor.
Fluid output from the pump powers the parallel
connected hydraulic motors, which drive the tram
gear boxes coupled by chains to the non-steering
front wheels. Figure 4 shows the main pump with
its integral charge pump.

7. Control of the variable feature of the pump
and motors is accomplished by mechanically
connecting levers in the operator's compartment
to servo valves on the units themselves.
These levers, duplicated on each side of the
machine, are connected together into one two-
directional control rather like an aircraft
"Joystick". Figure 5 shows the operators platform with the tram control "Joystick" and its
self centering spring cylinder in the centre.
This control also actuates the power steering
cylinder on the rear axle. Movement of the
"Joystick" from side to side varies the speed of
the two tram motors relative to each other:
movement to and fro in the direction of the
machine varies or reverses the pump output with
the output being zero in the central position.
Thus, to make a left hand turn while tramming
forward the "Joystick" is pushed forward and to
the left which causes the left hand tram motor
to run at slow speed relative to the right hand
motor, the speed and direction of the tram motors
being proportional to the position of the
"Joystick" relative to the central zero position.
It is a neat and effective system and though it
does require variable speed tram motors and a
variable output/reversible pump, i.e. three

rather complex units, the result is a very smooth
control of movement from zero to 270 feet per
minute, forward or reverse plus the ability to
turn round very sharp corners with all speeds
being proportional to the movement of the "Joystick"

8. The tram system is a connected closed
circuit. An 8 GPM charge pump mounted on the end
of the variable pump replaces system leakage,
supplies cooling oil to the closed system,
furnishes oil to operate the Servo control valves
and pre-charges the circuit to 125 - 250 p.s.i.
via the low pressure side of the system through
either of two check valves.

9. Pilot operated relief valves set at 3000 PSI
are built into the tram motors discharging into
the low pressure side of the circuit. In addition
there is a pressure compensator device in the tram
pump set for 2500 PSI to limit the pump output at
high pressures.

10. A pressure-actuated shuttle valve is used to
direct both high and low pressure to the respective relief valves. When one line is high
pressure, it moves the shuttle valve towards the
low pressure side; this in turn ports the high
pressure to its relief valve. At the same time
it ports the low pressure side to its relief
valve. It is also the valve used to direct the
high pressure relief valve discharge to the low
pressure side of the system.

11. Plumbing and associated hardware have been
minimised by building the charge pump and check
valves into the pump cover. The high and low
pressure relief valves and the shuttle valve are
built into the motor. Therefore, no separate
hoses or connections are needed for these items.

Cylinder and cable reel circuits

12. General description (see Figure 6)

The 15 GPM pump supplies oil for all cylinder
movements and the cable reel hydraulic motor.
These functions are controlled by a seven valve
unit, which consists of three inlet sections
having built-in reliefs, and seven spool type
operating sections. One inlet section feeds
cable reel and steer, another feeds boom and bar
swing, and the third feeds bar level, boom roll,
and boom elevate.

13. The maximum working pressure available for
each function is controlled by the setting of the
relief valve in the inlet section which feeds
that function. A separate relief valve set at
2000 PSI is provided to protect the 15 GPM pump.
In addition all cylinders are fitted with cushion-
ed flow at the end of the stroke to reduce shock.

14. Before entering the seven valve unit, the
output of the 15 GPM pump is divided into 9 GPM
and 6 GPM by means of a proportionator. The
9 GPM is fed to the cable reel and steering
sections, via a two function valve, one function
being the rear stabilizer and the other being
spare. Since operation of the cable reel
requires only one position of the four-way valve
section, the other position of this valve is used
to operate the filler pump. With the valve in
neutral, cable can be spooled off the reel by
hand.

15. The 6 GPM output from the proportionator is fed into an adjustable flow control valve. This valve has 2 outlets one being a controlled flow and the other a by-pass. The controlled flow is fed to the boom swing and bar swing sections of the 7 valve unit. The speed of these functions can thus be regulated by the lever on the flow control valve. The remainder of the 6 GPM not required for boom or bar swing, is discharged from the by-pass port of the flow control valve and fed to the boom elevate, bar level and boom roll sections of the 7 valve unit. When the boom and bar swing are not being used, the entire 6 GPM is available for boom elevate, bar level and boom roll.

16. A further split in the 6 GPM output from the proportionator has been added to provide fluid for the hydraulic four wheel power brakes to be described later.

Details of circuits controlled by the 7 valve unit

17. Cable reel circuit

The cable reel is powered by a planetary gear type fluid motor. Oil from the control valve section passes through a sequence valve (free flow) to the motor, to power the reel. Return oil from the motor is piped direct to the tank. The sequence valve is used as a brake, or drag, to prevent the reel from over-spinning when cable is spooled off with control lever in neutral. It is not set to any specific pressure, the proper setting being dictated by the type of cable being used and the amount of drag desired.

Stabilizer circuit controlled by the 2 function valve in series with the 7 valve unit

18. The rear stabilizer bar is raised and lowered by two double acting hydraulic cylinders, shown on Figure 7 which receive oil from one of the operating sections of the 2 function valve in series with the 7 valve unit.

19. The other section of the valve is not used, so the ports are plugged. This valve is installed in the line which feeds cable reel and steer, consequently these functions will be dead whenever the stabilizer is being positioned. A nitrogen filled accumulator is used to maintain pressure on the stabilizer bar when the control lever is in neutral with the oil locked in all cylinder lines by a double pilot operated check valve.

20. Oil fill circuit

This is a gear type double pump motor, one section being used as a fluid motor to drive the other section which is used as a pump for the oil fill. A 30 mesh strainer having built in magnets is provided in the suction line to the fill pump.

21. Steering circuit

Power for steering is obtained from one double acting cylinder. Two adjustable speed control valves are provided in the steering circuit to regulate the oil used for steering, and maintain a sufficient supply of oil and pressure for both steering and cable reel. The steering and tram valve linkage is interconnected so that both functions are operated by the tram control "Joystick".

22. Boom elevate circuit

Two double acting cylinders are used to elevate the boom. Meter discs located in the operating valve prevent the boom from dropping dangerously fast. A safety relief protects components and lines should the boom be forced up while the operating lever is in neutral.

23. Bar level circuit

One double acting cylinder is used for bar level, with meter discs in the control valve. The valve also has safety reliefs in both ports and anti-cavitation checks.

24. Boom & bar swing circuit

Two pairs of cross connected double acting cylinders are used for boom swing and bar swing. Each pair of cylinders is controlled by one of the operating valves in the seven valve unit. Both valve sections have built in crossover safety reliefs.

25. Boom roll circuit

Two cross connected special double acting cylinders create boom roll by a rack and pinion system. Counterbalance valves or meter discs prevent run-away when the boom is over centre and crossover relief valves are built in the control valve. Figure 8 shows the group of cylinders for boom elevate, boom roll, bar level and bar swing.

Circuits controlled by the 44 GPM 2 valve unit

26. Bugduster & cylinder boost circuit

The primary function of the 44 GPM pump is to supply oil to the hydraulic motor (vane type) for driving the primary Bugduster. When required, part of this oil can be used to boost the cylinder functions (except steering). The Bugduster and cylinder boost functions are controlled by a two valve unit which consists of an inlet section having a built in relief, and two spool type operating sections. The relief which is set at 1900 PSI limits the maximum pressure available for the Bugduster and also is a safety valve for the 44 GPM pump. Maximum pressure for the cylinder boost circuit is controlled by separate relief valve set at 1600 PSI.

27. This relief is set lower than the reliefs in the 7 valve unit to prevent oil from the 44 GPM pump from going out of the reliefs in the valve unit and creating excessive heat. Excessive volume is prevented in the boost circuit by dumping 16 GPM to tank through a flow regulator.

28. A secondary Bugduster when fitted, is driven by a vane type motor, identical to the one which drives the primary Bugduster. The hydraulic circuit remains the same except that the secondary motor is connected in series with the primary motor.

Filtration

29. A 10 micron filter having a vacuum gauge to show the need for replacement of the element, is provided in the suction line to the tram pump.

30. A 30 mesh strainer with integral magnets, located inside the oil tank, is provided in the suction line to the double pump.

31. Oil returning to the tank from the double pump passes through a 25 micron filter. A "spindicator" is provided to indicate filter element contamination.

32. All three filters contain built in by-pass valves, provided as a protection for the hydraulic units; however, they can permit contaminated oil to enter the system. It is very important therefore that the filters be cleaned soon enough to prevent the by-pass from operating.

33. Power brake circuit

Power brakes are fitted to all four wheels in addition to the manually operated disc parking brakes on the front wheels. The power brakes comprise double acting cylinder operated drum brakes on the rear wheels shown at Figure 9, and disc brakes on the front wheels. Circuits to front and rear wheels, though sharing a common 6 GPM supply from the proportionator, are completely separate in order to minimise the risk of a complete brake failure. Each circuit includes a check valve, a two way control valve i.e. brakes on and brakes off, a nitrogen filled accumulator to keep brakes on when machine has no power and a pilot line back to an 1800 PSI unloading valve. The unloading valve comes into operation to charge the brake circuit when the pressure in that circuit falls to about 1400 PSI and cuts the flow off when the pressure reaches 1800. Figure 10 shows the accumulators for stabilizer and brakes mounted in a compartment below the cable reel, the accumulators having sufficient capacity to operate the brakes six or seven times without recharge.

34. Cooling

Return oil from the double pump is cooled by passing through a heat exchanger consisting of a series of air cooled (natural ventilation) plates having oil passageways running through them. Additional cooling is obtained by passing oil through two auxiliary tanks, one being a rear bumper tank sited at the back of the machine, before it is returned to the main tank.

PREVENTATIVE MAINTENANCE

A few notes on the preventative maintenance procedures may be useful.

35. Instructions are given on the following points to check, and to the credit of the users of these machines these have been carried out unfailingly over several years.

1. Maintain proper oil level at all times - check daily or every shift.

   (a) Use only a good grade hydraulic oil (paraffinic base, 200 to 300 s.s.u.Vis.Max. at 100°F)

   (b) Keep stored oil in a closed container.

   (c) Be careful not to get dirt in system when adding oil. Clean storage container before removing cover.

2. Maintain proper pressure settings. Do not increase relief settings above prescribed values.

3. Change micronic filter elements when called for by indicators.

4. Make it a point to clean suction strainer periodically.

5. Keep all connections tight to keep oil in, and air out: check hoses for wear.

6. Keep air breather clean to prevent pumps from cavitating.

36. Hydraulic failures on these cutters, during a total working life on 5 machines of about 9000 production shifts, have been very few. A summary of the failures known to the Author is as follows:-

1. One bugduster motor seized up due to seal failure.

2. 4 cylinders reconditioned to correct piston seal wear.

3. Leakage past the seals of one section on one 7 valve unit.

4. Failure of elevating cylinder check valves on two occasions.

5. Power disc brake caliper failure on two occasions (believed to be faulty castings) These failures occurred recently and are still under investigation in conjunction with Goodman and the caliper manufacturers.

37. As a matter of interest it should be recorded that there have been no pump failures and no problems at all with the flexible hoses, which are numerous, work at medium to high pressures and have to exist in an arduous mining environment. Figure 11. giving a general view of the hoses etc. with the covers off the top of the machine, shows the complexity of the hose runs.

COMMENTS ON THE USE OF MINERAL OIL

38. The Goodman machines in use in this country all use inflammable mineral oil as their working fluid. The hazards involved with such fluids are well known but by taking great care and because the mines in which they operate cannot propagate fire i.e. these are salt mines, there has been no incident involving these fluids. Precautions taken against fire are very comprehensive and are strictly enforced and maintained, including frequent testing of the fire extinguishers carried on the machines. As a result of using mineral oil it is a fact that the reliability and availability of these machines has been outstanding - due in no small way to the lubricating properties of the oil. Indeed, it is only by being able to work with mineral oil that the intricate piston pumps and motors of the "Dynapower" infinitely variable tram transmission system could be used to provide the essential control required when cutting into a

rock face. This operation, known as "sumping in" is carried out by pushing the high speed cutter chain into the face. When this happens the chain unit, extending about 14 feet forward of the machine, reacts violently until such time as it gets three or four feet into the salt. Consequently, extremely gentle and finely controlled movement forward of this 20 ton machine working on a rough floor is necessary if damage to cutter chain, cutter picks and the machine itself is to be avoided.

39. The attitude in the United States towards the use of hydraulic powered mining machines of this type is, so far as the author could ascertain on a recent short visit there, as follows :-

    1. Face machines, such as these cutters, which are attended, and are working in coal mines must use either non-flam fluids or if mineral oil is used must have a fire prevention system on the machine. This system must be "fail safe" and may be either dry powder or water dump. Cutters, Continuous Miners, Loaders all seem to use dry powder systems - shuttle cars seem to have self contained water dump systems or carry hoses to plug into the mine water pipes.

    2. Unmanned machines, away from the working face must use non-flam fluids.

40. In the case of Goodman Cutters in the United States a choice of systems is available. They can either have a mineral oil hydraulic system with full "Dynapower" variable tram transmission protected by an extensive self contained dry powder fire extinguisher system using "Ansul" Foray type free flowing dry chemical or else they can work on Ester type fluids with a clutch/planetary gear type tram system.

CONCLUSION

41. These large, high powered mining machines have a complex system of hydraulic power circuits operating a wide range of movements and auxiliary devices. Experience has shown them to be reliable and relatively trouble free though unusually perhaps for a machine of this size working underground in this country, they do use mineral oil as a working fluid. They represent good American design, based on over 70 years of evolution in this specialised field where practical experience is perhaps the most valuable asset one can have.

ACKNOWLEDGEMENTS

42. Grateful acknowledgement is made to the Goodman Equipment Corporation of Chicago U.S.A., to Hydreco, a unit of General Signal Corporation of Kalamazoo, U.S.A. and to Distington Engineering Company of Special Steels Division, British Steel Corporation for the data and illustrations used in this paper.

43. The views expressed however are entirely those of the Author.

APPENDICES

Appendix 1

Definition of terms used to describe the cylinder movements used to position the cutting chain

44. Figures 1 and 2 show this machine to be a four wheeled vehicle fitted with a type of chain saw at the front end. This chain saw, known as the "bar" has to be capable of cutting in any plane to the front of the machine. Consequently the bar is connected to the machine chassis by the equivalent of a human wrist and elbow, the hand being the bar and the forearm, between wrist and elbow, being known as the boom. Like a hand, the bar can be swung, from the "wrist" to 45° either side of the bar centre line and this can take place in any plane up to 30° from the plane of the boom. Movement of the bar from side to side is known as bar swing, movement of its plane of swing is known as bar tilt or bar level.

45. The boom is also capable of being swung 30° to either side of machine centre line and its plane of swing can be varied from 30°, pointing upward, to about 5° pointing downward with these movements taking place at the "elbow" i.e. the front end of the machine chassis. Movement of the boom from side to side is known as boom swing and movement of the plane of the boom is known as boom elevate. In addition the boom can rotate through 270° - this is known as boom roll.

46. As a result of these movements the cutting chain can be positioned anywhere within the range of the cylinders. Thus, as examples, cuts can be made horizontally at floor level, below the floor to a depth of 10" and above the floor to a height of $65\frac{1}{2}$". By rotating the boom 180° and then elevating it, cuts can be made horizontally to a height of 8'6" above floor level. By rotating the boom 90° cuts can be made vertically on either the right or the left of the machine - indeed vertical cuts can be made from one position of the machine which will make an opening through which the machine can itself pass i.e. it can cut wider than its own width. Minor changes in cutting plane, during actual cutting, can also be made routinely - thus adjustments can be made so as to alter the gradient or slope of the heading during cutting.

47. All these movements are carried out effortlessly by hydraulic power, within seconds of deciding on a course of action. This is the measure of the machine's versatility and is why machines of this type are known as Universal Cutters - it also makes it possible to cut for example a uniformly graded kerf in salt 13 feet deep across a face 65 feet wide in about one hour, working with the machine on a rough rolling floor cut maybe months before.

Appendix 2

Makers of the main hydraulic components used on the machine

Cylinders, standard type :	Westinghouse Air Brake Company, Fluid Power Division, Lexington, Kentucky.
Cylinders, Special design for boom elevate and boom roll :	Goodman Equipment Corporation, Chicago, Illinois.
Variable Speed Transmission system :	"Dynapower" by Hydreco, a unit of General Signal Corporation Kalamazoo, Michigan.
Constant Volume pumps and motors :	Denison Division Abex Corporation Columbus, Ohio and Vickers Sperry Rand.
Check valves :	Republic Manufacturing Company, Cleveland, Ohio.
Relief Valves :	Westinghouse Air Brake Company, Fluid Power Division, Lexington, Kentucky.
Control valves :	Commercial Shearing & Stamping Company, Youngstown, Ohio.
Hoses, Fittings and self sealing couplings :	Aeroquip Corporation, Jackson, Michigan.
"ANSUL" fire extinguisher system	The Ansul Company, Marinette, Wisconsin.

Figure 1   View of a Goodman Universal Cutting machine at work in an American

salt mine.

Figure 2   Front view of a machine to show the bugdusters, cutting chain and

to demonstrate the manner in which the cutting chain can be positioned

at extreme angles.

Hydraulic Diagram – Tram Circuit

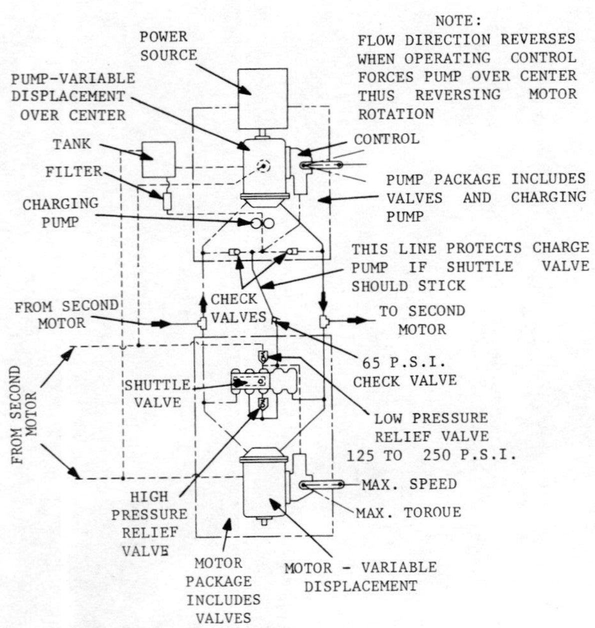

LOW SPEED HIGH TORQUE

HIGH SPEED LOW TORQUE

HIGH SPEED LOW TORQUE

LOW SPEED HIGH TORQUE

TOP

TOP

TRAM MOTOR

TRAM MOTOR

BOTTOM

BOTTOM

TRAM PR.
(MAX. 2500 P.S.I.)

6

REVERSE

NEUTRAL
FORWARD

CHECK VALVE
65 P.S.I.

TRAM PUMP

FILTER

NOTE
CHANGE FILTER ELEMENT
WHEN READING
REACHES 9" H.G.

TOP

BOTTOM

CHARGE PR.
125 TO 250 P.S.I.

5

AIR BREATHER
KEEP CLEAN

TANK

LEGEND

GAGE PORT

TANK

INTAKE

PRESSURE

INTERMITTENT PRESS

USE HYDRAULIC OIL, PARAFFINIC
BASE 200 TO 350 S.S.U. VIS-
COSITY AT 100°F. USE ONLY A
HIGH GRADE HYDRAULIC OIL.

#5 CHARGE PUMP - 125 TO 250 P.S.I.

#6 TRAM PRESSURE

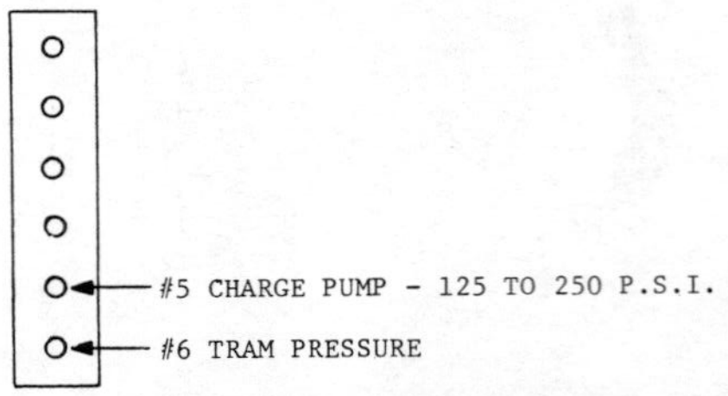

**ARRANGEMENT OF GAGE PORTS
ON RIGHT REAR FENDER**

NOTE:
FLOW DIRECTION REVERSES
WHEN OPERATING CONTROL
FORCES PUMP OVER CENTER
THUS REVERSING MOTOR
ROTATION

CONTROL

PUMP PACKAGE INCLUDES
VALVES AND CHARGING
PUMP

THIS LINE PROTECTS CHARGE
PUMP IF SHUTTLE VALVE
SHOULD STICK

TO SECOND
MOTOR

65 P.S.I.
CHECK VALVE

LOW PRESSURE
RELIEF VALVE

125 TO 250 P.S.I.

MAX. SPEED

MAX. TORQUE

MOTOR - VARIABLE
DISPLACEMENT

MOTOR
PACKAGE
INCLUDES
VALVES

HIGH PRESSURE
RELIEF VALVE

SHUTTLE
VALVE

CHECK
VALVES

FROM SECOND
MOTOR

FROM SECOND
MOTOR

POWER
SOURCE

PUMP-VARIABLE
DISPLACEMENT
OVER CENTER

TANK

FILTER

CHARGING
PUMP

SCHEMATIC OF TRAM LINE CIRCUIT

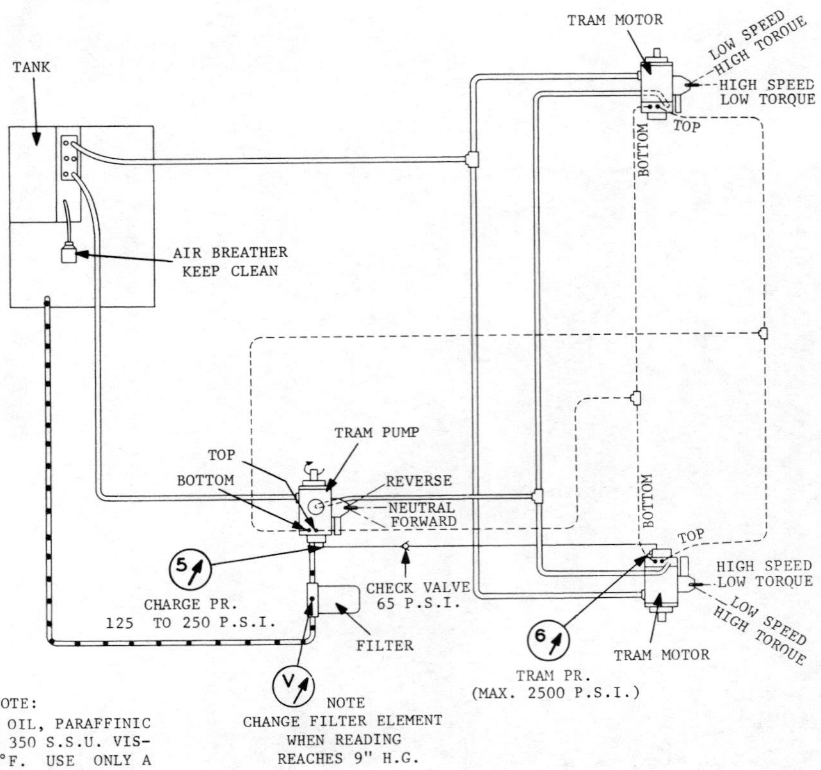

TRAM MOTORS - VARIABLE

PRESSURES FACTORY SET.

HIGH PRESSURE RELIEF SET AT 3000 P.S.I.
LOW PRESSURE RELIEF AT 125 TO 250 P.S.I.

TRAM PUMP - VARIABLE

PRESSURE COMPENSATED AT 2500 P.S.I.

CHARGE PUMP

APPROX. 8 G.P.M., RELIEF AT 125 TO 250
P.S.I. IN TRAM MOTOR

PUMP COMPENSATOR MUST BE 500 P.S.I.
LOWER THAN HIGH PRESSURE RELIEF IN TRAM
MOTOR

PUMP & MOTOR INTERNAL LEAKAGE APPROX.
1/2 G.P.M. EACH AT 1000 P.S.I.

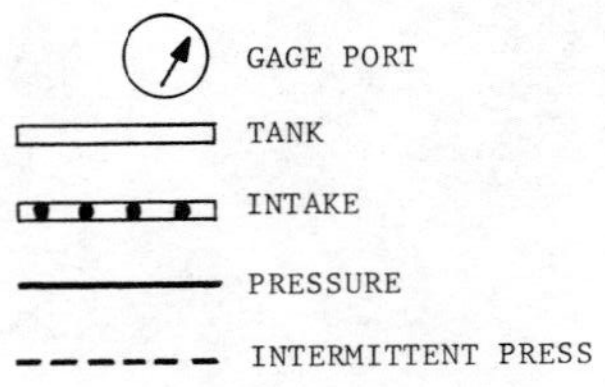

Figure 3   Circuit diagram of the tram circuit i.e. power to driving wheels.

Figure 4   Close up of "Dynapower" pump, charge pump, constant volume pumps

and filters sited behind operator's platform on right side of machine.

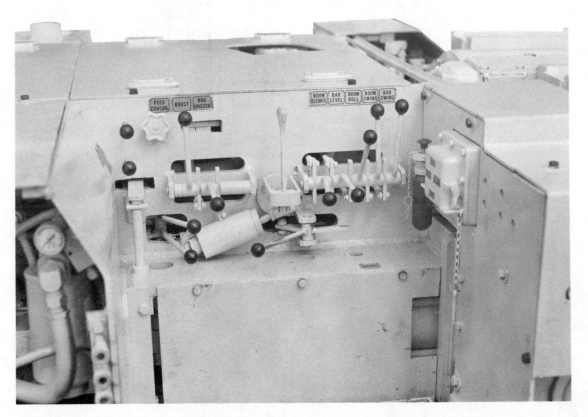

Figure 5   View of operator's platform on right side of machine showing control

levers.

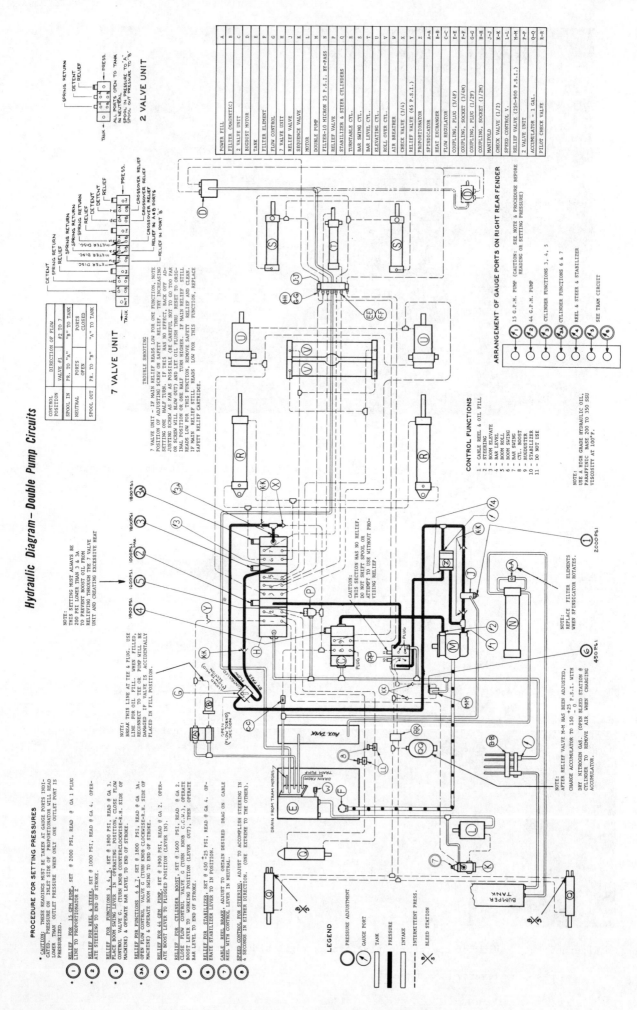

Figure 6   Circuit diagram of cylinder circuits.

Figure 7   View of back end of cutter showing cable reel, stabilizer to grip floor

behind machine and rear wheel with brake cylinder for drum brakes.

Figure 8   Close up of front end of machine showing turntable for boom swing,

cutting chain motor, and cylinders for bar tilt, bar swing, boom roll

and boom elevate.

181

Figure 9   Close up of rear wheel power brake cylinder and stabilizer control valve.

Figure 10   Accumulators, nitrogen filled, for stabilizer and power brakes accomodated beneath cable reel.

Figure 11   General view of top of machine with covers off to show complexity of
hoses, valves etc. behind the operator's platforms. Note how
operating controls are duplicated on each side of machine.

C37/74

THE APPLICATION OF FLUID POWER TO MINING AND TUNNELLING TRANSPORT AND MATERIALS HANDLING SYSTEMS

W. BROWN, CEng, HNC
Senior Engineer, Underground Mining Machinery Limited,
Aycliffe Industrial Estate, near Darlington, Co. Durham

G. A. GUPPY, BSc, CEng, MIMinE
Deputy Design and Development Manager, Underground Mining Machinery Limited,
Aycliffe Industrial Estate, near Darlington, Co. Durham

The Ms. of this paper was received at the Institution on 25th July 1973 and accepted for publication on 23rd October 1973. 33

SYNOPSIS In the drive to reduce costs, the Mining and Tunnelling Industry, in the post war period, progressively increased the degree of mechanisation applied to the mineral extraction process. Unfortunately, this progress was initially not matched by the development of transport and materials handling systems and indeed it is only in recent years that there has been a wide interest in this field.

Considerable effort is now being devoted to the development of more sophisticated systems specifically to transport men and handle materials. These systems generally use either a suspended monorail track or a floor mounted track of special configuration to prevent vehicle de-railment.

It has been convenient to use fluid power in these applications and this has brought together problems associated with the use of fire resistant fluids and those of working in a hostile environment. These problems have been largely overcome and systems using diesel hydraulic locomotives and incorporating a novel fluid induced traction system are operating successfully. Coupled with this locomotive development, high efficiency fluid controlled brake systems and fluid powered cranes provide safe and efficient means of transporting men and handling materials.

INTRODUCTION

1.   Early mine transport means relied upon rail mounted mine tubs to handle both mineral and materials, men normally being expected to walk. As mines developed in size and complexity the importance of an efficient mineral handling system first became apparent and belt conveyors were introduced to haul mineral; either to locomotive hauled main systems or in some cases direct to the shaft bottom.

2.   Where locomotive haulage was introduced for mineral handling this was used also for conveying men and material. Where conveyor belts were run direct from the coal face to the shaft bottom, however, no such facility existed. In these latter cases special men and material handling systems were required even on the main or trunk systems. In all cases some auxiliary means was required on the secondary roadways leading to the coal face. In many instances, until the recent demise of the pit pony, mine tub systems were preserved for material transport; manriding facilities still being the exception rather than the rule.

3.   In an effort to improve this position a number of manriding and materials handling systems have been developed, some utilising an overhead monorail while others use floor mounted track of either standard or special type. (Ref. 1,2). In the United Kingdom the monorail system, for various reasons, has never been fully exploited. Floor mounted systems using special track which prevent de-railment have however been extensively employed. In this paper some of the hydraulic features of the vehicles, locomotives and transfer stations developed, are described.

THE TRAPPED VEHICLE, 'COOLIE CAR' SYSTEM:

4.   One of the special track, trapped vehicle systems developed is the 'Coolie Car'. The vehicles are operated on a special track formed from two channel sections (fig.1). The cars are provided with both running wheels, which bear on the top web of the channels and side wheels which run in the side of the channel profile. The wheel assemblies are mounted on fully articulating bogies, two per vehicle, such that the vehicle is fully trapped to the track section.

5.   Various types are in use for the transport of men and materials, they can be rope or locomotive hauled, will negotiate curves of 3 metres radius and undulating track conditions commonly found in mining and are eminently suitable for operation on steep inclines. Indeed, one particular rope hauled installation is now operating on a gradient of 1 in 1.5. It will be appreciated from the foregoing that in order to operate on steep gradients, around small radius curves and in small roadways, special braking systems and locomotives are required.

Coolie Car Braking Systems:

6.   The braking systems provided on most material handling and manriding applications are emergency and parking brakes only, service braking being provided by the haulage means, be it a static winch or a locomotive. Typical of the emergency conditions under which these brakes are applied are the following:

(a) Overspeed of the train, due to overspeed of the haulage means.
(b) Overspeed of the train, due to parting of the haulage rope on a gradient.
(c) Parting of the train of vehicles due to broken drawgear.

(d) Operation by the guard due to the presence of a hazard.

These emergency brakes are required by the industry to have the following features:

(1) The system must be fail-safe.
(2) The brake shoes or members producing the braking effort should be applied directly to the track rails.

7.   The fail-safe feature is conveniently provided by employing a design in which the brake is applied by means of heavy coil or belville disc springs. Spring forces in the order of kilonewtons are required and an effective means to hold the brakes in the 'off' position is essential. It is also required that the brakes can be applied by means of an overspeed governor or manually by a guard who may be seated at either end of a train of vehicles. These requirements are best met by the use of an hydraulic brake 'hold off' and control system utilising fire resistant fluids.

8.   The means of applying suitable braking members onto the track rails has developed to produce increasing efficiencies and braking efforts. In the first instance brake shoes were forced onto the top surface of the track rails lifting the load bearing wheels just clear of the rail surface. This method has the distinct advantage of producing a rate of retardation which is a function of the coefficient of friction between brake pad and track and the gradient on which the vehicle is operating and is independant of the combined weight of the vehicle and its payload. This is a particularly useful feature if the payload varies widely, for instance, if the train has the dual function of transporting men and materials. This method is no longer used on 'Coolie Cars' since at a given gradient, the rate of decelleration is proportional to the coefficient of friction and no means exists to increase the braking effort other than such unreliable measures as track sanding.

9.   The only satisfactory alternative was found to be that of inducing a braking load on to the track thereby increasing the braking effort. An arrangement is shown (Fig.1) which utilises brake plates normally held clear of the side trapping wheels of the vehicle by hydraulic pressure. Release of the hydraulic pressure allows banks of springs to urge the brake plates into contact with the side wheels which in turn are forced into contact with the track. The spring force is therefore applied to the wheels on opposite sides of the track to produce a braking effort independant of vehicle weight. Several bogie designs of this type are in service each having a braking effort of 8000N. (the coefficient of friction is assumed to be 0.1). This brake has the disadvantage however that the retardation force is limited by the ability of the track to accept the required induced transverse load without permanent deformation.

10.   The application of Coolie Car to even steeper gradients led to the need for a brake which would not impose excessive loads onto the track section. This has been achieved by means of a caliper brake which grips the upper and lower faces of the top flange of the track. Undoubtedly the most effective brake so far available for steep inclines, this unit is capable of exerting a braking effort of 22 000N. As with earlier designs, the brake force is spring applied by means of a bank of beleville disc springs, the brake shoes being hydraulically held off.

Hydraulic Control:

11.   A typical hydraulic circuit for a train of vehicles is shown (Fig.2). A train generally comprises, a master or control car at one end and a terminal car at the other, with one or more intermediate cars. The assembly may incorporate braked bogies throughout or a mixture of braked and unbraked bogies depending upon the application. Fluid from a manually actuated pump, mounted on the brake control unit situated within the master car, is fed to the brake release cylinders until the relief valve setting is registered on the pressure gauge. At this pressure the brakes are fully held off, and the train is free to move. If the train should overspeed a centrifugal governor driven from one of the bogie wheels and usually set to operate at 3.6 m/s will open valve 1 and apply the brakes. Further means to apply the brakes are provided by valve 2 situated in the master car and valve 3 situated in the terminal car. The guard, travelling in the leading vehicle may bring the train to rest by operation of these valves. Any valve which has been operated to apply the brakes must necessarily be reset before operation of the hand pump will effect brake release. In the event of drawgear failure, the connection hoses between the cars are severed and the release of brake fluid allows the spring force to apply the brakes.

THE DIESEL HYDRAULIC 'MINERANGER' LOCOMOTIVE:

12.   The locomotion of manriding and materials vehicles within the smaller mine roadways, typical of gate roads leading to coal faces, is traditionally by means of a rope, hauled by a stationary haulage. The reliability of such systems is undoubted but serious drawbacks are evident when high rates of mining produce rapid changes in the roadway network which necessitate frequent adjustments to the rope layout. The Mineranger locomotive is the result of several years development which has attempted to produce a transport means unfettered by ropes.

13.   The machine employs an hydrostatic transmission using fire resistant fluid and an unconventional traction system resulting in a high drawbar pull to weight ratio and the ability to negotiate inclines well in excess of the maximum 1 in 15 laid down by transport within mines regulations for conventional locomotives. The locomotive comprises two permanently coupled units, a power pack and a tractor (Fig.3). This configuration is required so that the vehicle may negotiate 3 metre curves and operate in roadways of small overall height. In addition the arrangement provides the advantage of permitting alternative tractor units with different speed ranges to be coupled to the standard power pack.

Power Pack Unit:

14.   The power pack, with cabs at each end and mounted on two braked bogies, incorporates a fully flameproofed diesel engine delivering 53.5 kW at 2000 revolutions per minute. This unit is directly coupled to an over centre, tilting head, axial piston, hydraulic pump. Hydraulic oil tank, fuel oil tank, transmission control valve gear and brake circuit valve gear are all included on the power pack. The brake bogies as previously described (Fig.1) produce a

total braking effort of 2 x 8000N. Control of the locomotive by the driver is from the cab leading the direction of travel, the following cab being unoccupied.

Tractor Unit:

15. The unit consists of a chassis mounted on two induced adhesion bogies, each having four elastomer tyred driving wheels coupled in pairs through spur gear trains. Each pair of wheels is driven by one radial piston hydraulic motor. The four motors receive fluid energy from a common supply line, the quantity received by each individual motor being in direct proportion to the rotational speed of the output shaft. Thus the two pairs of driving wheels on each bogie, situated opposite each other and rolling on the track rails, can negotiate sharp bends with a true differential action similar to that of road vehicle drive axles.

16. The traction bogie drive wheel adhesion arrangement is shown (Fig.4). The wheels, with their axes vertical are mounted on a pivot in such a manner as to allow their peripheral surfaces to swing into contact with the outer web faces of the channel section track rails. Each pair of wheels is pressed onto the rails by the combined forces of compression springs which provide an initial or base adhesion force and hydraulic rams which provide an additional radial load on the drive wheels proportional to the pressure within the hydrostatic closed loop. This arrangement makes drive wheel adhesion directly proportional to the tractive effort being exerted and independant of the weight of the locomotive. The hydrostatic transmission of course facilitates stepless forward and reverse speed control with 'deadmans' lever control and trouble free power transmission to the hydraulic motors on the drive bogies which are subject to continuous movement and vibration.

Mineranger Hydraulic Circuit:

17. The Mineranger is fitted with a dual low and high speed range either of which may be selected to suit the prevailing duty. Speed range selection is achieved by operating either of the change-over valves (15), situated in the driving cabs (Fig.5). This is normally performed when the vehicle is stationary.

18. Low speed range: This is the condition shown on the circuit diagram. The change-over valve (15) is operated to exhaust the pilot pressure, acting on the directional valve (27), to tank and hence allow the spool to spring return to the position shown. In this mode the transmission pump (2) is delivering fluid to both pairs of motors (22) and (23) and therefore maximum tractive effort is available. The maximum speed will be approximately half of that attainable on high speed range.

19. High speed range: The directional valve (27) is pilot operated into the alternative position by means of change-over valve (15). In this mode the rear pair of motors (23) are isolated from the transmission circuit, the transmission pump (2) now delivering fluid to one pair of motors (22) only, therefore maximum linear speed is attainable.
　　　　　In the high speed mode, the two motors (23), which are isolated from the transmission circuit, are driven by the wheels which are in contact with the track and therefore act as pumps. In order to prevent cavitation it will be

seen that boost fluid is flushed across this secondary closed loop.

20. The brakes are spring applied and hydraulically released by means of brake rams (18). Fluid to release the brakes is provided by a vane pump (5), the pressure being limited by the balanced spool relief valve (7). Flow of the brake control fluid is governed by the block ball valve (11) which has three positions, brake on, brake off, and run.

21. Brake on: This is the position shown on the circuit drawing. Fluid from the vane pump (5) is allowed to flow to tank under no pressure. The brake rams (18) are also connected directly to tank and therefore the brake circuit is exhausted and zero pressure will be registered on both brake pressure gauges (16) within cabs 1 and 2. In this condition unloading cylinder (12) will unbalance the 190 bar relief valve in the composite valve block (1) and if the tilting head within the transmission pump (2) is moved, the flow thus produced in the closed loop will short circuit the traction motors. Simultaneous application of brakes and tractive effort is therefore impossible.

22. Brake off: In order to release the brake, block ball valve (11) is manually moved into the centre position and held there until brake pressure gauge (16) registers a static pressure.

23. Run: When the above operation is completed the block ball valve (11) is further moved into the right hand position and fluid from vane pump (5) is thus again allowed to return flow to tank under no pressure. The brake circuit is now fully charged and escape of fluid prevented by non-return valve (21). Furthermore, unloading cylinder (12) is now loaded and consequently tractive effort can be applied.

24. An additional safety feature is provided by interlock valve (6) which ensures that boost pressure must constantly be available when the brakes are in the 'off' position. If the boost pressure should fail the brake circuit would be instantly exhausted, resulting in application of the brakes. Failure of boost pressure could arise due to the demand exceeding the supply, e.g. exceptionally high rate of leakage due to, say, burst transmission hose.

Performance Data:

Maximum static tractive effort	- 27000N	)4 motor
Maximum speed at above T.E.	- 0.63 m/s	)drive.
Maximum speed	- 5.7 m/s	)2 motor
Maximum T.E. at above speed	- 3000N	)drive.
Vehicle weight	- 5600 Kg	

MATERIALS HANDLING - MONORAIL AND CRANES:

25. With production at the coal face increasing, the need to remove bottle necks caused by inadequate supplies and materials handling facilities is thrown into greater relief. Thus, recent years has seen the installation, at the mine surface, of gantry cranes. These cover the whole stocking area providing maximum storage space with minimum manpower requirements and the ability to handle heavy or light loads in pallets or containers with the maximum of safety and efficiency. The use of such arrangements is now being increasingly extended underground in the

shape of monorails, transfer stations and travelling cranes, thereby considerably simplifying the flow of materials into and out of the colliery.

26. Hydraulics using fire resistant fluids provide an ideal flameproof means of power transmission for such units, the components generally possessing low volume/horsepower ratios compared to their electrical equivalents - e.g. hydraulic versus electric motors.

Monorail/Transfer Stations:

27. Overhead monorails suspended from the mine arch roof supports are sometimes employed to perform extensive materials transport duties over routes having inclines. In these circumstances the load trolleys will be rope hauled and fitted with hydraulically released, spring applied brakes similar in principle to those of Coolie Cars. Manriding on monorail systems is not undertaken in British Mines.

28. Often, however, the monorail installation will be in the form of a localized level station where, for instance, materials are transferred from trunk road mine cars onto coolie cars. Here, lifting and travelling of the loads can be hydraulically powered from a stationary power pack located nearby.

Travelling Cranes:

29. Although a relatively recent underground introduction, travelling cranes of varying designs are now in use. For example, the Goliath crane with its overhead structure running on floor mounted rails, the gantry type suspended from twin parallel runway beams attached to the roof of the mine roadway or the alternative type, more commonly associated with the factory workshops, where the gantry beams are attached to the walls of the roadway. All of these types have their particular attributes depending upon the handling duty required and the mining conditions at the installation. The latter, for instance, is obviously applicable to situations where the marshalling of materials over a large area is involved.

30. While the cranes, which are generally of under ten tonnes capacity and two metre lift, may vary in design, however, the application of hydraulics to provide flameproof power to all of the motions is a common feature. A simple hydraulic circuit diagram for a crane in which the long and cross travel motions are driven by hydraulic motors and the hoist by an hydraulic cylinder, is shown (Fig.6). The crane operator standing on the floor of the roadway controls the crane, pedestrian fashion, by means of the pendant mounted pilot controls. The controls have the fail to safe feature of returning to the neutral position with all motion ceasing as soon as they are released.

Electric Supply Cable Handling:

31. On account of the difficulty of handling long lengths of multiple hydraulic hose, it is usual to have the electric prime mover on the travelling crane to power the hydraulics. This focuses attention on the safe handling of the single electric cable, particularly where long travel distances are involved. Here again, in a particular instance hydraulics have been employed with advantage (Fig.7). On the crane carriage, the tandem gear pump (1) is driven by the electric motor (2) which is mounted inside the cable reeling drum (3). The shaft of

the flange mounted motor protrudes from one end of the drum whilst a stub shaft integral with the drum protrudes at the other end, the whole assembly being free to rotate in bearings (4). The electric supply cable (5) is led from the electric motor and wound around the outside of the reeling drum, which has helical grooves to suit. From there it passes between guide pulleys (6), into the cable laying trough (7) and then into a fixed electrical supply source (8) half way along the gantry. The pulleys are fixed on travelling nut (9) which is on lead screw (10) journalled in bearings (11). The lead screw is geared to the cable drum by means of chain drive (12) such that one revolution of grooved drum traverses pulleys (6) an axial distance equal to the outside diameter of cable (5) or the drum groove pitch.

32. When the electric motor shaft is rotating and exerting torque by virtue of the resistance to motion offered by the hydraulic pump, the electric motor case and with it the cable drum will try to turn, in the opposite direction to the motor shaft. This will be prevented from so doing by the electric cable which is thus pulled taut. If the crane moves towards point (8) the slack cable will be taken up by the drum which is always trying to wind on more cable. Conversely, when the crane moves away from point (8) the taut cable will rotate the drum in the opposite direction thus paying out more cable. Unfortunately, the motor case, cable drum and cable upon it, possess sufficient inertia to force the assembly to continue to pay out cable after the crane travel has ceased. This results from the load on the electric motor being suddenly released due to the directional control valve diverting live fluid away from the long travel drive motor. The electric cable therefore becomes displaced from its helical grooves on the drum and subsequent travelling can cause entanglement and damage of the costly flexible cable. To eliminate this effect the hydraulic motor (13) is coupled to the leadscrew and supplied with low pressure fluid so as to impose sufficient tension in the cable to keep it taut even when the electric motor is off loaded. It should be noted that the permissible travel distance is twice the amount of cable that can be accommodated on the drum. This system is now working successfully in an installation where the gantry length is 140m.

CONCLUSIONS:

33. Material handling and transport systems in mines remain very labour intensive but the development of equipment to improve this situation is proceeding with increasing speed. The continuing use of hydraulic power in this field will provide compact and flexible equipment although care must be exercised to maintain simplicity in concept and design.

REFERENCES:

1. Stams J. Track Guided Means of Haulage (Schienenzwangsgefuehrte Flurfoerdermittel. Glueckauf 1971 Vol.107.May Pp.399-405.

2. Roehrs H. New Developments in Manriding Underground. (Neuere Entwicklungen bei der Personen befoerderung). Glueckauf 1972 Vol.108.March Pp. 170-176.

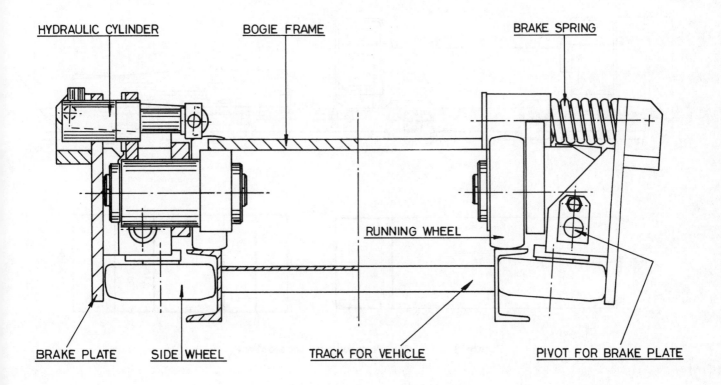

HYDRAULIC CYLINDER   BOGIE FRAME   BRAKE SPRING

RUNNING WHEEL

BRAKE PLATE   SIDE WHEEL   TRACK FOR VEHICLE   PIVOT FOR BRAKE PLATE

BRAKE SHOWN IN "HELD OFF" POSITION   BRAKE SHOWN IN "ON" POSITION

Figure 1   Coolie Car bogie with brakes.

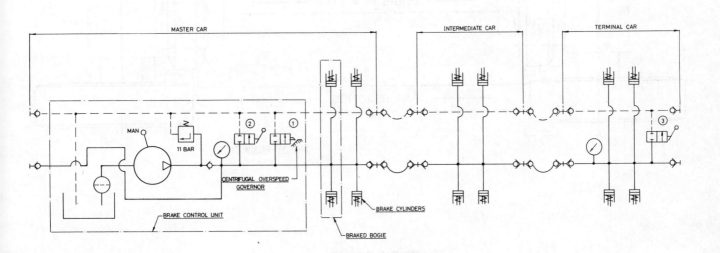

Figure 2   Typical Hydraulic Circuit for
a train of Coolie Cars.

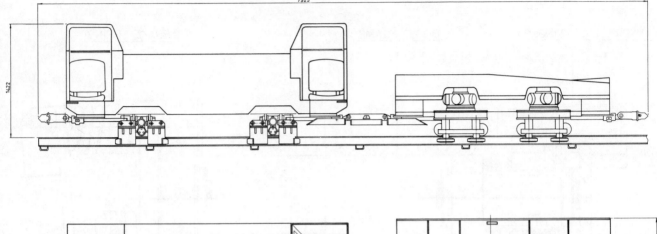

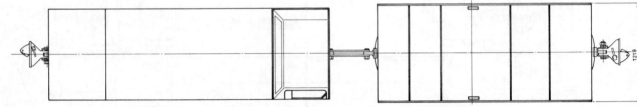

Figure 3   The 'Mineranger' Locomotive.

**COMPRESSION SPRINGS
AND HYDRAULIC RAM THRUST**

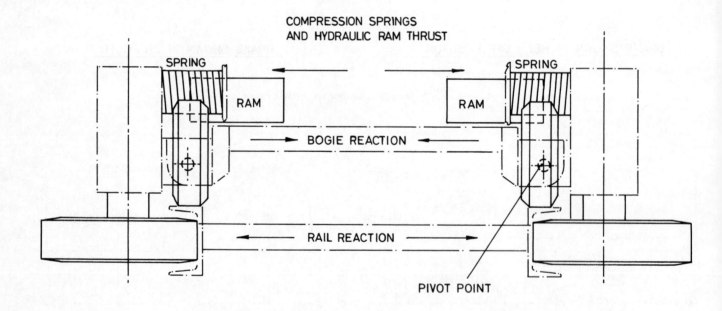

TRACTION BOGIE

Figure 4   Traction Bogie Arrangement for the
                'Mineranger'.

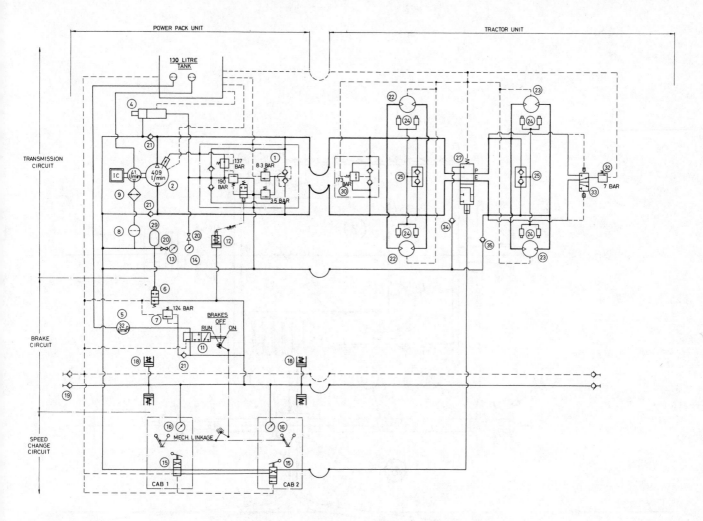

Figure 5   'Mineranger' Hydraulic Circuit.

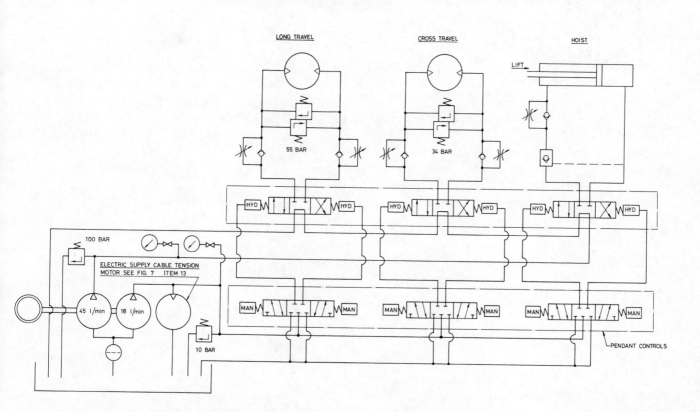

Figure 6   Circuit Diagram for 4 tonne Crane.

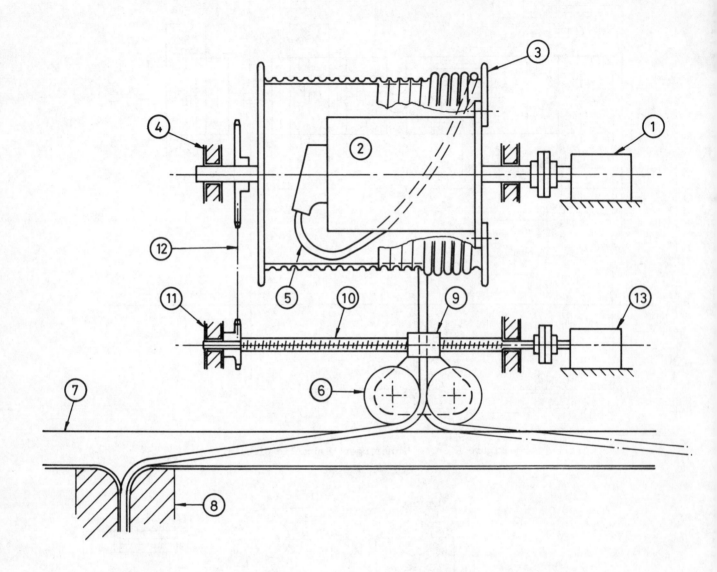

Figure 7   Cable Handling Arrangement.

C38/74

HYDRAULIC OPERATION OF A SHEARER LOADER

S. L. WILSON, CEng, MIMechE

Divisional Hydraulics Engineer, Anderson Mavor Limited,
Mining and Engineering Division, Motherwell, Scotland

The Ms. of this paper was received at the Institution on 13th August 1973 and accepted for publication on 23rd October 1973. 34

SYNOPSIS   This paper describes the functioning of the hydraulic equipment on a modern power loading mining machine for underground use and the reasons behind the choice of the equipment.   This includes a description of the hydrostatic transmission used for traction, which is integral with the machine, the automatic control system coupling the transmission system to the electric motor load and so varying the speed to keep the machine working at full power and the operation of the various auxiliary functions. These comprise of hydraulic tilting of the machine to make it capable of following undulations in the coal seam and ranging of the cutter units to accommodate variations in the seam thickness.

A system of remote control of the machine is described which uses low pressure hydraulic power as its medium.   This allows the operator to control the machine from a safe or convenient position which may be remote from the control valves.   The safety features incorporated in this system are also discussed.

THE MACHINE

1.   The Anderson Mavor D.E.R.D.S. (Double Ended Ranging Drum Shearer) was the logical development of the single ended machine and, as the name suggests, is capable of cutting in either direction, therefore taking the full seam section for each pass through the coal face.

2.   The machine as shown in figure I consists of several major units bolted together and mounted on an underframe which sits astride an armoured face conveyor.   Gearheads at each end of the machine carry the rotary cutting elements which are driven through reduction gearboxes directly from the electric motor.   These gearheads can be ranged by means of a hydraulic ram so that the height of the cutter can be varied in relation to the coal seam. Cowls are attached to the gearheads which shroud the cutters and channel the cut material onto the conveyor.   The cowls are mounted in a manner such that they will maintain their position relative to the cutter during the ranging operation of the gear-heads.   They are positioned by means of a hydraulic motor through a gearbox and chain sprockets and can be rotated 360° round the axis of the cutter.   The underframe is hinged about an axis parallel to the coal face and hydraulic rams mounted in the under-frame can tilt the machine relative to the coal face to allow control of the cutting horizon.

3.   The traction of the machine is provided by a haulage unit built into the machine between the electric motor and the right-hand gearhead.   A chain stretched the full length of the coal face is anchored at each end and engages with two idlers and a driving sprocket on the haulage unit.   A hydrostatic transmission in the haulage unit operates the driving sprocket enabling the machine to travel in each direction at a speed infinately variable between zero and 6 m/min.

4.   The mode of operation is to cut with the leading cutter raised and the trailing cutter lowered.   Controls are located at a central point and also at each end of the machine for selecting the required height of the cutters, the position of the cowls and the tilt of the machine.   The end station controls take the form of push buttons and provision is also made on these for starting and stopping the haulage.   A chain extending the length of the machine provides the facility for stopping the electric motor and hence the haulage in the event of an emergency.

THE HAULAGE

5.   The most important hydraulic facility on the machine is the haulage unit and its construction incorporates purpose designed components which have been developed to operate in the arduous and space limiting environment of a longwall coalface.

6.   The pump, shown in figure 2, was based on the early National Engineering Laboratory design of an axial piston pump. This was developed over a lengthy period to the degree of contamination tolerance and compactness which this particular unit now exhibits.   In this application it delivers 1.78 l/s (23.5 GPM) at pressures up to 20,700 kPa (3000 PSI) yet its overall dimensions are 150 x 200 x 250 mm.

7.   The hydraulic motor, shown in figure 3, is a slow speed high torque unit of the radial piston type with a multi-lob cam.   The capacity per revolution is 4.2 l (254 ins^3) and the motor measures 495 mm dia x 250 mm deep (19.5" x 10") excluding the shaft extension.   All the other units were designed so that they could be accommodated in the space available inside the haulage casing incorporating a through shaft transmitting the drive from the electric motor to the cutter gearhead.

8.   An arrangement of the haulage unit is shown in figure 4.   The main pump is driven from the through shaft via spur and bevel gears.   A priming pump is mounted directly to the main pump

and is driven from an extension of the pump shaft. This is a gear type pump delivering .38 l/s (5 GPM) which is passed through a filter and cooler, both of which are housed in a separate box mounted above the pump compartment, before entering the circuit at the manifold block. The manifold block contains most of the hydraulic circuit valve gear, i.e. relief valves etc., and is bolted directly to the main pump. The servo control valve mounted on the rear of the main pump controls the direction and magnitude of oil flow to the hydraulic motor housed in a compartment which is connected to the pump compartment by a tunnel through which the connecting pipes pass. The hydraulic motor drives through a 3.6:1 gear reduction onto the driving sprocket. The shaft to the driving sprocket drives a small lubricating pump for the idler sprocket bushes. The incoming electric cables pass through the compartment containing the torque motor for auto-control which operates through a push rod onto a pilot valve contained in the adjacent compartment. The pump and pilot valve compartments are dry having all drains piped back to the sump while the hydraulic motor is directly connected to the sump and has to be drained should access to it be required. The sump occupies the space under the pump and pump drive compartments and contains 52 litres. An accumulator assembly is situated on the top of the haulage to give a reserve of energy to ensure a smooth relaxation of chain tension when the electric motor is switched off with the haulage still in engagement.

9. The hydraulic circuit is shown diagrammatically in figure 5. The system forms a closed loop between the pump and the hydraulic motor, with the pump supplying oil to the motor and the exhaust from the motor being returned directly to the pump inlet port. The closed loop is pressurised by the priming pump. The main pump output can be varied from zero to maximum, and also reversed, by the movement of the swashplate. The swashplate is controlled by a servo mechanism which is linked to the haulage control handle and also to the auto control circuit in such a manner that the direction and maximum speed required can be selected on the control handle and the auto-control will then adjust the speed to suit the current being taken by the electric motor.

10. While the haulage control handle is in the "STOP" position the swashplate is held in the centre position by the servo valve. When the handle is moved to the "FORWARD" or "REVERSE" position the swashplate is moved either clockwise or anti-clockwise, which gives forward or reverse flow to the hydraulic motor. The magnitude of the flow and hence the speed of the machine is proportional to the distance moved by the handle between the "STOP" and the "FULL" speed position.

11. For satisfactory operation the swashplate pump (A) depends upon leakage from the main pressure for hydrostatic balancing of certain parts. This leakage is replenished by the priming pump (C) which draws oil from the sump through a gauze strainer and pumps it through a 20 micron paper element filter (D), fitted with by-pass valve and tell-tale unit. The oil subsequently passes through cooler (H) before entering the circuit, via non-return valve (G), through one or other of check valves (E) depending on which of the lines to the motor is low pressure, the check valve on the high pressure line being held closed by the working pressure. The output of the priming pump considerably exceeds the

leakage from the main circuit and the excess is blown off through the low pressure relief valve(F) and the back pressure valve (K) thus maintaining a pressure at the main pump inlet. The exhaust flow from the priming circuit passes through the main pump casing before returning to the sump.

12. Because the circuit operates on a closed loop any heat generated within the loop tends to remain causing a considerable increase in the circuit temperature. In order to minimise this temperature rise, a valve is incorporated into the circuit which ensures a consistent rate of transfer of hot oil out of the circuit. The valve (T) is connected to both lines going to the hydraulic motor. When a particular direction of travel is selected one or other of the lines is pressurised. This pressure acts on the end of the valve spool moving it across thereby connecting the low pressure line to the back pressure valve (K) via pilot operated check valve (P.O.). In this condition the pressure setting of the low pressure relief valve is such that all of the priming supply is pushed into the low pressure line, through the appropriate check valve (E), mixes with the hot oil returning from the motor before being bled off through the transfer valve (T) and the back pressure valve (K) to return to the sump via the pump casing.

13. The pilot operated check valve (P.O.) situated between the transfer valve and the back pressure valve, ensures that when the electric motor stops the low pressure line bleed across the transfer valve is immediately blocked. This is necessary to keep the circuit 'closed' during runback and prevents the capacity of the accumulator (BB) being discharged back to tank. As long as the electric motor is running the pilot operated check valve is held open by priming pressure. By-pass valve (J) avoids the necessity for finding the exact centre position of the handle when it is desired to stop the haulage. This valve is operated by a cam on the spindle of the operating handle, and is opened approximately 1° on each side of the centre position of the pump swashplate. This action short circuits the remaining pump output through the valve, dropping the system pressure and allowing the motor (B) to be driven back by the haulage chain thus releasing the tension imparted in the chain during hauling. The valve is spring loaded towards the open position and requires a pressure to be applied to the opposite end of the spool before it will close. This pressure is created by back pressure valve (K) and is applied to the end of the by-pass spool opposite the spring, moving the valve to the closed position provided the cam on the operating spindle allows it to do so. This means the by-pass valve can only be closed when the priming pump and hence the electric motor is running. Therefore, if the electric motor is switched off and the haulage control handle left in the operating position, the spring will open the by-pass valve thus releasing the tension in the haulage chain. Accumulator (BB) maintains the system 'tight' during this condition thus avoiding violent runback from occurring.

14. The speed of the haulage is controlled by the current in the main electric motor through the Auto-Control System. The working of this is as follows :- A torque motor is connected in series with the main electric motor and produces a torque proportional to the current in the main electric motor. This torque is balanced in a spring unit from which a linkage acts on the spool of the pilot valve (M). While the motor is working within 15%

of full load current, all ports in the pilot valve remain closed. If the current increases above 115% full load current the spool of the pilot valve is pushed in, and oil at priming pressure supplied to port (N) is directed via port (P) and speed control orifice (R) to the large end of the speed control cylinder (S). Priming pressure is constantly applied to the small end of the speed control cylinder tending to retract it. The supply from the pilot valve to the large end has a 2:1 advantage and so the piston moves out at a rate controlled by orifice (R), thus reducing speed at a controlled rate until the motor current drops to full load current bringing the pilot valve back to the closed position. This reduction is achieved by a mechanism on which the speed control cylinder operates, which urges the servo spindle towards the centre position against the action of spring (U). If the overload increases to above 150% full load current, the pilot valve spool would be pushed further in, connecting port (N) to port (Q) which admits oil direct to the speed control cylinder by-passing the orifice (R) and reducing speed immediately. This oil is simultaneously admitted to the spring end of the by-pass valve (J) opening the valve and thus releasing the tension in the haulage chain thereby immediately relieving the load on the main electric motor. When this load is relieved and also when the electric motor is working below 85% full load current, the pilot valve spool moves out connecting port (P) to tank port (O), allowing the large end of the speed control cylinder to be exhausted and permitting spring (U) to restore the servo to the original speed as set by the operating handle. Any oil which has been admitted to the spring end of the by-pass valve would bleed off to tank through orifice (V). Check valve (CC) prevents the by-pass valve being opened when a slight overload of the electric motor admits a controlled supply of oil to the speed control cylinder.

15. The system is protected against hydraulic overload by the main overload valve (L) which is set at 15,500 kPa (2,250 PSI). If the pressure in the system exceeds 15,500 kPa the main overload valve opens allowing oil from the high pressure line to flow through the appropriate check valve (W) into the low pressure line through the appropriate check valve (E). Orifice (X) is set to allow a flow of 0.02 l/s (¼ GPM) through the overload valve before sufficient back pressure is created by check valve (Y) to force oil through check valve (Z) to speed control cylinder (S), thus reducing the output of the pump sufficiently so that it is pumping just enough to maintain 15,500 kPa in the system. When the pressure subsequently falls below 15,500 kPa the oil which has been admitted to the speed control cylinder is allowed to bleed off through the speed control orifice and pilot valve provided that the load on the electric motor is such that the pilot valve is in the speed up position.

16. Low pressure switch (DD) protects the main pump from damage due to loss of priming pressure. It is set to open a switch in the pilot circuit of the main electric motor if the priming pressure drops below 345 kPa (50 PSI).

17. Thermostat (TH) stops the electric motor if the oil temperature rises above 72°C.

18. The pilot valve is fitted with an auxiliary piston which permits the haulage to be controlled remotely with respect to 'stopping' and 'starting' only. This feature is operated through the hydraulic push button stations situated at the machine ends.

THE AUXILIARIES

19. All auxiliary functions on the machine are hydraulically operated and the circuit diagram is shown in figure 6.

20. The hydraulic power is supplied from two 0.1 l/s (1.3 GPM) pumps, one mounted in each gearbox. The outputs are coupled together and supplied to a manifold on which are mounted the control valves for each operation. An unloading valve is also mounted on the manifold and is mechanically linked to all the control valves such that it is closed when any service is selected but otherwise unloads the pump output to tank through a filter and a back pressure valve which creates 1,400 kPa (200 PSI) in the return line.

21. Each ranging gearhead is positioned by a hydraulic ram. The supply to the ram passes through a valve block which is subplate mounted on the ram and incorporates pilot operated locking valves to retain the gearhead in position in the event of a hose failure, 55,000 kPa (8000 PSI) relief valves and check valves to keep the ram full when an overload occurs. These check valves are fed from the 1,400 kPa back pressure. The tilting of the underframe is achieved by 2 small rams built into the underframe which are locked in position by a double pilot operated check valve.

22. Each cowl is rotated by means of a small radial piston motor. The control valves for the cowls connect both service ports to the return line in the neutral position thus allowing the cowls to float and rest on the base of the coal seam cut by its associated cutter. The 1,400 kPa back pressure in the return line keeps the motor cylinders full while it is in the floating condition.

23. These control valves are all capable of pilot as well as manual operation and the gearhead and underframe valves are connected to the low pressure push button controls situated at the ends of the machine for the convenience of the operator. The push buttons are simply 2 position valves supplied by the 1,400 kPa back pressure and when a button is pressed a single service is selected and this service receives a supply until the button is released. Where a common service can be selected from either end check valves are incorporated to ensure that the signal from one end is not exhausted at the other. These are shown on the underframe control lines.

24. The push button blocks also contain one valve which provides a remote STOP/START of the haulage. This is not a spring returned button and it is retained in the STOP position by a latch. Since this facility is provided at each end of the machine it is essential that an interlock exists so that the haulage cannot be started by an operator at one end while a second operator at the other end thinks he has it safely latched off, and it must be failsafe. To this end the remote control cylinder on the haulage has haulage priming pressure permanently applying a stop signal and this must be overcome by the start

signal from the push button station before the haulage will start. Thus failure of the start signal pressure for any reason will automatically cause the priming pressure to stop the haulage and failure of the priming pressure would stop the electric motor via the low pressure switch. The interlock between the two ends is provided by a double check valve block on which it is physically impossible for both check valves to be closed at the same time, thus a start signal from one end will be blocked by the check valve and the haulage cannot start until a start signal is received from the other end.

25. These hydraulic systems have been applied to some 200 machines in this country and overseas during the past few years. The components must operate in conditions of contamination which are worse than the average encountered in normal industrial and mobile applications. Mr R D Lee's Paper (Ref.1) showed the results of a survey of hydraulic systems including contamination levels and reliability ratings. With his permission some of his findings are shown in Table I with typical values for a haulage unit shown on the bottom line of the table. (Contamination classification is according to NAS1638 as shown in Table 2). From this it can be seen that a high degree of reliability is being achieved in spite of the heavy contamination by solids which in some cases may be supplemented by 6% of pit water. Units have been in operation for up to 500,000 metres of cutting but are usually replaced at a somewhat lower figure on routine overhaul schedules. These machines operate on mineral oil but similar components in particular the axial piston pump are now being applied to power packs operating on 40/60 emulsion with equal success which appears to substantiate the use of purpose designed hydraulic equipment in the mining industry.

Ref(1)   LEE R.D.
          "ARE HYDRAULIC SYSTEMS OVERDESIGNED".
          FIRST EUROPEAN FLUID POWER CONFERENCE
          SEPTEMBER 1973

TABLE I

Machine		Approx. Age (years)	Filtration (Nominal)	Contamination Level NAS.1638	Hydraulic Reliability Class (this & similar m/cs)	Most Frequent Replacement Parts
No.	Class					
8	FMH	8/12	190 um?	10-14	2	Gear pump chamber wear
13	FMH	6/12	Coarse Mesh	10-13	95% 1; 5% 2	-
18	HM	1½	(Main 25 um	6-8	2	Pumps(? system fault))
			(Servo 2½ um	5-7	1-2	-)
19	F	10/12	½ um	4-7	1	Solenoids of valves
21	F	3	15 um	12-14	2	Piston Seals (2 months)
22	HM	15	149 um	7-11	2	Pumps (1 yr), Filters (6 months)
23	HM	9/12	10 um	5-9	1	Piston Seals, valve seals
24	F	1½	36 um	9-13	2	Pipe Joint 'O' rings
25	OME (HM)	14	74 um	11-13	2	Pumps (2 months)
26	F	12	Filling Strainer	16 +	3-4	(Pump packings, valve (stem seals, Copper (pipe joints
28	FMH	*	25 um	5-10	2	-
29	FMH	*	74 um	-	2	-
30	HM	*	20 um	7	1	-
31	FMH	*	74 um	7-11	2	-
32	HM	*	15 um	7-8	1	-
34	HM	1	15 um	-	2	Piston, pump & valve seals
35	HM	1	15 um	11-12	3	Piston Seals, Blocked Relief Valve jets
7	AM		20 um	15-16	1-2	-

NOTES:- 1. * The age of machines 28-32 at the time of test was probably 2-3 years.

2. NAS 1638 classification ceases at class 12 but, for the purposes of this work only, has been extended to class 16 by the same mathematical progression (i.e. each class contains twice as many particles as the preceding one for each size).

3. The hydraulic reliability class number represents answers given by the user to questions as follows:-

Class 1   Trouble free (e.g. 1 minor breakdown/year)

Class 2   Only occasionally gives trouble (e.g. 1 breakdown/month or two)

Class 3   Fairly frequent maintenance needed (e.g. most weeks)

Class 4   Always breaking down (e.g. several times each week)

TABLE 2

Size Range Microns	CLASSES													
	00	0	1	2	3	4	5	6	7	8	9	10	11	12
5 - 15	125	250	500	1000	2000	4000	8000	16000	32000	64000	128000	256000	512000	1024000
15 - 25	22	44	89	178	356	712	1425	2850	5700	11400	22800	45600	91200	182400
25 - 50	4	8	16	32	63	126	253	506	1012	2025	4050	8100	16200	32400
50 - 100	1	2	3	6	11	22	45	90	180	360	720	1440	2880	5760
Over 100	0	0	1	1	2	4	8	16	32	64	128	256	512	1024

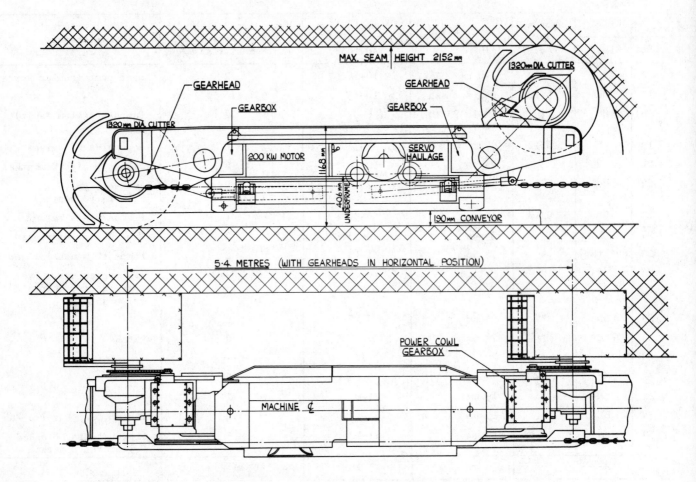

Fig.1. Double ended ranging drum shearer

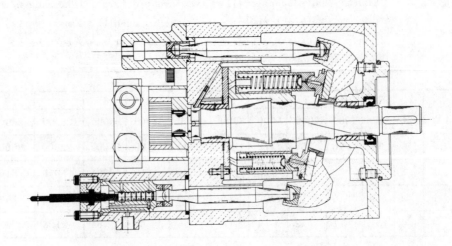

Fig.2. AM Axial piston pump

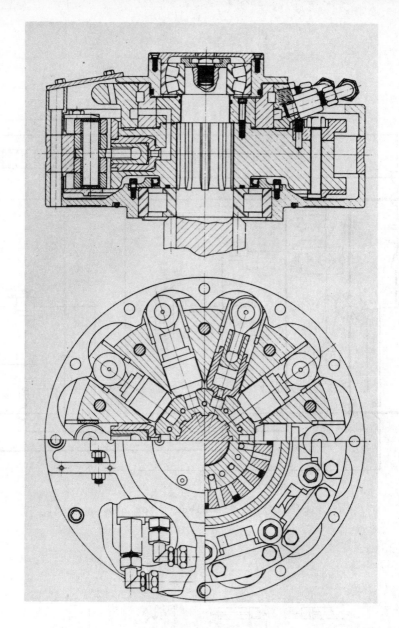

Fig.3. Radial piston motor

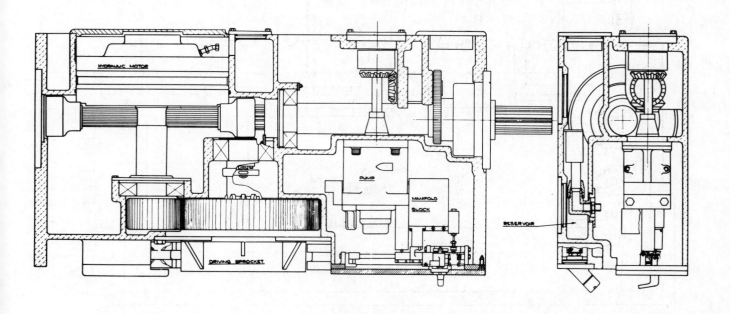

Fig.4. Layout of haulage unit

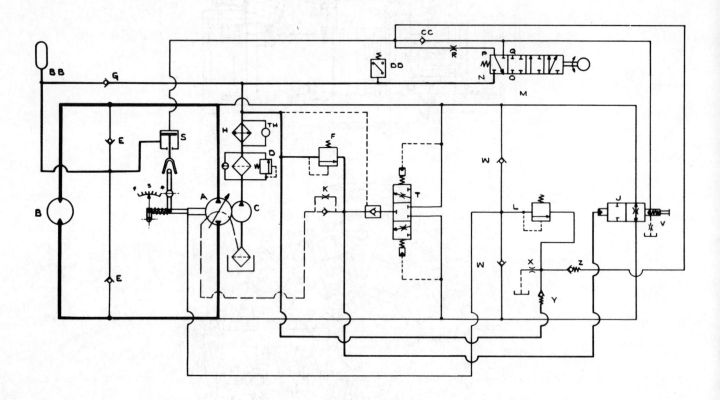

Fig.5. Hydraulic circuit for haulage unit

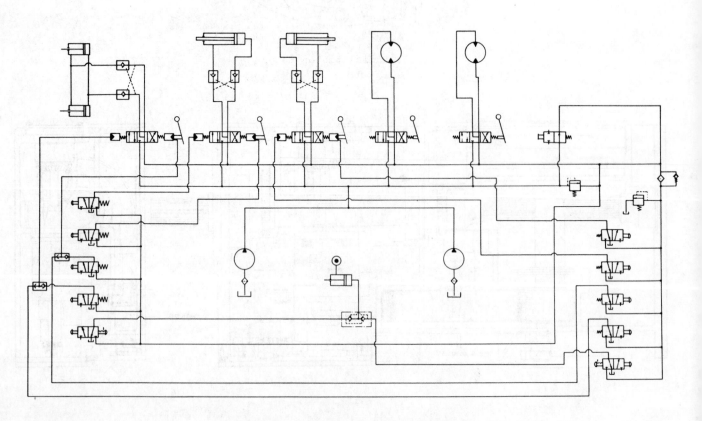

Fig.6. Hydraulic circuit for auxiliary system

C39/74

THE DEVELOPMENT OF A HYDRAULIC HAULAGE TRANSMISSION FOR A 300,000 WATTS (400 h.p.) ROTARY DRUM COAL FACE SHEARER

E. BROOK, MIMechE

Design Engineer, British Jeffrey-Diamond Limited, Wakefield, Yorkshire

The Ms. of this paper was received at the Institution on 21st August 1973 and accepted for publication on 23rd October 1973. 4

SYNOPSIS. A survey of the commercially available hydrostatic units showed that if the stipulated frame size of the machine was to be maintained, new units would have to be produced. The application of these is described and test results given.

INTRODUCTION

What is a haulage unit

1. A modern Shearer Loader may be likened to a milling machine with one or two rotary cutters driven by an electric motor. The machine box which carries the cutters is moved along by a round link chain (Remote Haulage) or winches itself along a stationary chain (Integral Haulage).

2. Although in remote haulage installations the winch is at the end of the face and size and heat dissipation are no problem, integral haulage which needs the winch to be part of the moving element is more preferred by Mining Engineers and is the subject of this paper.

3. Integral haulage is a power take off from the cutting unit supply and thus is readily controllable at the point of working. However, the height of the seam dictates the size of the machine with attendant design problems.

DESIGN PARAMETERS

4. A chain pull up to 310kN (70,000 lbs) and speeds up to 9 metres (30 ft) per minute were called for in both directions. Full load efficiencies of 92 % each for two power units and a train of gears indicated that a haulage input of about 65000 watts (85 HP) would be required within an available machine section of 685mm x 508mm (27" x 20").

5. The highest possible standard of reliability to be attained.

6. Haulage speed has in the past been satisfactorily controlled by the induced load on the electric motor which drove the whole machine but which could be connected to rotate, without pre-indication, in either direction of rotation. Small overloads of 10% above full, reduced speed but allowed the machine to keep progressing; excessive overloads of 40% above dropped the speed to zero.

7. Whatever overload protection devices are fitted it is a fair assumption that they will be removed or otherwise nullified by the coal-getters. The transmission should therefore have ample capacity to cope with this type of misuse.

8. An N.C.B. requirement indicates that wherever haulage is produced by winching along a chain, when the load is removed from the chain, tension thus released has to be dissipated in a controlled and gradual way.

9. An additional coal face hazard is that if the machine is picked up by the coal conveyor running beneath it and accelerated, then the transmission is rotated at speeds and loads far in excess of what it was designed to withstand.

10. The power losses due to mechanical inefficiencies require adequate cooling capacity. The through driving shaft, needed for a double-ended machine must almost certainly be in the middle of the haulage unit. At a possible 300,000 watts (400 HP) transmitted, a set of gears at each end, necessary if the shaft were to be offset, would introduce an unacceptable amount of heat.

11. The machine should be driveable in a smooth and responsive way with no complicated sequence of control actions. Interlocks should prevent starting or changing direction whilst under load. Its nature, hopefully, should be to instill confidence in the operator.

Why hydraulics

12. A hydrostatic drive offers automatic and infinitely variable speed changing whilst full power is being transmitted and makes safety devices and radio control possible without serious design complications. Its constant torque output lends itself to the application and overload protection is at constant pressure throughout the speed range.

13. Hydraulic transmissions have for a long time been working in coal face environments with predictable success. Although few units which were commercially available have been used for haulage, the main factor in this has probably been the size of the machine casing allowed.

Designer's choice ?

14. "If it works down the pit, it will work anywhere".

"Breakdown at the coal face should be accepted .... as being totally unnacceptable".

15. What then hydraulically meets the case if working pressures are preferably below 135 bar (2000 p.s.i.) and all materials of the sort which will allow spares to be obtained or made without delay anywhere in the world?

16. Presented with all these requirements the decision is not an easy one and because of the ever increasing powers transmitted, not often helped by what has been used before.

VARIABLE DELIVERY PUMP

Types available

17. Any units intended to work much above 200 bar (3000 p.s.i.) are at a disadvantage because their close limits of manufacture need a close limit of filtration and usually work better on an oil of lower viscosity than may be available at the coal face. Any overload valves would be operating at pressures around 270 bar (4000 p.s.i.) which may affect their effective life.

Axial piston port plate

18. This is a well proven design but suffers from the disadvantage of needing inlet and outlet check valves for dual rotation. For a 300,000 watts(85 HP) transmission these could be quite space consuming. It would be at least difficult to foolproof a control system which could set a reversing swash-plate in the correct attitude to give the same direction of flow for the opposite direction of rotation. The larger sizes do tend to produce some manufacturing difficulties.

Radial Piston

19. In the space available it is difficult to provide piston bearings which are capable of carrying the oil loads. For more than 19000 watts (25 HP) they tend to a multiplicity of pistons which complicates manufacture.

Vane Pump

20. In the variable delivery type it is nearly impossible to design one of appropriate size with shaft bearings capable of giving a useful working life. They need also almost clinically clean oil for the higher pressures.

Axial Piston - sliding port

21. This fairly recent innovation was not available in the capacity required. The ones that **were seem-ed** oversize for their delivery, but the method by which their flow is varied is simple and reliable.

Ball pump

22. Not enough was known about these at the time but one of the required capacity would present many design and leakage problems.

Design Selected

23. Reliability has to be the dominant feature. In any arrangement which has more than ten of the same size of bearing, the life of all units made trends towards the B10 life of an individual bearing. No rolling contact swash plate bearing has yet appeared (of a useable size) which is totally safe. Hydrostatically balanced slippers have been proved in many applications. Nine axial pistons make for the most compact arrangement with low pressure peaks. Non-return valves will simplify dual rotation's problems of oil flow direction. A rotating swash plate is convenient if the delivery can be varied otherwise than by tilting it. If the pistons have a slot which bleeds oil into a bypass which is altered by moving the cylinder body then a variable flow will ensue in the delivery line.

24. From here onwards the pump design mostly involved applying well known materials and methods to produce a design with the apparently best features of several models included in the one.

25. A development unit was made to deliver 340 l/min(75 gpm) at 135 bar (2000 p.s.i.) pressure and 2200 r.p.m. Its installation dimensions were 254 mm (10") diameter and 560 mm (22") long. The swash plate (E 36 cyanide hardened) was carried in one taper roller thrust, and one roller journal, bearing. This appears to be the first time that bearing manufacturers had been asked to approve such an arrangement .

26. To carry oil from the sliding cylinder block (Meehanite) to the static valve block (EN24), tubes fitted with square section rubber seals were used.

27. The nine axial pistons (EN36) cyanide hardened) had slippers made from $500 MN/m^2$ (32 tons/sq.") bronze and worked on a constant stroke of 23 mm (.9 ").

28. The piston slippers were held in contact with the swash plate by a spring loaded plate (EN36 cyanide hardened) which was designed to have low inertia and to pivot about a point in line with the rear face of the slippers.

29. The inlet and outlet non-return valves (EN36 cyanide hardened) were loaded to close by springs of about .5 Kg (1 lb) load.

30. The operating servo and ram were fitted into the centre of the cylinder body.

31. The pump thus delivers its full swept volume all the time with a chosen portion going to the pressure line and the remainder being shunted into the return line at charge pressure.

MOTOR

Types available

32. A two-speed motor would show a more advantageous use of the available pump delivery but would introduce a further control function. A fixed delivery motor should be suitable provided that its starting torque was about equal to its running torque.

33. More variety was available in the fixed type such as the slowspeed - radial piston and the multi-lobe cam motors. Without exception, however, these would not fit into the machine casing.

34. After a survey of all available it seemed that the most likely motor was a double ended swash, axial piston type but this was not made in the required size at the time and appeared to need a higher standard of filtration than was possible.

Design selected

35. The high capacity/size ratio and general reliability of vane motors was known well and the desirability to operate at about 135 Bar (2000 p.s.i.) pressure and eliminate as much reduction gearing as possible made a slow speed model seem a suitable answer. Up to 250 r.p.m. the physical size deterrent would be compensated by lower tip speeds and the working pressure acceptable without the use of intra-vanes.

36. A development model (figure 1) was therefore designed, with fixed delivery, to have a provisional torque output of 2700 Nm (2000 lbs ft). Its swept volume 2.27 litres (.5 gall) per revolution and its overall dimensions were 280 x 280 x 280 mm (11" x 11" x 11").

37. The cam (Meehanite) had four lobes and the rotor (EN16) having the minimum number of vanes to work with four lobes, i.e. eleven. Because dual rotation was required, the vanes had semi-circular tips. Alternative sets of vanes were made, one from "Sulfinuzed" tool steel, the other from High Speed steel. The cheek plates (Meehanite) were hydraulically balanced, space not allowing the outward loads to be retained by thick walls. The centre shaft (EN24) was carried in needle roller bearings.

38. Two driving keys were fitted to transmit torque from rotor to shaft. They were round in cross section to minimise stress concentrations in the rotor and made from stainless steel to minimise fretting corrosion. To simplify manufacture, the cam lobes were arcs of circles and the slots in the rotor were plain milled.

39. Oil enters and leaves the lobes via ports in the cheek plates, which are connected to annulii in the cam ring. Pressure under the vanes was supplied by a continuous annulus in the cheek plates.

DEVELOPMENT TESTING

40. Two prototype motors were built, one to drive and the other to load, the connection between them being a B.H.C. Torquemeter shaft.

41. One prototype pump was built and driven by means of a toothed belt at 2200 r.p.m.

42. The rig used is best described by the photograph (Figure 3). Flexible pipes connecting the units allowing many different circuits to be tried.

43. Filtration was a charge suction strainer at .1mm (.005)" and a charge delivery filter at 25 microns. Although the joints were broken and re-made many times no piston sticking or other seizure was experienced.

44. To approximate chain tension release, three 10 gallon accumulators were piped to deliver together into the low pressure side of the load vane motor. They were charged through non-return valves by the delivery pressure. When the drive was stopped, the oil they released turned the load motor backwards.

DEVELOPMENT RESULTS

Pump

45. Typical results from log sheets are:

Oil temperature °C	60	Tellus 33.
Charge pressure p.s.i.	200	
Delivery pressure p.s.i.	1500	
Flow g.p.m.	75	
Leakage to drain g.p.m.	1.5	
Speed r.p.m.	2200	

* This pressure is artificially high for rig protection.

Oil temperature °C	60	Tellus 33
Charge pressure bar	13.5 *	
Delivery pressure bar	100	
Flow l/min	340	
Leak to drain l/min	7	
Speed r.p.m.	2200	

46. The delivery could be varied from full to zero in a smooth way at all pressures, the relationship between flow and servo position being approximately linear.

47. No wear was experienced on any component, after many hours running. Particular attention was paid to the edges of the bypass grooves in the cylinder bores over which the slots in the pistons were sliding. They were undamaged.

48. The minimum charge pressure at which the pump would run without cavitation was 5.5 bar (80 p.s.i.)

49. More than 1000 operations of the overload valves (paragraph 76 circuit) were performed, collapsing the pump delivery with no significant failure.

50. At reduced flows the port-to-port leakage between the slots in the pistons and the bypass grooves is greater than it is a full flow. This is because at full flow the slots are always closed off by the cylinder walls, whereas, at partial flow, increased opportunity for leakage occurs as the slot becomes covered in delivering oil to the pressure line.

Motor

51. The first discovery was that for power to be transmitted the pressure under the vanes holding them in contact with the cam ring needs to be some 8% greater than the working pressure. This differential was obtained for all flow rates by a specially designed valve. (see paragraph 74).

52. The units then produced their rated torques with no discernable fluctuation. Typical results from logsheets are:-

	Full load	No load	
Oil temperature $^{\circ}$C	60	60	Tellus 33
Charge press p.s.i.	200 *	210	
Working press p.s.i.	1600	400	
Under vane press p.s.i.	1800	500	
Return press p.s.i.	250 *	300	
Torque lbs.ft.	2000	50 (less than)	
Speed r.p.m.	90	98	
Leakage to drain pints/min	2	-	

* The charge pressue is artificially high
for rig protection.

Oil temperature $^{\circ}$C	60	60	Tellus 33
Charge pressure bar	13.5	14 *	
Working pressure bar	107	26.6	
Under vane pressure bar	120	33	
Return pressure bar	16.7	20 *	
Torque Nm	2700	68 (less than)	
Speed r.p.m.	90	98	
Leak to drain 1/min	1.135	-	

53. The motors would run at the maximum speed of
140 r.p.m. but due to rig limitations, full
torque could not be applied at this speed.

54. Both units were notable for the almost total
absence of wear on any component. The eleven
vanes of each unit weighed at start, totalled for
Sulfinuzed tool steel 1181.7 gma and for High
Speed steel 1306.8 gms. At the end of approximately 700 hours running at various loads and 1000
operations of the chain tension release test, their
respective weights were 1179.5 gms. and 1306 gms.

55. An increase of about 6% of the output torque
could be obtained if the under vane pressure was
ported to the return line in the region where
the vanes are pushed radially inwards by the cam
adjacent to the exit port. (See Fig. 6 D to E)
For the opposite rotation, however, this feature
causes the vanes to lose drive where they are
travelling radially outwards and thus is not
practical for dual rotation motors.

56. The average time of run-down for the chain
release tests was found to be 28 seconds at a
temperature of 60°C. This was obtained by the
oil passing over the tips of the vanes from high
to low pressure. (See Fig. 6) This time
was shortened artificially by introducing an
orifice valve between the high and low pressure
ports of the motor.

57. Rotation of the driving motor was halted and
re-started many times by simply cutting and re-
connecting the under-vane pressure supply without
detriment to any component. This overload
protection feature is utilised in the transmission
overpeed condition.

58. By a happy coincidence about this time it was
learned that a slow speed vane motor was being
introduced in America but beyond the fact that it
would not go into our casing, no details were
available. A similar unit also appeared to be
being developed in Russia. This news seemed to
indicate that they were on the right track.

PRODUCTION MODELS

Pump

59. The production model, due to metrication,
was designed to produce 355 litres/minute
(78 g.p.m.) at 1800 r.p.m. (Fig. 2). The main
changes in detail from the development pump were
metal piston rings which were used instead of
rubber for the sliding oil transfer tubes, 620 MN/m^2
(40 tons/sq.in) bronze for the slippers and the
inlet and outlet non-return valves were shortened
and made from High Speed steel, all to improve
reliability. The delivery collection manifold also
forms the pump mounting bracket.

60. The servo valve, but not the piston, was
brought to the outside of the casing for easier
servicing.

61. The retaining plate for the slippers was now
made from Nitride hardened steel to simplify
manufacture.

62. Typical Rig test results were:

	Full load	No Load	
Oil Temp.	75°C		Tellus 41
Charge pressure p.s.i.	230	230 *	
Delivery pressure "	1650	400	
Flow g.p.m.	72.2	75.8	
Leakage to drain gpm	1.5	.5	
speed rpm	1785	1800	

*This pressure is artificially high for
rig protection.

Oil Temp. $^{\circ}$C	75	75	Tellus 41
Charge Pressure bar	15.3	15.3 *	
Delivery " bar	110	26.6	
Flow 1/min	328	345	
Leak to drain 1/min	6.8	2.27	
Speed r.p.m.	1785	1800	

63. On test, the pump behaved very much as the
development model for controlability and the
absence of wear. It was, however, found necessary to limit the lift of the inlet and outlet
non return valves to approximately 2mm (.080").
Less than this caused cavitation behind the
pistons with cold oil, and more than this caused
some loss of delivery at full stroke due to the
longer time taken for the valves to close.

64. The pump will function if the return springs
are removed from inlet and outlet valves, but the
delivery is then slightly reduced.

Motor

65. The production motor, also to metric dimensions was designed to give 4000 Nm (3000 lbs/ft) at
110 r.p.m. with a swept volume of 3.4 litres
(.72 gallon) per revolution. (Refer to paragraphs
102 to 106 for calculation). Figure 5 shows how
its casing is manifolded to carry the reversing
and relief valves and profiled to fit within the
haulage unit.

66. The volume delivered to the lobe entry ports
is 355 l.p.m. (78 g.p.m.) and in order to give the
biggest area to the flow paths, wall thicknesses
are kept to the minimum. The cam ring is therefore
made from EN24 steel which has been "Tuftride"

hardened. The vanes are of high speed steel and the
the rotor is again EN16.

67. Typical results obtained from the test rig for
the production motor are:

		Full load	
Oil Temperature	°C	50	Tellus 41
Charge pressure P.s.i.	*	200	*
Working pressure p.s.i.		1700	
Under vane pressure p.s.i.		1900	
Return pressure p.s.i.		300	
Torque lbs.ft.		3000	
Speed r.p.m.		80	
Leak to drain pts/min		11	

* The charge pressure is artificially high
for rig protection.

Oil temperature	°C	50	Tellus 41
Charge pressure	bar	13.5	*
Working "	bar	113	
Under vane "	bar	127	
Return "	bar	20	*
Torque	Nm	4070	
Speed	r.p.m.	80	
Leak to drain	1/min	6.25	

68. Up to temperatures of 55°C the leakage to
tank and reduction in speed due to loading compared
favourably with the other hydraulic equipment. At
temperatures above this, up to 90°C the total
leakage was sufficient to cause the under vane
pressure differential to be reduced and the motor
lost its drive at speeds less than ¼ of full.
When the total clearance between the side plates
and the rotor was lessened, by selective assembly,
full power was regained from zero speed upwards.

CIRCUITRY (Figure 4)

69. "If there are any valves on this machine that
stop it, then leave them off. Put some on that
make it go".

70. Several apparently good ideas such as chain
tensioning control and hydraulic stall valve
were discarded after much discussion. Variable
rate of increase of speed is provided, but not
variable rate of decrease.

71. Manifolding and 'O' ring bobbin joints are
used everywhere except for one flexible main
circuit connection and the pilot lines.

72. A closed circuit was necessary and the charge
pump (1) is in fact a gear motor, for dual
rotation, of 45 litres/min. (10 gallons) capacity
at 80 bar (1200 p.s.i.). The total system
leakage could be 18 litres/min (4 gallons) and the
charge pressure 13 bar (200 p.s.i.) so these ample
margins were considered to be assets.

73. For reversed rotation of the sprocket, working
oil is diverted by a pilot operated 1½" change-
over valve (2), chosen because it was the only
one of its capacity to fit into the casing.
Following this, the main circuit relief valve (3)
and the servo flow control valve (4) are from the
same manufacturer.

74. To obtain the required under vane pressure
differential, all the working oil passes through a
valve (5) which maintains the set margin at all
flows. It is a pilot-controlled throttling valve,

conveniently manifolded in the system. The pilot
piston is 10% larger in area than the spool and
senses the main working pressure. Metal piston
rings minimise friction when sealing against
leakage on both spool and pilot.

75. All the main pressure is thus running 10%
higher than is needed for the load. The alternative, to pressurise only the amount needed for the
under vane would have meant another high duty pump
and introduced one more point of possible failure.

76. Control of direction and of overloads (whether
by haulage pull or by the rotating cutter) is
obtained electrically by four solenoid operated
miniature directional valves situated on the electric motor, (6, 7, 8, 9.) These are two position,
three port valves with overall dimensions of
38 x 38 x 22 mm (1½" x 1½" x ⅞"). Here again,
space and F.L.P. requirements meant that several
good commercial models had to be passed over and a
valve designed for the application. Additionally,
all solenoid functions can be obtained manually and
the main circuit relief valve limits the haulage
speed hydraulically.

77. The return line is pressurised by a simple
cone valve (15) manifolded in, but adjustable from
the top of the case. A non-return valve (16) into
the cooler allows the circuit to prime itself in
the event of charge failure, which, if continued,
stops the main electric motor via a pressure switch
(17). If the main relief blows continuously, its
discharge zeroes the pump delivery via a pressure
switch (18).

78. A pressure sensing interlock valve (10) is fitted which prevents the direction being changed
manually as long as the chain is under tension. A
pilot-operated orifice valve (11) is ported across
the vane motor to shorten the time of chain tension
release.

79. In the under vane line is fitted a trip valve
(12) which cuts off the supply in the event of
either pressure or return overload (13,14). This
is a detent version of the miniature directional
valve. It is pilot operated and its function is to
render the vanes unsupported and allow the rotor to
revolve unrestrictedly if the machine is carried
away by the conveyor. A manual reset button is
provided, to reactivate the vanes.

Filtration

80. Fortunately the filter makers were now
introducing new types of disposable element and
were able to show that a 450 litres/min (100 gallon)
filter could fit within the space of 150 mm (6")
diameter and 250 mm (10") length. Several different products were available with pressure drops
less than 1 bar (15 p.s.i.).

81. The main filter is fitted in the return line
preceding the pump inlet and it follows that most
of the oil is cleaned some of the time. However,
a good rule is to find a filter of the stipulated
capacity and then fit one twice as big, for the life
factor is inevitably minimised.

82. The charge oil is made to flow through the
main filter before entering the circuit. Additionally a smaller element filters the pilot oil down
to 10 microns and a suction strainer filters the
charge inlet down to .1mm (.004").

Cooling

83. Some 11,000 to 15,000 watts (15 to 20 h.p.) equivalent of heat require to be dissipated and as radiation is almost nil, water cooling is necessary.

84. A multicoil assembly using 7.6 metres (25 ft) of wire wound tube was made to fit beneath the pump and its enclosed chamber is part of the return circuit. Approximately 27 litres (6 gallons) of water flow through the tubes per minute.

Working Fluids

85. Oils of the "Tellus" type from 29 to 56 are all useable, with pre-start ambient temperature helping selection. The lower viscosities are used to meet the colder conditions with "Tellus" 41 being the standard at 28°C.

Controls

86. The controls for speed and direction are located on the electric motor and interlocked, both electrically and mechanically, so that the pump delivery must be zeroed before any change of direction can be achieved. Every stop function also returns pump delivery to zero, but chain tension remains until the directional valve centres.

CASE DESIGN

87. The paramount need is ease of servicing and for the hydraulic units this means replacement. Both units are tailored to fit above and around the through shaft. Their retaining screws act as jacks to lift them and break the 'O' ring joints.

88. Both filter elements are replaceable from the goaf side, the main filter housing being part of the structure.

89. The total length of the haulage unit was in fact dictated by sprocket room and is 1500 mm (59"). It holds about 160 litres (35 gallons) of oil with the closed circuit of two units, cooler, filter and pipes holding 45 (10) of them.

90. Drive is transmitted from the vane motor to the sun wheel of the epicyclic sprocket drive by means of a layshaft. The total reduction can be varied between 1/15 to 1/20 by changing the number of teeth in the layshaft pinion. A disengaging mechanism allows the hydraulics to be run without turning the sprocket. This can be locked out for safety.

91. The main and charge pumps are driven by helical gearing from the through shaft.

92. A steel plate fabrication was decided upon because of the real difficulty of obtaining satisfactory steel castings.

HAULAGE UNIT

93. For test purposes the haulage unit was loaded by friction brake (Figure 8), the power transmitted of 73,000 Nm (54,000 lbs.ft.) being measured by a Torquemeter shaft.

94. The total gear reduction between the vane motor and drive sprocket was 18.9/1.

95. Typical test results are:

	Load	No load	
Oil Temperature	80°C		Tellus 41
Charge pressure p.s.i.	215	225	*
Working " p.s.i.	1750	510	
Under vane " "	1950	730	
Return pressure "	340	400	*
Torque lbs.ft.	54000	-	
Sprocket speed r.p.m.	4.8	5.2	

* These pressures are artificially high for protection purposes.

		Load	No load	
Oil temperature	°C	80	80	Tellus 41
Charge pressure	bar	14.3	15	*
Working "	bar	117	34	
Under vane "	bar	130	48.5	
Return "	bar	22.6	26.6	*
Torque	Nm	73,300	-	
Sprocket speed	r.p.m.	4.8	5.2	

96. The full torque was transmittable from zero speed upwards at a temperature of 85°C.

97. The loss of speed which occurred when the load was applied must be attributed to the main pump and vane motor together.

98. With full load applied by the brake and the transmission not rotating, if the main pump delivery was brought to approximately 1/16 of full, the motor would start up with the working pressure momentarily increasing to the 10% above norm at which the main relief valve was set.

99. The unit is currently on life test, more than 200 hours having been accomplished. First results indicate that the temperature stabilises at 85°C after five hours running at full load with 27 1/min (6 g.p.m.) of cold water through the circuit cooler. An additional cooling element of 7.6 metres (25 ft.) of wire wound tube has been fitted in the sump, to improve the heat exchange. Results indicate that when both coolers are used in series then the stabilized temperature of 85°C can be held with 20 litres (4½ galls) of cold water per minute flowing.

100. With a completely dry unit it is necessary to fill the circuit with oil before starting. A bleed screw is fitted to the top of the pump and filling takes place at a tapping point which makes the ingoing oil flow through the main filter before entering the transmission passages. Excess then passes through the charge relief valve until the required sump level is reached, i.e. within 50 mm (2") of the top flange.

THEORETICAL ANALYSIS

Pump. Production Model

101 Swept volume = 191 ccs (11.75 cu.ins) per revolution.
Oil velocity through valve ports = 6.6 metres (22 ft) per second.
B.10 life of swash plate bearings = 3000 hrs.
Input power of pump per 100 p.s.i. at 1800 r.p.m. = 4500 watts (5.33 HP).

Vane Motor. Production Model

102. The values of - f x Radius x facewidth x pressure - for the four lobes taken simultaneously at vane intervals of 360 ÷ 11 ÷ 6 can be summated to produce a torque curve. (Figure 7.)

103. This can readily be done on a 2 x full size drawing of the cam lobes with the vane positions accurately marked out on a rotating disc.

104. The curve repeats itself after 8.18^o, 16.36^o, 25.54^o, and 32.7^o and if the four are plotted on one graph, an approximation of the torque fluctuation is created.

105. The average value of the torque with a working pressure of 93 bar (1400 p.s.i.) is 5100 Nm (3752 lbs. ft.)

106. The swept volume by incremental methods (Figure 6) is - area bounded by the lobe periphery and the angle between A and B x facewidth x 4 x 11. This is:
8.34 sq.cm. x 8.9 cm x 44 = 3260 ccs.
(1.29 sq.ins. x 3.5 ins. x 44 = 198.5 cu. ins.)
or 3.26 litres (.72 gallons) per revolution.
A pressure of 93 bar (1400 p.s.i.) then gives a torque of 5000 Nm (3700 lbs ft.)

RETROSPECT

107. Though, from the outset, no attempt had been made to produce a unit with high efficiencies, the transmission in this respect is adequate. Under-vane differential pressure reduces efficiency but in view of the robust way the vanes stand up to the chain run back condition, this should be acceptable.

108. A single direction vane motor with reversal obtained by gears would probably show better output efficiency. It would, however, need an appreciably longer haulage unit casing and would, most likely, rule out radio control.

109. No other hydraulic motor appears to be challenging the slow speed vane for this application.

110. For other applications than at the coal face the rated output could be increased probably by $33\frac{1}{3}$%.

111. The opinions expressed are those of the author and not necessarily those of British Jeffrey-Diamond Limited.

Fig.1. Development model of vane motor

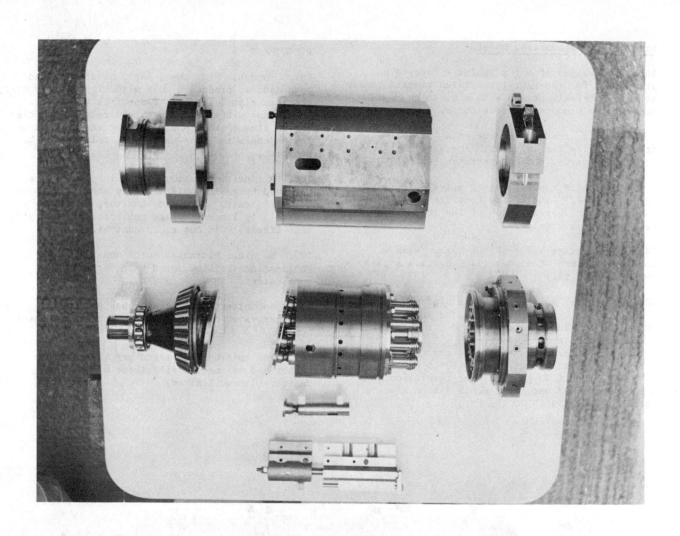

Fig.2. Production model of pump

Fig.3. Development test rig

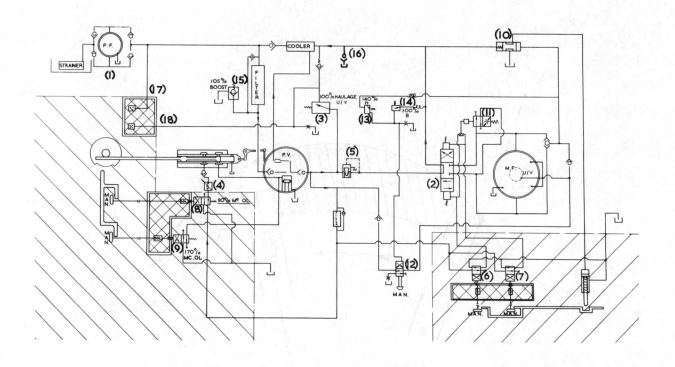

Fig.4. Hydraulic circuit diagram

Fig.5. Production motor

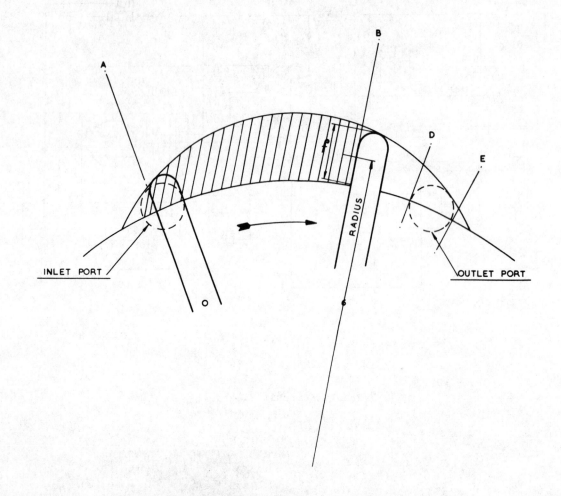

Fig.6. Swept volume of vane motor

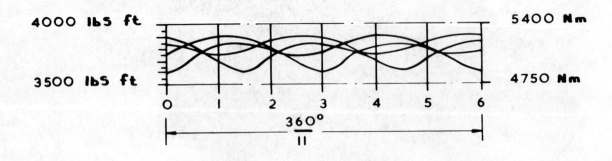

THEORETICAL TORQUE

Fig.7. Torque diagram - vane motor

Fig.8. Haulage unit on test

Made and printed in Great Britain by William Clowes & Sons, Limited, London, Beccles and Colchester